Contents

Rabindranath Tagore
Omnibus

IV

Rabindranath Tagore
Omnibus
IV

RUPA

Published by
Rupa Publications India Pvt. Ltd 2005
7/16, Ansari Road, Daryaganj
New Delhi 110002

Sales centres:
Allahabad Bengaluru Chennai
Hyderabad Jaipur Kathmandu
Kolkata Mumbai

Edition copyright © Rupa Publications India Pvt. Ltd 2005

ISBN: 978-81-291-0638-4

Eighth impression 2014

10 9 8

Typeset by Mindways Design, New Delhi

Printed at Gopsons Papers Ltd, Noida

TWO SISTERS

Sarmila

Women are of two kinds, the mother-kind and the beloved-kind—so I have heard some learned men say. If a comparison may be drawn with the seasons, the mother is the rainy season. She brings the gift of water and of fruit, tempers the heat, and dissolving from the heights drives away the drought. She fills with plenty. The beloved, on the other hand, is the Spring. Deep its mystery, sweet its enchantment. Its restlessness rocks the blood into waves and swings over into the jewel-chamber of the mind where the solitary string of the golden *vina* is lying mute, waiting for the vibration to set the body and the mind ringing in some wordless melody.

Sasanka's wife Sarmila was the mother-kind. Her large, gentle eyes had a deep, steady look. The dark, well-rounded limbs had the comely grace of the first rain-laden clouds. The vermilion mark at the parting of her hair, the broad black border of her sari, the thick *makar*-shaped bangles on her wrists bespoke homely grace rather than elegance of style.

There was no outlying region in the territory of her husband's life over which her empire was not actively exercised. The extreme solicitude with which she had surrounded his life had made him careless. If by any chance the fountain pen was so misplaced on the table as not to be readily at hand the moment he needed it, his wife would have to discover it for him. If he could not remember where he had left his wristwatch before going to bathe, his wife was sure to know where it was. So, too, she must be there to repair his error when, having put on socks of different shades, he was ready to go out. He mixed up English dates with Bengali months and sent out invitations to friends accordingly, and when the unexpected guests made their untimely appearance, it was his wife who had to bear the brunt of it. He knew full well that any negligence in the day's routine would be set right by her. To perpetrate negligences therefore had become second nature with him.

"It's the limit," his wife would complain, half derisively, half lovingly. "Will you never learn?"

If he had learnt, Sarmila's days would have lain idle as untilled land.

One day Sasanka was at some friend's, playing bridge. It was getting rather late at night. Suddenly his friends burst out laughing. "Ah! Here comes your bearer with the summons! Your time is up." Sure enough, there was the inevitable Mahesh, with his moustache gone grey and the hair still black on his head, wearing a vest, with a coloured duster on his shoulder, and a bamboo rod in his hand.

"The mistress has sent me to inquire if the master is here. She is afraid of some mishap to the master on his way back in the dark night. She has sent a lantern as well."

Irritated, Sasanka threw down the cards and got up. The friends taunted, "Ah, the lonely, unguarded male!"

On reaching home Sasanka addressed his wife in no gentle terms or peaceful manner. Sarmila quietly accepted the scolding. What was she to do? She simply could not get rid of her fear that when her husband was not with her, all sorts of impossible perils were conspiring to waylay him.

Another day some stranger had called on business. Every now and then a chit would be handed in. "You know you were indisposed yesterday. Do come in early to dinner." Sasanka lost his temper, but yielded nevertheless.

Once in extreme exasperation he had told his wife. "For goodness' sake, get hold of some god or deity like that Chakravarty wife. It's too much for me to withstand your attentions all by myself. Sharing them with a god would make it easier. The gods can stand excesses, but man is frail."

"Indeed!" retorted Sarmila. "Have you forgotten your condition that time when I went to Hardwar with my uncle?"

He had himself related to his wife, adding embellishment for effect, how very pathetic his condition had been in her absence. He knew that such exaggeration would make her feel at once penitent and happy. How could he now go back on his own immoderate version! And so he swallowed the retort and kept quiet. Nor did it end there. Fancying that in the morning he had a slight touch of cold, she made him swallow ten grains of quinine as well, with juice of *tulsi* leaves in tea. He dared not object, for, having refused to take quinine on a previous occasion, he had developed fever—which incident had remained ineffaceably engraved in the domestic annals.

As she was solicitous of her husband's well-being and comfort at home, so was Sarmila jealously mindful of his dignity abroad. Let me recall an incident.

Once they were going to Nainital on holiday and had their compartment reserved "through". At a junction where they changed trains, they went out to dine. Returning they found a villainous looking figure in livery actively occupied in dispossessing them of their berths. The station-master came and explained that the compartment had been actually reserved for a certain celebrated general, though through inadvertence their name had been affixed to it. Opening his eyes wide, flabbergasted, Sasanka made ready to shift, when up jumped Sarmila into the compartment and standing against the door challenged:

"Let me see who dares pull me down! Call your General here!"

Sasanka, who was a government servant, and was well accustomed to keeping a safe distance from the path of the superior official tribe, grew nervous and began to protest: "But what's the use? There are plenty of other carriages—"

But Sarmila would not heed. In the end the General who had returned from the refreshment room, cigar in mouth, and was witnessing this spectacle of feminine wrath, himself retired to another compartment. Sasanka turned to his wife: "Do you know how big that man is?"

"Don't care to know. In a compartment reserved for us, he is no bigger than you."

"What if he had insulted us?" ventured Sasanka

"What are you for then?" retorted Sarmila.

Sasanka was a graduate of the Sibpur Engineering College. However irresponsible he might be in the other walks of his life, he was careful enough in his official duties; the main reason being that the planet presiding over his official world was not his wife but the ruthless eye of the "Bara Sahib".

When he was acting as the district engineer his newly won promotion was suddenly reversed and he was superseded, despite his superior claim, by an inexperienced English youth, with the mere down of a moustache—an unsuspected proof of what right connections in high quarters can achieve. Sasanka knew that he would still have to carry on the real work, while that white booby would be installed in the chair. The big boss patted him on the back and said consolingly:

"Very sorry, Mazumdar. As soon as feasible, we'll push you up."

Both of them were Freemasons.

But despite this hope and consolation, the whole affair was exceedingly unpleasant for Mazumdar. At home he found cause for quarrel with every little thing. Suddenly he noticed soot in a corner of his office room; suddenly he felt that he couldn't bear the sight of the green cover of his sofa. He thundered at the office-boy who was sweeping the verandah for blowing dust in his direction. The inevitable specks of dust blew daily, but the master's thunder was something new.

He kept the news of his humiliation from his wife, afraid she would only add one more complication to the already complicated affairs of his service. She might even go and pick a quarrel with his boss, in no pleasant language, specially as she already nursed a grudge against Donaldson. Once, while engaged in suppressing the monkey pest in the garden of the circuit house, he had instead marked holes in Sasanka's sola hat. Fortunately there was no accident, but an accident there might easily have been. People blamed Sasanka, which only added to Sarmila's wrath against Donaldson. What inflamed her wrath most was that Sasanka's enemies made much of the joke that a bullet aimed at a monkey had landed on Sasanka.

However, she herself found out all about the reverse in her husband's official status. She had suspected from his manner that somewhere a thorn was pricking. It did not take long to discover the cause. Rejecting the way of "constitutional agitation", she went straight for "self-determination". She told her husband:

"Have done with it. Hand in your resignation immediately."

Resignation would no doubt remove the leech of humiliation from his breast. But then there stretched before his mind's eye the rich field of regular monthly income and beyond that the golden prospect of a pension.

In the very year in which Sasankamauli had topped the pinnacle of the M.Sc. degree, his father-in-law, unwilling to delay the auspicious event, married him off to Sarmila. With the wealthy father-in-law's help he passed the engineering course. Seeing his speedy rise in service, Rajaram Babu had felt assured of his son-in-law's steady progress in prosperity. The daughter too never suspected till now that the contrary could happen. Not that any want was actually felt in the house; the ways of her father's house had been maintained here too, the reason being that in the domestic dyarchy all management was in Sarmila's control. She had no child, nor any longer the hope of one. Whatever her husband earned was delivered into her hands to the last copper. If any special need arose he had no alternative but to go and beg from the *Annapurna* of his home. If the demand was unreasonable, it was refused; he accepted the decision, scratching his head. But there was always some other sweet compensation to make up for this disappointment.

"To give up the job," said Sasanka, "matters little to me. It's for your sake that I hesitate. You'll be put to hardship."

"It's a worse hardship to try to swallow injustice which sticks in the throat."

"But," remonstrated Sasanka, "one must work. If I give up the certain, where shall I go about looking for the uncertain?"

"Where you don't care to look now. You jokingly call your government service your *luchi-sthan*—beyond the arid wastes of *beluchisthan,* and you are so obsessed with it that you ignore the whole wide world outside it."

"Good Heavens! The whole world is too big for me. Who is going to survey all its highways and byways? Where am I to find a telescope big enough for that?"

"No big telescope is needed. My cousin Mathurdada is a big contractor in Calcutta. If you join him as a partner, we'll manage to make both ends meet."

"It would be an unfair sharing, for the weight on this side of the scale would not be enough. To hobble in such partnership seems too undignified."

"The weight on this side of the scale would be not one whit too light. You know the amount father had deposited in the bank in my name—well, it's there, only bloated with interest. You would not have to feel small before your partner."

"How can I take that? That money is yours." Saying which Sasanka got up. There were visitors waiting outside. Sarmila caught hold of his dress and pulled him back into the seat. "I too am yours," she said. And added: "Pull out that fountain-pen from your pocket, here's the paper, write out your resignation. I can have no peace till I have posted that letter."

"Nor can I have any peace either, it seems." He wrote the letter of resignation.

The very next day Sarmila went to Calcutta and straight to Mathurdada's house. Petulantly she greeted him:

"Not once have you cared to inquire after your sister."

One of her own sex would have retorted: "Nor have you." But the male brain could think of no such retort. Mathurdada admitted his fault:

"Have I even the time to breathe? Sometimes I even forget whether or not I exist. Besides, you two are always on tour."

"I read in the papers," said Sarmila, "that you have secured the contract for building a bridge at Mayurbhanj or Mathurganj or some such place. I was so delighted that I thought, let me go and congratulate Mathurdada in person."

"Wait a little, *Khuki*. It's not time yet."

The trouble was that liquid capital was needed for which he had offered to enter into partnership with a wealthy Marwari. In the end it turned out that the Marwari's conditions were such that while the Marwari would have all the juice, he would be left only the refuse. So he was trying to back out.

"Impossible," cried Sarmila excitedly. "It can't be allowed. If you needs must enter into partnership, then let it be with us. It would be too bad to let such business slip from your hands. I simply will not allow it, say what you will."

It did not take long to render all this into a written deed. Mathurdada's heart too was touched.

The business went ahead. Formerly Sasanka's work had been "service", it limits were well defined. Working under a boss, his responsibility ended with the demand made on it. Now, however, he was his own boss, subject to no will but his own. The claim of duty and his response to it were now merged in one. The days were no longer woven in a network of work-days and holiday, but became one compact whole. Because he was now free to ignore his responsibility, its hold on his mind became all the more tenacious. If nothing else, he must at least pay back his debt to his wife; after that there would be time enough to set the pace slow and easy. And so in khaki pants, his leather belt fastened tight, wearing thick-soled shoes, a sola hat on his head, his sleeves rolled up, a watch strapped to his left wrist, and sun-glasses to protect his eyes, Sasanka plunged headlong into his work. Nor was the pressure of the steam relaxed, even when the debt had been wellnigh liquidated; the mind was still in full heat.

Formerly his income and expenditure had flowed through one single channel; now they branched into two, one flowing bankwards, the other homewards. Sarmila continued to receive her old portion and dispensed it as before, Sasanka remaining a stranger to its mysteries. On the other hand, Sasanka's leather-bound ledger of business accounts was to her inaccessible, incomprehensible. There was no harm in that. But the fact that this path of her husband's business life ran outside her domestic orbit did, however, mean that her jurisdiction to that extent had suffered.

"Don't overdo it please," she pleaded, "your health will break down."

To no avail. Strangely enough, his health did not break down. Impetuously ignoring all pleadings of conjugal solicitude, her anxiety for his health, her complaints at his lack of rest, her fussy concern over the details of his comfort, et cetera, Sasanka left the house early in the morning, blowing the horn of his second-hand Ford, himself at the wheel; returned at about two or half-past two, received a scolding and then his food which he gulped down.

One day his car ran into another. He was unhurt, but the car was damaged and had to be sent to the garage for repairs. Sarmila was greatly upset.

"You must not drive any more," she beseeched, her voice hoarse.

"An accident at another's hands can be equally fatal," replied Sasanka, laughingly dismissing her concern.

One day, while he was supervising some repair work, a packing-box nail pierced through the shoe right into his foot. At the hospital the wound was bandaged and he was given an antitetanus injection. That day Sarmila was all tears.

"Stay in bed for a day or two at least," she pleaded. But Sasanka replied laconically: "Work."

It is not possible to improve on such brevity of expression.

"But," remonstrated Sarmila,—but Sasanka had left, without even a word, and with bandage on.

Sarmila dared not test her powers any more. The man's masterfulness in his own field was now evident. Beyond all argument, entreaty, pleading, was the one phrase, "I've work to do."

For no reason Sarmila was uneasy, anxious. The slightest delay in returning home and she thought of an accident to the car. When she saw her husband's face flushed with the sun's heat, she thought it must surely be influenza. Timidly she would suggest the doctor—and immediately stop, seeing the reaction on him. Nowadays she was afraid even to express her anxiety fully and freely.

In no time Sasanka became sun-burnt and dry. His dress, like his leisure, was cut short to tightness; his movements became hurried; his speech abrupt like sparks. To this quick rhythm Sarmila's ministry strove to adjust its motions. Some

food must always be kept ready and warm near the stove—
for who knew when the husband might suddenly and untimely
declare: "I'm off. Shall be late in returning." A provision of
soda water and dry food-stuff in a tin was neatly stored in
his car; a bottle of eau-de-cologne carefully concealed from
view—in case of headache. She looked into them carefully
each time the car returned home, only to find that nothing
had been used. It was distressing. Every day a clean change
of clothes, neatly folded, was prominently displayed in his
bedroom, nevertheless, at least four days in the week he
found no time to change. Domestic consultation reduced to
the briefest, in the staccato style of an express telegram, had
to be carried out in a most casual manner, standing, walking
or calling from behind, "Just a word, dear." The little
connection which Sarmila had with his business also came
to an end with the repayment of her loan, interest and all.
The interest too had been paid to the penny and a formal
receipt taken.

"What a pity!" wailed Sarmila. "Even in love men cannot
wholly lose themselves. A portion of themselves they needs
must set apart for the exercise of their masculine ego."

From his share of the profits Sasanka built a house in
Bhowanipore, after his own heart. To astound Sarmila he
planned the latest devices of hygiene, comfort and order.
Sarmila too was not remiss in allowing herself to be properly
astounded. There was the laundry machine installed by the
engineer. Sarmila looked at it from this side and that and
praised it profusely; but to herself she added: "Nevertheless,
the clothes will continue to be sent to the *dhobi* as they have
been till this day. I've known the donkey carry soiled clothes,
but have not known science take its place yet."

Seeing the potato-peeling machine she was all amazement.
"Three-fourths of the drudgery of cooking potatoes is gone
now," she declared. Later on it was rumoured that this machine

had earned its liberation from toil in some limbo of oblivion, alongside many a leaking pot and broken kettle.

When the house was completed, Sarmila's repressed affection found a stable object for its exercise. The infinite patience of a brick-and-mortar body makes it a convenient object of affection. The endless pother of setting and fitting, furnishing and arranging drove the two bearers to the end of their tether; one of them gave notice. The interior decoration was for Sasanka's benefit. He hardly ever sat in the drawing room; yet cushions of various patterns were devotedly spread for his tired back-bone; tables and teapoys were there, with fringed covers embroidered with flowered patterns; and many a flower-vase. He no longer entered the bedroom during the day, the reason being that in his current calendar Sunday had been adopted as twin-brother of Monday. Even on other holidays when the office was closed he managed to find some little work or other to do and went and sat in his study with his files or with his tracing cloth. Nevertheless, in the bedroom the old order persisted. In front of the spacious, cushioned sofa were the knitted slippers; beside it the *pans* ready as of old in the betel box; on the rack a *punjabi* of fine silk and a *dhoti,* pleated and crinkled, ready for wear.

It was a risky business to meddle with Sasanka's study; despite the risk Sarmila ventured in with a duster when he was not there. With unremitting diligence she strove to bring order and harmony in the medley of things useful and useless.

Thus Sarmila continued to be serviceable, but her service went a great deal unobserved. Her devotion which was once offered directly to its object was now directed to its symbols— in looking after the house and the garden, in knitting a cover for Sasanka's sofa, embroidering flower patterns on his pillow-case, in setting on a corner of his office-table bouquets of tuberoses in blue crystal vases. It cost her no little pain to worship her deity from so great a distance. She was still bathing with her secret tears the wound inflicted on her only the other day. It was the 29th of *Kartik*, Sasanka's birthday, the most festive day in her life. And usual, invitations had been sent out to friends and the house and the gate specially decorated with flower and leaf. Returning from work just before noon, Sasanka inquired: "What's the matter? A doll's wedding, I suppose!"

"Dear me! You have even forgotten it's your birthday today. But say what you will, you must stay in this evening."

"Business bends its head before no day, save the day of death."

"I won't ever ask you again, but today I have already sent out the invitations."

"Look here, Sarmila, don't you ever try to set me up as a plaything and call in the crowd to watch you play."

Saying which Sasanka hurriedly left. Shutting the bedroom door, Sarmila cried awhile.

In the afternoon the guests arrived. They readily acknowledged the paramount claim of "business". Had it been Kalidasa's birthday instead, the plea that he had to finish the third Act of *Sakuntala* would have been dismissed by them as too frivolous to be seriously entertained as an excuse for his absence. But business! However, there was enough of amusement and gaiety. Nalu Babu made everyone laugh by his caricatures of the current stage-acting; even Sarmila joined in the hilarity. Sasanka's birthday, bereft of Sasanka, prostrated itself before the business presided over by him. Even Sarmila's heart, aggrieved as it was, made its distant obeisance to the flying banner on the racing chariot of that business.

Unbending was this work, which cared for none, which ignored everything, the wife's entreaties, the invitations to friends, his own comfort even. Such faith in his work gives man faith in himself; it is the homage of self to its own power. Standing on one bank of their river—the bank of daily domestic routine—Sarmila watched with awe Sasanka's work on the other bank which made itself felt far and wide, beyond the boundaries of the household, in distant lands, on the shores of distant seas, gathering in the net of its authority men both known and unknown.

Man is at daily war with his fate; if the soft entwining arms of woman hinder him in his rugged onward march, it is but natural that he should ruthlessly break away. With loving faith Sarmila had accepted this ruthlessness. But there were times when she could not help herself, and impelled by love, her tender solicitude trespassed on forbidden ground. Rebuffed, she acknowledged the rebuff as well-merited and sorrowfully retraced her steps, praying to the Deity to watch her husband's steps where access to her was barred.

Nirad

When the prosperity of this family, riding on bank investments, was running into six figures, Sarmila was attacked and laid prostrate by a disease which could not be diagnosed. It is necessary to explain why this fact caused so much consternation.

Sarmila's father, Rajaram Babu, had owned a considerable estate in Barisal, near the mouth of the Ganges, besides holding shares in a ship-building yard at Salimar. He was born at the junction of the old times and the new. He could wrestle, hunt, wield a lathi like an expert, and was also famous for his skill at *pakhwaj*. He could recite from memory passages from *The Merchant of Venice, Julius Caesar* and *Hamlet,* held Macaulay's English as his ideal, and was an ardent admirer of Burke's orations. His appreciation of Bengali literature extended as far as *Meghnadbadh Kabya.* In his middle age he had looked upon the taking of alcoholic drinks and proscribed food as a *sine qua non* of modern culture. In his old age, however, he gave it up. Handsome and dignified in appearance, of tall and sturdy build, he dressed with meticulous care, and was of a hearty and sociable disposition. He never could say "No" to needy importunity. Though he himself was indifferent to religious forms, they were nevertheless observed in his house with great pomp, for such impressive observances add to the prestige of the family. As regards the actual worship of the deity there were the ladies of the house and many others to look after it. Had he been keen, he could easily have secured the title of a Raja for himself. If any one asked him why he was indifferent to it, Rajaram laughingly replied that his father having already conferred on him the name Raja, it would be belittling that honour to add a duplicate to it. At the Government House he was honoured with entry by the special gate. On the occasion of the customary *Jagadhatri Puja* in his house, champagne used to flow freely and high English officials had their fill of it.

After Sarmila's marriage, his widowed home was left with only his eldest son Hemanta and his youngest daughter Urmimala. "Brilliant!"—that is how the teachers had always spoken of the boy. His appearance was such that when one had passed him one turned to look at him again. There was no subject in which he did not secure the highest marks at every examination. In athletic achievements too he promised to live up to his father's reputation. It is superfluous to state that he was constantly besieged by eager agents of prospective brides, but he was averse to marriage as yet. For the present his heart was bent on the prospect of a degree at a European University, with which object he had even begun to study French and German. Meanwhile, for want of anything better, he began the study of law as well, though there was hardly any necessity for it.

About this time, however, Hemanta was suddenly attacked by a disease, whether of the intestines or of some other organ, the doctors failed to diagnose. The mysterious ailment was lodged in his robust body as in a citadel; it was as difficult to locate it as to attack it. Rajaram Babu had implicit faith in an English doctor, who enjoyed at that time high reputation as a surgeon. The surgeon began an exploration of his patient's body and, as is the way of surgeons, came to the conclusion that the trouble was rooted in some inaccessible organ which must therefore be uprooted. But when, accordingly, his skilful instruments cut open the outer layer of the flesh and exposed the interior, neither the alleged enemy nor any trace of its havoc was discovered. The mischief was irremediable and the boy died. The father was disconsolate with bitter grief. It was not the death so much as the picture of a strong, beautiful and palpitating body being mutilated which, like a black bird of prey, dug its piercing claws into his mind, and sucking his vitals day and night, brought him to the very verge of death.

Dr. Nirad Mukherjee, an old class-mate of Hemanta's, who had recently qualified as a doctor and was helping in the nursing of his friend, had protested from the very beginning that the case was being wrongly treated. He had given his own diagnosis and had advised a change of climate and a long stay in some dry place. But the prejudices of an older generation were too firmly fixed in the mind of Rajaram, who believed that only an English doctor could effectively combat the fierce onslaught of death. But after this experience his affection for Nirad and confidence in him rose disproportionately high. His young daughter Urmi too suddenly realized that here was a man of uncommon genius and said to her father:

"So young in years, father, and yet how strong his confidence in himself! See, how boldly and without any hesitation or doubt he asserted his judgment even against that of such a big and hefty foreign doctor!"

The father replied: "A doctor does not learn from books alone. Some are endowed with a rare, God-given insight—which I find Nirad has."

Thus under the impact of sorrow and in the pain of remorse, a slight proof of merit was sufficient to give rise to their loving admiration which, once born, went on growing without waiting for any further evidence of worth.

One day Rajaram called his daughter and said:

"Urmi, I almost hear Hemanta calling to me,—calling upon me to alleviate the suffering of diseased humanity. I have decided to found a hospital in his name."

"Excellent!" exclaimed Urmi exultingly, carried away by her natural enthusiasm. "Send me to Europe. Let me return as a doctor and take charge of the hospital."

The suggestion appealed to Rajaram.

"This hospital will be a *Debottar* property," he said, "and you shall be the *Shebait*. Great pain was Hemanta's portion; he loved you much; your devoted service will bring him peace in the other world. You served him day and night on his sick bed; now that service will attain a larger scope in your hands."

It did not strike him as preposterous that a girl of aristocratic family should take to medicine as a profession; for he had now deeply realized what it meant to rescue life from the clutches of disease. His own son could not survive, but the sons of others might; which would be some compensation for his loss, some lightening of the weight of his sorrow. He said to his daughter:

"Finish your science course at the University here, and then proceed to Europe."

From now on, one thought constantly recurred to Rajaram's mind, the thought of that boy Nirad. A veritable piece of gold. The more he saw him, the more he liked him. Having covered the tedious course of examinations, how smoothly he was swimming his way through the deep ocean of medical knowledge! Despite his young years, he was unmoved by the pleasures of light-hearted gaiety, deeply absorbed in the latest discoveries, discussing them, analysing them and putting them to the test, even at the risk of his professional career. He had great contempt for those who had only built up a practice, and would say: "The foolish achieve success, the worthy glory." An epigram taken from a book.

At last Rajaram told Urmi one day: "I've been thinking that it would be best for the success of the mission if you and Nirad join hands in this work. I too would feel reassured. It's rare to come across a boy like that."

Whatever else Rajaram could do, he could not be indifferent to Hemanta's opinions; and Hemanta used to say that it was barbarous of parents to ignore the daughter's wishes in the matter and to force on her a marriage of their own choice. Rajaram had once argued that marriage was not a mere personal affair but involved the whole family, and that therefore in its making not only desire but experience also should count. But argue as he might, and despite his own likes and dislikes, so great was his affection for Hemanta that in this family it was really the latter's will that prevailed.

Nirad Mukherjee had always been a frequent visitor. Hemanta had nicknamed him the Owl. When invited to explain the significance, Hemanta used to say: "This man is mythological; he has no age, only learning; hence I call him Minerva's mount." Nirad was a frequent guest at their tea-table, where he would often enter into a terrific argument with Hemanta. No doubt, Urmi was in his mind; if his behaviour gave no indication of the fact, it was because his nature had not fitted him for the ways appropriate to such expression. He could discuss, but could not converse. Even if the heat of youth was in him, he was without its glow. Hence he took a particular delight in running down those in whom the exuberance of youth was self-evident. Naturally, therefore, no one had reckoned him as a suitor for Urmi's hand, though now it so happened that this very apparent indifference raised Urmi's respect for him to the point of veneration.

When Rajaram had made it quite clear that, provided his daughter had no objection, it would make him happy to see her wedded to Nirad, Urmi signified her consent by a nod of her head; only adding that the wedding would have to wait till she had completed her course of education, both here and in Europe.

"That's as it should be," replied the father, "as long as the engagement is accepted and made definite by both the parties."

It did not take long to get Nirad's consent, though his manner implied that for a scientist marriage was a kind of self-abnegation, almost amounting to suicide. Perhaps as a partial alleviation of this calamity, he made it a condition that in education as in other matters Urmi would be guided entirely by him, so that he might gradually mould and fashion her as his future wife. This training would be scientific, rigidly prescribed and regulated, infallible as a laboratory process.

"The birds and beasts," explained Nirad to Urmi "come out ready-made from Nature's workshop. But human life is in a raw, unformed state. It's for man to put it into shape."

Urmi gently replied: "You may by all means experiment. I'll make no difficulties."

"The life-force in you is dispersed," went on Nirad. "It has to be mobilized and marshalled round one single object of your life. Then will your life gain a meaning. When that which is scattered is gathered and concentrated towards a single aim and becomes intense and dynamic, then alone can we call it a moral organism."

Urmi was thrilled. So many young men frequented their tea-table and their tennis court, but not one ever said anything thought-provoking or did anything but yawn, if some one else happened to say it.

Indeed, Nirad did have a way of imparting the utmost profundity to anything he uttered. In whatever he said Urmi discovered a wonderful depth of meaning. Amazingly intellectual!

Rajaram would often invite his elder son-in-law to his house and tried to encourage intimacy between the two sons-in-law.

"What an insufferably cheeky blighter!" remarked Sasanka to Sarmila. "He thinks we are all his pupils—and that too at the very bottom of the very lowest Form."

"That is your jealousy," replied Sarmila laughing. "Why, I rather like him."

"Why not change places with your younger sister?" asked Sasanka.

"That might mean a great relief to you," replied Sarmila, "but to me—it is different."

Nirad too did not seem to feel any particularly brotherly regard for Sasanka. "A mason—not a scientist!" he said to himself. "He has hands—but what of the brain?"

Sasanka would often chaff his sister-in-law about Nirad.

"It is time you changed your name."

"In the English manner?"

"No, in the pure Sanskrit way."

"Let's hear the new name."

"Vidyut-lata. Nirad will like it. He is familiar with this thing in his laboratory. Now he will have it harnessed at home."

To himself he said: "Indeed, the name does suit her." A secret pang pricked him. "Pity that such a girl should fall into the hands of so great a prig." In whose hands it would have consoled and pleased Sasanka to see her fall, it is hard to say.

Shortly after, Rajaram died. The future rightful master of Urmi now wholeheartedly took upon himself the responsibility of guiding her mind to its full maturity.

Good-looking as Urmimala was, she seemed even better looking than she was; the luminous intensity of her mind scintillated in the lively movements of her body. She was eager about everything: interested in science, even more so in literature; greatly excited at the prospect of witnessing a football match on the maidan; not indifferent to the cinema; must be present when the physicist from Europe lectured at the Presidency College; listened to the radio and though she might now and again ejaculate an "ugh!" was nevertheless interested; ran out to the verandah to watch a wedding party pass by, with its bride-groom and the fanfare of trumpets; was a frequent visitor to the Zoo which she enjoyed greatly, specially when she stood watching the monkeys in their cage; would accompany her father and sit by his side when he went angling; played tennis; was particularly good at badminton. All these interests she had derived from her brother. Slender and delicate as a frail creeper, she swayed with every breath of the wind. She dressed simply but elegantly; knew how to bring out the full beauty of the figure in a *sari* by a slight turn here, a right twist there, a little tightening here and a little loosening there—in a way whose secret no one could catch. Though she could not sing well, she could play on the *sitar*. When she played, it was difficult to say whether it was a thing to hear or a sight to see—it seemed as though her wild unruly fingers were in an uproar. She was never in want of a topic for conversation, never waited for a proper excuse for laughter. She had an inexhaustible talent for creating company out of dullness and filling emptiness with her mere presence. Only in Nirad's presence she became an altogether different person, as though the wind had left the sail and the boat had to be slowly and gently towed.

Every one said that Urmi's nature was like her brother's, full of vitality and liveliness. Urmi knew that it was her brother who had released the current of her mind. Hemanta used to say: "Our homes are like moulds for fashioning human beings of clay, which is why the foreign juggler has succeeded so long in keeping thirty-three crores of puppets dancing to his tune. When the time comes, I'll break into this puppet-dom and wreak the havoc of a Kalapahar." The time never came—but he left Urmi's mind very living indeed.

What caused all the trouble was the extreme rigidity of Nirad's method of work. He prescribed a course of study for her, and admonished her thus: "Look here, Urmi, if you let your mind spill over in its onward march, what will be left in your pitcher at the end of the journey?" He added: "You are like a butterfly, restlessly flitting about without gathering anything. You should be like a bee. Every moment is of account. Life is not dalliance."

Of late Nirad had been studying books on Pedagogy borrowed from the Imperial Library. All these maxims were to be found in them. His very language was of the books, for he did not know how to put things in simple and natural words of his own. Urmi was left in no doubt that she was at fault. Great was her mission and yet every now and then her mind wandered away from it, leaving her in a state of perpetual self-reproof. Before her was the example of Nirad. How amazingly steadfast, how single-minded of purpose! How sternly he had set his face against all fun and frivolity! If any work of fiction or light literature caught his eye on Urmi's table, it was immediately forfeited. One day when he came to pay his supervisory call, he learnt that she had gone to spend the evening at an English theatre to see Gilbert and Sullivan's *Mikado*. She had never missed such chances while her brother lived. She was severely taken to task by Nirad. He spoke in English in a tone of the utmost gravity:

"Have you already begun to forget that you have dedicated your life to the mission of making your brother's death fruitful in service?"

The words stung Urmi with extreme remorse. She said to herself: "What an uncommon power of seeing through the mind this person has! Indeed, it does seem that my grief is losing its intensity—I myself couldn't realize it. Shame on this fickleness in my character!'

She began a strict watch on herself, removing every trace of attractiveness from her dress. The *sari* was now coarse, its colour all gone. The chocolates were still in the drawer, but the desire for them was gone. She leashed her unchained mind to the dry post of duty within a severely restricted orbit. Her elder sister scolded her; as for Sasanka, the bitter epithets he showered on Nirad were too strong and too foreign to be found in the dictionary—they were not exactly pleasant to hear.

Sasanka and Nirad had one thing in common: both took to English—Sasanka when in a furiously abusive temper, and Nirad when he was discoursing on something profound. Nirad disliked it most when Urmi was invited to her sister's house. It was not that she merely went—she was most eager to go. This intimacy of blood relationship seemed to cut through his own rights over her.

One day with a grave countenance he said to Urmi:

"Please don't mind the unpleasant words which my sense of responsibility towards you obliges me to say. I must warn you that this intimacy is injurious to the development of your character. Family attachment makes you blind—but I can see quite clearly the likelihood of degradation."

The first mortgage deed of the thing called Urmi's character being in Nirad's strong box, the loss would naturally be his if anything happened to that character. As a result of Nirad's ban, Urmi, on various pretexts, made her visits to Bhowanipore very rare. This imposition of restraint on herself she regarded as a sort of repayment of her huge debt. For, what sacrifice could be greater for a votary of science than that which Nirad had made by encumbering his work for his own ideal with this life-long charge of her life?

Though in a sense Urmi had got used to the unhappy strain of withholding herself from every enjoyment, now and again her mind was seized with a painful yearning which she could not wholly suppress as a mere frivolity. Nirad merely directed her—why did he never for a moment woo her? For such an expression of ardour on his part her heart ever waited, and for want of it, remained unfulfilled; her very acts of duty became dry and lifeless. Sometimes when she suddenly caught a look of wistfulness in Nirad's eyes, it seemed to her that the deep secret of his heart would now be laid bare. But, God knows, even if deep yearning was in him anywhere, its language was not known to him. And because he could not express himself, he found fault with the urge for self-expression and prided himself on the very dumbness of his agitated heart, which he thought was but a proof of his strength of character. "Sentimentality is not in my grain," he declared. On such occasions Urmi felt like crying, but so hypnotised was she by her own devotion that she too thought that this indeed was manliness. And then she would begin again ruthlessly chastising her "weak" mind. But try as she might, she could not get away from the consciousness that the spontaneous readiness with which, under the impact of great sorrow, she had at first undertaken her arduous mission had steadily flagged until now it had to cling for support to another's will.

Nirad put it quite plainly to her: "You had better understand, Urmi, that it is no good expecting from me the kind of adulation which girls commonly hope for from men. What I give you is something far more true and valuable than all their made-up pretty talk."

With bent head Urmi silently wondered: "Can't anything ever remain hidden from him?"

She is unable to fix her mind on anything. On the roof-terrace she paces about alone. The afternoon fades into dusk. Across the uneven heights of the city mansions, the sun sinks to its rest beyond the distant masts of ships on the Ganges. The clouds with their many-coloured bars raise barricades at the day's frontier. Gradually the barricades fade out of sight. The moon climbs above the church spire. In the misty light the city looks like a dream, like an enchanted land. She wonders, is life really so uncompromisingly severe? Can it be so niggardly as to allow no holiday, no gift of joy? And then a maddening impulse seizes her, a desire to do something wicked, to shout at the top of her voice, "I don't care!"

Urmimala

Nirad finished the piece of research he had taken in hand, and sent the thesis to a scientific association in Europe. It brought him recognition as well as a scholarship. He made up his mind to cross the seas for a degree at a European university.

The moment of parting was not marked by any tender words. He merely kept on repeating "Now that I am leaving, I am afraid you will slacken in your efforts."

"Have no fear," replied Urmi.

"I am leaving detailed instructions in writing," said Nirad, "to guide your future conduct and studies."

"I shall follow them faithfully."

"I'll remove these books from your almirah," went on Nirad, "and leave them locked up in my house."

"You may take them," said Urmi handing him the key.

He glanced once at her *sitar* but hesitated and said nothing. But he felt obliged by his sense of responsibility to utter the last admonition.

"My only fear is that if you start once more frequenting Sasanka Babu's house your steadiness will again falter. There's no doubt of it. Please don't imagine that I am out to malign Sasanka Babu. He is an excellent man. I've seen very few Bengalis with his zeal and aptitude for business. His only drawback is that he acknowledges no ideals. To tell you the truth, at times I feel very apprehensive about him."

This led to further elaboration of Sasanka's many drawbacks. Nirad could not help giving vent to his grave concern at the several other shortcomings in Sasanka's character which, though dormant then, were bound to become more active with age. But that, nevertheless, he was an excellent man, Nirad was anxious vociferously to admit, adding in the same breath that it was imperative for Urmi to guard herself against his house. It would be a sure degradation for Urmi if her mind ever came down to their level.

"But why are you so apprehensive?" asked Urmi.

"Shall I tell you why? You won't resent it?"

"You have taught me to bear the truth. I will stand it though I know it won't be easy."

"Then listen. I've observed a sort of likeness between your temperament and Sasanka Babu's. It's this very light-heartedness of his that appeals to you, isn't it?"

'Is this man omniscient?' Urmi wondered. Undoubtedly she liked her brother-in-law very much—and mainly for his capacity for rollicking laughter, his pleasantries and his waggish pranks. Then also he knew just what flower Urmi loved best and what colour pleased her most in a *sari*.

"Yes, that's true, I like it," she admitted.

"Sarmila-didi's love," proceeded Nirad, "is serene and deep; her care and devotion are like an act of religious merit; her duty knows no holiday. It's by virtue of these that Sasanka Babu is enabled to give his whole mind to his work. But the day you go to Bhowanipore the mask falls off his face—there he is with his tomfooleries, pulling out your hair-pins and letting loose your coiffure, snatching your book and hiding it on the almirah-top. His interest in tennis suddenly becomes overwhelming despite other engagements."

Urmi could not help admitting to herself that it was this very naughtiness of Sasankada's which drew her to him. Her own irresponsible girlishness surged up in her when she was with him, and he too was no less a victim of her pranks. Her Didi would smile her gentle, serene smile at their wild frolics. Sometimes she would mildly chide, though the chiding was but a pretence.

"You should stick only to that," said Nirad, winding up, "which gives the least scope to your own nature. There was little fear so long as I was there, for my nature is the exact contrary of yours. While I was your guardian it was impossible that any of my acts should ever vitiate your mind."

"I'll always bear in mind what you have said," said Urmi, her head bent low.

"I am leaving behind some books for you," said Nirad. "Read specially the chapters I have marked. You will find them useful."

Urmi needed this tutoring. Of late she had been assailed by doubts that perhaps she had been misled by the first fervour of her enthusiasm in selecting medicine as her line, that perhaps she had no aptitude for it. The books marked by Nirad would act like a rope tied to her, towing her upstream.

After Nirad's departure Urmi subjected herself to even harder severities. Except that she went to college, she practically shut herself up as if in a zenana. Returning home at the end of the day, she would again ruthlessly chain her mind to study, however much the tired mind yearned for rest. She made no progress whatsoever, her listless wandering mind vainly lingering over the same page. But she would not admit defeat. Because Nirad was not there, his will from its distance began to work all the more effectively on her.

She particularly despised herself when in the midst of work she was haunted by memories of the past. Many were her admirers among the young men; to some she had been indifferent, towards some she had felt drawn. Though in no case had it yet matured into love, the longing to love, like the sweet and gentle breeze of spring, played about her mind; so that now she would be humming a tune all by herself, now copying a poem that had caught her fancy, now playing on the *sitar,* if the mind were stirred a little too deeply. Nowadays it was not uncommon that as she sat in the evening, her eyes fixed on the pages of her book, she was suddenly startled to discover that her mind was haunted by the memory of a face and of a day which had moved her but little at the time. Sometimes the face would be of one whose persistent wooing had actually irritated her, though today that very memory seemed to stir in her mind a pang of discontent, as the light, fleeting wings of the butterfly leave on the flower a touch of spring.

The more fiercely she tried to fling these thoughts away from her mind, the more surely they boomeranged back into it. She had placed a photograph of Nirad on her desk at which she would look long and steadily. The light of intellect was in that face, but no trace of the heart's ardour. If that face did not call, to what was her spirit to respond? All she could do was to work up her mind into a state of exalted contemplation of his genius, his heroic striving, his unblemished character and her own undreamt-of good fortune.

We might as well state here that in one respect Nirad had triumphed. At the time of his engagement to Urmi, Sasanka, as well as several other skeptics, had laughed and had mockingly declared: "The simple-minded Rajaram Babu has convinced himself that Nirad is an idealist. An idealist indeed! No pious platitudes can hide the fact that his idealism is secretly worming its way into Urmi's purse. True he has 'sacrificed' himself— but to the deity enthroned in the Imperial Bank. Where we would plainly and bluntly tell our father-in-law that we need money, which won't be wasted but will on the contrary be used for his daughter's benefit, this great man condescends to marry only for the sake of a great mission! And then he will daily translate that mission into figures in his father-in-law's cheque book."

Knowing that such comments were inevitable, Nirad had told Urmi that the one condition of his marriage was that he would not touch a penny of her money, but would depend entirely on his own earnings. When the would-be father-in-law proposed to send him to Europe, Nirad did not agree, even though it meant that he would have to wait long. He had moreover told Rajaram Babu: "Whatever money you choose to donate for the founding of the hospital should be put down in the name of your daughter. When I take charge of the hospital I'll draw no remuneration for my work. I am a doctor. I don't have to worry about my livelihood."

Such extreme disinterestedness only confirmed Rajaram Babu's love and admiration for Nirad and gave Urmi cause for much pride. On the other hand, the fact that this pride had a legitimate cause turned Sarmila's mind against Nirad. 'Pshaw! Let's see how long these heroics last!' Henceforth whenever Nirad was in the midst of one of his usual, profound discourses, Sarmila would suddenly get up and walk out of the room, her head mockingly cocked sideways, her steps audible from a considerable distance. For Urmi's sake she said nothing but her silence by its very irony was withering enough.

At first every mail brought from Nirad four or five pages of long-winded counsel. After some time, however, there came a startling telegram, demanding a considerable sum of money, urgently needed for his study. Though the pride which Urmi had cherished as her supreme treasure received a blow, the telegram was also in a way secretly comforting. For as the days passed and Nirad's absence was prolonged, her original nature had begun to seek ways of escape from the barricade of duty she had erected round it. Under various pretexts she would deceive herself and then reproach herself. Nirad's appeal for money therefore came as a consolation to her contrite mind.

Handing the telegram to the estate-manager, Urmi said hesitatingly, "Kaka-babu, the money—"

"I can't make out what it means," said the manager. "All along we have been under the impression that your money was unacceptable to him." The manager did not like Nirad.

"But in a foreign land—" Urmi faltered, unable to finish the sentence.

"That the foreign soil can change our native character, I know well enough," said Kaka-babu. "But how are we going to keep pace with such changes?"

"But he might be landed in difficulties if the money is not sent to him," protested Urmi.

"Very well then, I'll send it. Don't be anxious. But mark my words, this is only the beginning, not the end of it."

That this was not the end was speedily proved when another call arrived for a still bigger sum—this time for reasons of health.

"I had better consult Sasanka Babu," said the manager, looking grave.

"Please, do not let Didi and others come to know of it," pleaded Urmi greatly flustered.

"I don't like to take all the responsibility on my shoulders."

"But all this money will in any case be his one day."

"Before that we must see to it that it is not thrown away."

"But we must also consider his health."

"Ill-health is of various sorts. Exactly what he is suffering from is not known. May be, if he returned here the change of climate would restore him to health. We might arrange his passage back."

The proposal to get Nirad back greatly perturbed Urmi. She attributed it to her concern for his studies.

The Kaka was saying: "Well, let the money be sent this time,—though I fear it will only aggravate the doctor's malady."

Radhagovinda was a near relation of Urmi's. The innuendo in his words stirred a faint breath of suspicion in her mind. "May be, it's better to let Didi know." On the other hand the question kept recurring to her, poking her:

"Why don't I feel dejected—as I should?"

About this time Sarmila's disease had begun to cause anxiety, the tragedy of her brother's case adding alarm to anxiety. A number of doctors were set on the trail of its mysterious source. Smiling her wearied smile, Sarmila remarked: "The culprit will elude the C.I.D., only the innocent will be harassed to death."

"Let the Inspectors carry on their legitimate investigation— but third degree methods, no, never!" Sasanka assured her.

Sasanka had two heavy contracts on hand, one with a jute mill on the Ganges' bank, the other at Tollygunge in the garden house of the Mirpur Zamindar. The workers' tenements at the jute mill which had to be completed within three months, besides the several tube-wells in different localities he had taken in hand, left him no time to spare. Between the pressure of his work and the frequent claims of Sarmila's illness on his time, he was in a state of constant anxiety.

In the many years of their married life he had never had to worry on account of his wife's health, with the result that this time the strain of her illness drove him into a state of almost childish flurry. Leaving his work unattended he would return home and sit helplessly by her side. Gently caressing her hair he would inquire how she felt that day.

"I'm all right," Sarmila would promptly answer. "Please don't worry unnecessarily."

Encouraged by his own wishful thinking, Sasanka believed the obviously unbelievable and felt greatly relieved.

"I've been entrusted with a huge contract by the Raja of Dhenkanal, and have to discuss the plan with the Dewan. I'll return at the earliest—before the doctor comes."

"I beg of you," pleaded Sarmila anxiously, "don't let unnecessary hurry spoil your work. Don't I understand that your presence is needed there! Of course, you must go. If you don't, I'll only get worse. There are enough people to attend to me."

To build up a magnificent fortune had become Sasanka's obsession day and night. It was not wealth but the magnificence of it which drew him on. Man is made that way; he responds to the call of glory. One may despise wealth only when it barely and meagrely suffices; but the moment its summit is raised high, men flock to admire it. Not that they are any the better for it, but because they delight in watching the splendour of eminence. As Sasanka sat by his wife's side, his uneasy mind could not help apprehending where lay a possible obstacle to his career of achievement. Sarmila knew that this apprehension in her husband's mind was not due to any miserly greed but was rooted in a manly ambition to build up from the very bottom a tower of triumph. Considering his glory as her own, she did not like him to neglect his work in order to attend to her, however pleasing such attentions in themselves. She therefore constantly urged him to return to his duty.

Her own duties caused her endless anxiety. Now that she was laid up in bed, who knew what mess the servants were making—no doubt using bad ghee in cooking, neglecting to keep hot water in the bath at the appointed hour or to change the bed linen in time; no one to see if the drains had been properly cleaned. Well she knew what confusion it meant if the clothes from the washer-man were not properly received and checked. Unable to bear the strain she would secretly leave her bed to see things for herself. The pain would increase, the temperature shoot up, and the doctor would be puzzled.

At last she sent for her sister Urmimala. "Never mind your college for a few days—come to the rescue of my household, otherwise I can't even die in peace."

Those who have read the story so far will at this stage smile knowingly and declare, "We know the rest." Indeed, it does not need much intelligence to anticipate. What must happen does happen, and no more need happen. Nor is it necessary to imagine that in the game of life Fortune will necessarily keep back her cards, throwing dust into Sarmila's eyes.

Urmi was enthusiastic at this opportunity of serving her sister and was ready, since there was no alternative, to set aside all other tasks. Moreover, so she argued, nursing a patient was quite in line with her future medical career. She got ready a leather-bound book of charts for recording graphically the daily variations of disease. She also made up her mind to read up from books all she could gather about her sister's illness, lest the attending physician look down upon her for her ignorance. Physiology being her subject in M.Sc., she would have no difficulty in following the therapeutic terminology. In short, having convinced herself that attending on her sister would mean no snapping of the thread of duty but would rather help her to pursue it the more arduously and steadfastly, she packed all her books and papers in a bag and presented herself at the Bhowanipore residence. She did not have to pore over the bulky medical manuals, for not even the specialists were able to diagnose the disease.

Imagining herself as the sole warden of the sick room, she very gravely announced to her sister: "Since I am here to see that the doctor's instructions are strictly carried out, you will have to listen to whatever I say."

Amused at the elaborate earnestness of her attitude, Sarmila replied, smiling: "Indeed, what teacher has coached you in such earnestness—this fanaticism of a new convert? As a matter of fact, I have called you here only because I must have some one to carry out my instructions. Your hospital is not yet ready, but my household is in full swing; so meanwhile take charge of it so that your Didi may have some relief."

And so she was relieved of her duty in the sick room at her Didi's own insistence.

Now Urmi became the viceregent in the kingdom of her sister's household. Things were in chaos there and needed immediate measures. In the scheme of this household every activity of each member, high and low, was directed and subordinated to one great purpose, namely the comfort and convenience of the gentleman who presided over it. That this gentleman was utterly helpless and pathetically incapable of looking after his own physical needs—this impression was too firmly rooted in Sarmila's mind to be ever dislodged. When she found that he had not even noticed the hole which his cigar had burnt in his sleeve, she was not a little amused, but was at the same time filled with a great tenderness. The engineer would bustle off in the morning to his duty in such a great hurry as to forget to turn the tap off after his wash, only to find on his return the bed-room floor one sheet of water and the carpet in a mess. At the very outset when the tap was being installed, Sarmila had objected, knowing that a tap so near the bed would only result in his hands in a daily recurrence of an all-round mess in the room. But the great engineer must set up every sort of complicated nuisance in the name of scientific amenities. Once in a fit of originality he had contrived an entirely original model of a stove, with shutters and funnels on all sides for conserving heat and for the speedy discharge of ash, and fitted inside with a variety of special devices of cells and shelves for baking, grilling, boiling and what not. If, in the interest of peace and good will, the invention was accorded a warm domestic welcome, the reception was in words and manner only, not in any use made of it. Adult babies have their hobbies, which they forget in a day but which, if resisted, lead only to friction. Bored with the monotony of daily usage, they break into something spectacular, to which women need pay no more than lip-service, while free to do as they choose. This responsibility of husband-tending Sarmila had long enjoyed.

A long time indeed. It was impossible for Sarmila to conceive of Sasanka's world without herself in it. But now she was afraid that the courier of Death would intervene between that world and its presiding goddess. She even feared that after death her bodiless spirit would have no peace if Sasanka's bodily comforts were not well looked after. Fortunately there was Urmi. Though not so gentle as her sister, Urmi could nevertheless carry on the work, for after all hers was a woman's touch. Without the tender grace of such a touch the daily provision of a man's life is left dry and flavourless, devoid of charm. And so as she watched Urmi's beautiful hands peel and cut an apple, rind and slice an orange, neatly pick out the seeds of a pomegranate and tastefully set everything on a plate of white stone, Sarmila seemed to realize her own self in her sister. A stream of directions would issue ceaselessly from her sick bed:

"Do fill his cigarette case, Urmi."

"Can't you see it won't occur to him to change his soiled kerchief?"

"He won't have the sense to ask the bearer to clean his shoes—see how stiff they look with their coating of cement and sand!"

"Do have the pillow cases changed, dear."

"Put away these paper scraps in the wastepaper basket."

"Do peep into his study, Urmi, I'm sure he has left the key of his cash box on the desk."

"Don't forget it's time to transplant the cauliflower seedlings."

"Please ask the *mali* to prune the rose plants."

"Look at those daubs of lime on the back of his coat! Do wait a moment, why this hurry? Please, Urmi dear, brush them off."

Though Urmi was used to books rather than to domestic work, she thoroughly enjoyed her new duties. Having broken away from the rigid discipline of her life, these varied ministrations gave her a sense of freedom. The under-current of anxiety and devotion beneath the smooth running of this household was little realized by her, for the strain of its direction was borne by her sister. To Urmi it all seemed a play, a kind of holiday, occupation without an aim. Here was a world in itself, wholly different from her own old world; here no aim, no object to be achieved held up its warning finger before her; and yet the day was full of activity, delightfully varied. She had not to account for each mistake, each shortcoming. If her Didi tried to chide her, ever so mildly, Sasanka would laugh it all away, as though the very shortcomings of Urmi added a special relish to his enjoyment. Indeed, the fact that their little world had now lost its look of earnest responsibility, that in the new atmosphere of laxity, mistake and inadvertence no longer mattered, was to Sasanka a source of great relaxation and amusement. Life seemed a picnic now. The fact that Urmi never seemed worried, never looked miserable, never felt ashamed of little mishaps, but always overflowed with enthusiasm in whatever she did helped considerably to lighten the strain on Sasanka's mind of his own heavy responsibility of work. Nowadays he was always eager to return home as soon as his work was over—sometimes even when the work was not over.

It must be confessed that Urmi was no expert at household management. Nevertheless, it was evident that, if not by virtue of her work, by the charm of her personality she filled a great and longstanding void in this house. What this void was, it is difficult to define in words. And so when Sasanka returned home these days, he experienced the buoyancy of a playful, holiday spirit in the atmosphere. This enjoyment was not of domestic comfort, nor was it merely in the atmosphere. It had a rapturous embodiment. Indeed, it was Urmi's own holiday spirit which filled the void in this house, making day and night radiant with her liveliness, sending waves of blood pulsing through the work-weary Sasanka. On the other hand, the unmistakable consciousness that she was a source of joy to Sasanka made Urmi happy. For the satisfaction that her mere presence could make another happy had long been denied to her, causing her no little humiliation.

The care and attention to his personal needs to which the master of the house had been so long accustomed, now began to seem to him of but secondary importance. He was pleased with everything now, delighted almost without any cause. He remonstrated with his wife:

"Why do you worry over trifles? An occasional change of routine does not necessarily mean inconvenience—in fact, it is quite a relief."

Sasanka's mind was now like a river in the interval between ebb and flow. The pressure of work had slowed down. The tempestuous protests that the work would suffer, the loss would be serious, et cetera, which had been so frequent before, were hardly audible now. At any such manifestation Urmi would blow out the solemnity with her laughter. If she found him looking unusually serious, she would inquire: "Has your bogy been here today—that green-turbaned broker, from God knows where—has he been frightening you?"

"How on earth did you know of him?" asked Sasanka in surprise.

"Oh, I know him very well. I found him sitting in the verandah that day. You had gone out, so I kept him engaged in conversation. He is from Bikanir; his wife was burnt to death when her mosquito-net caught fire. He is looking for another."

"In that case he will come here daily at the right time— just when I am out. As long as he has not discovered a wife, the dream will grow on him."

"Just let me know what you want of him. I believe I can get it out of him."

If nowadays the fat figure of profit in Sasanka's income-ledger came for a while to a standstill in its numerical progress, he was not greatly perturbed. Never before had Sasanka Mazumdar's enthusiasm for listening-in to the evening radio been so pronounced. When Urmi dragged him to it, he did not spurn it as frivolous, nor think the time wasted. He even went to Dum Dum one early morning to watch the aeroplanes take off. Nor was scientific curiosity the main attraction.

He learnt for the first time to go shopping in the New Market. It was Sarmila who used occasionally to visit the Market to buy fish, meat, fruits and vegetables. She looked upon this work as her own special responsibility and never dreamt nor even desired that Sasanka should accompany her on such errands. But Urmi never bought anything, she merely picked up things, handled them, looked them over and haggled with the shopkeeper. If Sasanka attempted to buy anything for her, she snatched away his purse and locked it up in her bag.

Urmi did not in the least share Sasanka's concern for his work. Sometimes when she wasted too much of his time, he lost his temper with her; the result was so disastrous that to retrieve the tragedy he had to sacrifice twice as much time.

Between the imminence of tears in Urmi's eyes and the urgent claims of his work he did his best to finish as much of his work as he could in his office before returning home. But even there he found it difficult to stay beyond the afternoon. If sometimes he was detained for any reason, he found awaiting him on return Urmi's stony, impenetrable silence. Sasanka was secretly thrilled at this expression of aggrieved affection in Urmi's eyes misty with suppressed tears.

Very innocently he would plead: "If you have sworn not to talk to me, I must respect your *satyagraha,* but for heaven's sake, Urmi, don't give up playing—it was not included in your vow." And forthwith he brought the tennis rackets. When about to win the set, he deliberately chose to lose it. Next morning on waking up he would be seized with remorse for having wasted his time the previous day.

In the afternoon of a holiday, as he sat at his desk deeply absorbed in some difficult problem, a red-and-blue pencil in his right hand, the fingers of his left hand needlessly ruffling his hair, Urmi came and announced: "I've fixed it up with that broker of yours—he'll take me to see the Temple of Pareshnath. Come with me—please!"

"No, not today, please," pleaded Sasanka, "it's impossible to get away."

But Urmi was undaunted by the majesty of work.

"How can you," she protested, "without any compunction leave a young, helpless and unprotected girl in the hands of that green-turban? Is that what you call your chivalry?"

In the end, unable to resist, Sasanka left his desk and drove the car.

If Sarmila came to learn of any such outrage, she was greatly annoyed, for she considered it an unforgivable liberty on the part of a woman to intrude on man's field of activity. She had always treated Urmi as a child and thought her so even now; nevertheless, in no case was she going to let her turn her husband's office into a play-room. She sent for Urmi and talked to her severely. Her words might have borne fruit, if Sasanka, overhearing his wife's angry tone, had not come and stood behind the door, winking encouragingly at Urmi and beckoning to her with a pack of cards to slip away to his office to learn poker from him. It was no time for playing cards, nor had any such idea been in his mind. It was only to spare Urmi the painful humiliation of her sister's bitter scolding which hurt him almost more than it hurt Urmi. He himself might, by pleading, cajoling or mild reproof, restrain her from interfering with his work, but that Sarmila should take Urmi to task for it was more than he could bear.

Sarmila sent for him and remonstrated. "Why must you indulge her so much—at all hours of the day? Your work is bound to suffer."

"Ah, the poor lonely child," commiserated Sasanka, "if she finds no playmate, how can she live in this lonely house?"

So much for her childish pranks. But it also happened that when Sasanka sat engrossed in some architectural plan, Urmi would pull up a chair by his side and ask him to explain it to her. She was quick of understanding and could steer through mathematical formulae. Sasanka was delighted and would set her problems which she solved. She insisted on accompanying him when he went out on inspection in the steam launch of the jute company. And she not merely accompanied him, but challenged his figures and conclusions, thrilling him with her arguments, which Sasanka found more delightful than any poetry. So that now he was not afraid of bringing some of his office work home. Whether drafting plans or working out problems, she was at his side, listening to his explanation and following his arguments. Though the progress in Sasanka's work was rather slow, it seemed to him that the long hours spent at it were fruitfully employed.

Sarmila was scandalised. While she could appreciate Urmi's childish waywardness and might affectionately tolerate her shortcomings in the management of the household, she could not but strongly disapprove of her unrestrained frequent excursions into her husband's workaday world which she herself had looked upon as absolutely beyond the reach of the feminine mind. Sheer impertinence, it seemed to her—directly contravening the teaching of the Bhagavat Gita which enjoined that one should keep within the limits of one's own nature, one's *svadharma*.

Unable to restrain herself, she asked Urmi one day: "Can it be that you really enjoy all this tracing and drafting and calculating?"

"I do indeed—greatly, Didi."

"Really!" exclaimed Sarmila skeptically. "Or is it only to please him that you pretend this interest?"

Well, why not? we might ask, since all that Sarmila desired was to make Sasanka happy. But while she would have done it by attending to his personal comforts, this particular way of making him happy did not accord with her conception of happiness. She would repeatedly send for her husband and expostulate:

"Why do you waste so much of your time with her? Your work suffers. She's a child, what will she understand of all this?"

"She understands no less than I do," replied Sasanka, thinking that praise of her sister must please his wife. The simpleton!

In the beginning when in the excitement and pride of his work Sasanka had cooled in his attentions to his wife, Sarmila had not only accepted the fact as inevitable but had actually felt pride in it, and had steadily taught her devoted heart to restrain the ardour of its solicitude, saying, "Man belongs to the race of kings; he must perpetually extend his empire of heroic achievements, otherwise he would be less than woman; for while the natural grace and sweetness of woman, her inborn wealth of love, are sufficient in themselves for the fulfilment of her function in this world, man has to vindicate himself by constant battle and strife. In the old days kings marched out to new conquests, not always out of greed of territory, but to vindicate over again their proud claim to manliness. Far be it from woman to stand in the way of this pride!"

And so Sarmila had not stood in the way; of her own accord she had effaced herself completely from the path to which he had set himself. Once she had held him tight in the net of her devoted attachment, but gradually, at no little cost to her happiness, she had loosened the bonds, until she had learnt to serve him from behind the scenes.

And now, alas! she was shocked to see him sink lower day by day. From her sick bed she could not watch everything, but what she could sense was sufficient. Looking into Sasanka's face she could see that he was always in a kind of trance. That this mere slip of a girl should in a few days have shaken that stern worker out of his arduous striving—the ignominy was more agonising to Sarmila than the actual pain of her disease.

There was no doubt that the little details of his personal comfort to which Sasanka had been used so long were being neglected; for example, it would be suddenly noticed that his favourite dish was missing at the table. Some sort of excuse would of course be offered. But in the old days no excuse was ever tolerated in this house, no such inadvertence was ever overlooked, but was severely rebuked. What a great revolution indeed that in this very same disciplined household the direst negligence was now looked upon as more amusing than reprehensible! Whom to blame! If Urmi did as her sister desired and sat on her cane stool in the kitchen, supervising the culinary operations—while at the same time carrying on

her investigations into the life-history of the cook—suddenly
Sasanka would storm into the kitchen with his peremptory,
"Come along! Have done with all this!"

"Why, what do you want me to do instead?"

"I'm off duty now. Come along, let's go and see the
Victoria Memorial. I'll explain to you why it looks so
ludicrously pretentious."

Urmi's impressionable mind found it hard to stick to her
duties in face of so great a temptation. Sarmila was well aware
that her sister's absence would make little material difference
to the excellence of the cuisine, nevertheless the solicitude of
a feminine touch did impart grace and charm to a man's
comfort. But what was the use of worrying when each day
it became clearer that comfort hardly mattered to him any
longer—he was so happy!

Thus a sort of uneasiness grew upon and possessed Sarmila's
mind. Tossing about in her sick bed she kept on repeating to
herself: "This much I have learnt before death—whatever else
I could do, I could not make him happy. I thought I should
see myself in Urmi, but Urmi is not myself, she has her own
individuality." She looked through the window and thought:
"She cannot replace me, nor could I replace her. My absence
would make some difference, but hers would create a void."

In the midst of these thoughts she suddenly remembered
that winter was approaching, and it was time for the warm
clothing to be put out to dry in the sun. She sent for Urmi
who was playing table-tennis with Sasanka.

"Here's the key, Urmi. Please have all the winter clothes
taken out and spread on the roof in the sun."

Hardly had Urmi turned the key in the lock when Sasanka
turned up and said: "There's plenty of time for all that. Come
and finish the game first."

"But Didi—"

"All right, I'll get you your Didi's permission."

Didi did give her permission—with a deep sigh. Calling
the maid-servant she asked her to put a cold compress on her
head.

Although this spell of sudden freedom after a long confinement
had tended to make Urmi forgetful of herself, there were
times when she was suddenly reminded of her life's stern
mission. She knew that she was not free; she was bound by
her own self-imposed vow, bound also by that very vow to
another individual, bound to his guardianship, bound to
follow the daily routine he had set for her. She could in no
way refute his life-long claim over her. It was easy enough
to acknowledge this claim when Nirad was there. She seemed
to draw strength from him. But now while the heart was
estranged, only the conscience was insistent, making the
heart still more rebellious. The very difficulty of excusing her
transgression made it possible for her to indulge it. In order,
as it were, to drug this uneasiness with opium, she tried
constantly to forget herself in fun and frolic with Sasanka,
saying: "It'll be all right in the end. Let me make the most
of this little holiday."

Another day she would suddenly shake her head and
taking out all her books and papers from the trunk sit and
pore over them. Now it was Sasanka's turn to snatch the
books from her hands, shove them back into the trunk, and
sit tight on the lid.

"How wicked of you, Sasankada!" Urmi protested. "Please
don't waste my time."

"I can't waste your time," retorted Sasanka, "without
wasting my own as well. So we are quits."

After a little pushing and jostling, Urmi had to give in.
It didn't seem that she very much resented the fact either.
Thus thwarted, her conscience, after a brief offensive of four
or five days, gradually flagged.

"Please don't imagine I am weak-minded," she warned Sasanka. "What I have resolved upon I shall carry out."

"That is?"

"That is, after getting my degree here, I shall proceed to Europe for medical study."

"And then?"

"And then I shall found and maintain a hospital."

"Whom else will you maintain? That fellow Nirad Mukherjee, that insufferable—"

"Shut up!" cried Urmi, literally shutting his mouth with her palm. "If you talk like this, we'll fall out."

She struggled hard to keep her faith. "I must be true, true to myself." She thought that if she failed in the relationship which her father had established between her and Nirad, she would prove herself faithless. Her real trouble was lack of adequate inspiration from the other party. She was like a tree, well rooted in the soil, but bereft of any light of the sun, its leaves turning yellow. Sometimes she found it intolerable and cried out:

"Why can't the fellow write as men write?"

Having received her early school training for many years in a convent, Urmi, whatever the other defects in her education, knew English well. Nirad was aware of it and was therefore all the more keen to dazzle her with his mastery of that language. It would have been better if he had written in Bengali, for the poor fellow did not know how little English he knew. His sentences, packed with long, cumbrous words and phrases culled from books, creaked along like overloaded bullock-carts. Urmi felt like laughing but was too ashamed to do so and would reprove herself:

"It's snobbish to find fault with the English of a Bengali."

When formerly Nirad used to lecture to her, as he always did, his presence and manner lent weight and dignity to his words, which struck her imagination as even mightier than they sounded. But there is little room for such effects in a long letter. His long-winded pomposities sounded silly and easily betrayed their lack of substance. All that she had grown used to while he was with her now began to jar upon her from a distance. The fellow was utterly devoid of any sense of humour. His letters exposed this want most glaringly and she could not help contrasting him with Sasanka.

What happened one day only emphasised this contrast. As she was rummaging for some clothes in her trunk, she discovered an unfinished knitted slipper at the bottom, which brought back to her the memory of an episode that had happened four years ago. Her brother Hemanta was living then. They had all gone up to Darjeeling. There was no end of fun. Hemanta and Sasanka between them seemed to have released a regular cataract of gaiety. Urmi, who had just learnt knitting from an aunt, had begun a pair of slippers intended as a birthday gift to her brother. It was a subject of constant chaffing by Sasanka. "Whatever else you may give to your brother, please don't give him slippers. That way one insults one's elders, says Lord Manu."

"For whom has Lord Manu prescribed them then?" asked Urmi with a mischievous side-long glance.

"The ancient prescriptive right to be insulted," replied Sasanka gravely, "is the brother-in-law's. Moreover, you owe it to me, interest and all."

"Owe it to you? I don't remember."

"Nor can you. You were a mere child then and hardly of age to play the Puck in your sister's bridal chamber on the auspicious occasion of our wedding. The privilege your tender hands then missed of pulling the ears of this lucky chap now waits to be exercised in fashioning a pair of slippers for him."

The debt was, however, never paid, for that particular pair of slippers found its way to the feet of Urmi's brother.

Soon after, Urmi received a letter from Sasanka which caused her considerable amusement. The letter was still in the box. She opened it and re-read:

"You left yesterday. Before the memory of your visit could fade, a scandal has been associated with your name which it would be wrong of me to conceal from you.

"Many eyes have observed the slippers I habitually wear. What they have observed even better is the way my toe-nails jut out of the holes—like a wreath of moons breaking out of clouds. (*Vide* Bharat Chandra's *Annadamangal.* In case of doubt as to the authenticity of the simile, refer to Didi.) This morning in the office as Brindaban Nandi took the dust of my slippered feet, the dilapidated state of their dignity was exposed. Shocking! I asked my servant Mahesh what had happened to my new pair of slippers. On whose holy usurping feet had it found its refuge? He replied, scratching his head: 'When you went to Darjeeling with Urmi Mashi, the pair went with you. On your return only one slipper came back, the other—' Here Mahesh grew red in the face. I also thundered at him to shut up, for there were other persons in the room. Stealing a pair of slippers is a base thing to do, but the human mind is weak and the temptation too great. Let us hope God forgives. Of course when the theft is ingeniously carried out, it wipes away much of its shame. But to steal *one* slipper! Fie!

"I have suppressed the name of the thief. But if she allows her own natural sauciness to be provoked by this charge, she will only publicise it the more widely. If her conscience is clear, it may be worth while to create a scene even over one slipper. If now you want to shut the mouth of that vile calumniator Mahesh, you had better have immediate recourse to a pair of hand-embroidered slippers. Fancy the fellow's cheek! Herewith is enclosed the measure of my foot."

Urmi, delighted with the letter, had immediately set her hands to knitting a pair for Sasanka, but she could not finish it as she soon lost interest in knitting. Today when she discovered this unfinished slipper in her trunk, she resolved to present it, as it was, to Sasanka to mark the anniversary of their journey to Darjeeling, which was only a few weeks ahead. A deep sigh escaped her. Where were those light-winged days under that laughter-lit sky? All that lay in front of her was a prospect of a dreary life of duty, bleak and unrelieved like a desert.

It was the 26th of *Falgun,* the day of the Holi festival. Busy with his work, Sasanka had no time for this play and the day had been forgotten. Urmi went to where her sister lay in bed and putting the ceremonial mark of the red powder on her feet, *pranaamed* her. Then she went in search of her brother-in-law and found him at his desk immersed in his work. Creeping behind him she smeared his head with the colour, which fell profusely on his file of papers as well. A regular skirmish ensued. The ink-pot being handy on the desk, Sasanka threw the red ink over Urmi's sari, and then catching hold of her hand, he snatched the powder wrapped in an end of her sari and rubbed it over her face. Then began an uproar of chasing and scuffling. Though it was getting late for lunch and Sasanka had not yet had his bath, the house went on ringing with the notes of Urmi's pealing laughter. It was only when Sarmila, concerned for Sasanka's health, began to send message after message that the hilarity came to an end.

The day had long receded, the night was far advanced. Over-topping the flowering branches of the *krishnachura* tree, the moon rose clear in the unclouded sky. In the sudden gusts of the spring breeze, the green denizens of the garden murmured and swayed, the web of light and shade at the foot of the trees blending in the harmony. Urmi sat by the window, silent and still. Sleep was not in her eyes, for the waves of excitement had not yet quieted down in her blood. The scent of the flowering mango tree filled her mind with its intoxication. The *madhavi* creeper thrilled with pain in the creative agony of its sap to burst into flower. Urmi's whole being too seemed filled with the same ecstasy. She went into the bathroom and poured water on her head and cooled the burning flesh with a wet towel. Then she lay on her bed, tossing about, until sleep dragged her down into the world of dreams.

At about three in the morning she suddenly woke up. The moon was no longer visible from the window. The room was in darkness; outside, the row of areca palms seemed caught in a network of light and darkness. Urmi broke into a fit of sobbing. Unable to control it, she threw herself on her bed and hid her face into the pillow. It was the wail of the spirit; language cannot lend it either words or meaning. If asked, could she have explained from where came this flood of sorrow that overwhelmed her mind, sweeping away the day's record of duties, the night's repose of sleep?

When she woke in the morning, the sun was already in the room. She had missed her morning duty. Sarmila had excused her absence, attributing it to the strain of fatigue. What was this regret that had overcome and dejected Urmi and filled her with a sense of defeat! She went to her sister and said: "Didi, since I am not of much use to you here, I might as well return home, if you would permit me." Sarmila could no longer protest: 'No you can't go—please don't!' She readily agreed. "All right! You may go—since your studies suffer. Come and see us now and again when you have leisure."

Sasanka was out on duty. Taking advantage of his absence, Urmi left for her home that very day. When Sasanka returned from office he brought with him a set of instruments for mechanical drawing he had bought for Urmi, having promised to teach her the technique. Not finding her in her usual place, he came and asked Sarmila: "Where on earth has Urmi disappeared?"

Sarmila replied: "It was not convenient for her studies here, so she's gone home."

"But she had come prepared to put up with this inconvenience for a few days. Why then this objection today, all of a sudden?"

From her husband's tone Sarmila divined that he suspected her as the cause. Without wasting any words on that score, she merely said: "Please bring her back here—tell her I want her to return. I'm sure she won't object."

Returning home Urmi found awaiting her a long-overdue letter from Nirad. She was afraid to open it, knowing what a pile of guilt she had accumulated. So long she had been citing her sister's illness as her excuse for indiscipline. The excuse had very nearly lost its validity, ever since Sasanka had insisted on engaging trained nurses for Sarmila both for day and night. In accordance with the doctors' instructions the nurses did not allow the relatives to frequent the patient's room. Urmi knew that her sister's illness would not carry weight with Nirad who would dismiss it with, "That's no excuse." Indeed, it was not, since her attendance was not needed. Full of repentance, she made up her mind to confess her wrongdoing and to beg for Nirad's forgiveness. She would swear never to go astray again, nor take any more liberties with the discipline of her life.

Before opening the letter, she took out again that photograph of Nirad which she had not seen for so long, and placed it on her desk. She knew that if Sasanka saw it he would jeer at it. Never mind, she would remain unaffected by his ridicule. That would be her expiation. While in her sister's house, she had hitherto refrained from raising the topic of her impending marriage with Nirad, nor did any one else there ever allude to it. The engagement had met with no one's approval in that house. Urmi now resolved, with clenched fists, to proclaim the fact in every act of hers. She put on her finger the engagement ring which she had so far kept hidden. It was a very cheap ornament which Nirad, by way of flaunting the pride of his "honest poverty", had valued far above any diamond. His manner had said: "The price of the ring is no measure of my value; it's my worth that lends value to the ring."

Having thus made due amends, Urmi very slowly opened the envelope. No sooner had she perused its contents than she gave a leap of joy. She felt like dancing, but not being used to that art, she snatched the *sitar* lying on her bed and, without bothering to tune it, began to draw all sorts of frenzies out of it. Just at that moment Sasanka entered the room. "What on earth is the matter?" he asked. "It seems the date of the wedding is fixed after all!"

"Indeed, Sasankada, it's fixed."

"Fixed beyond any possibility of change?"

"Beyond all possibility of change."

"Let me send for the pipers then and order sweets at Bhimnag's."

"You don't have to bother."

"What! Will you arrange everything yourself? Bravo Amazon! What about the wedding gifts?"

"The wedding gifts have gone from my own pocket."

"The fish being fried in its own oil, eh? I don't quite understand."

"Here, take this letter and read it."

She gave him the letter to read. Having finished it, Sasanka roared with laughter. Nirad had written that having discovered that it was not feasible to carry on in India the highly difficult line of research to which he had dedicated his life, it had become necessary for him to make a supreme sacrifice. He had no alterative but to release himself from his engagement to Urmi. A European lady had agreed to marry him and to devote herself to his work. But of course the mission was the same, whether it was carried on in India or over there. Hence it would be no injustice to the spirit of Rajaram Babu's will if part of the money he had set apart for the mission were to be handed over to him. Indeed such an act would but bring honour to the deceased.

"At any rate, it wouldn't be bad," commented Sasanka, "to help to keep this creature alive in that distant land. If you stop sending him money, there's the danger of the fellow turning up here one day, driven by hunger."

"If you are afraid of that," laughed Urmi, "you had better send him the money yourself. I won't give a penny."

"Sure you won't change your mind any more?" asked Sasanka. "Will the pride of the proud one last?"

"If I should change my mind, what's that to you, Sasankada?"

"To answer that question truthfully would only add to your conceit. For your own good therefore I'll keep quiet. But really, I wonder at the fellow's impertinence—what the English call cheek."

A great weight seemed to have been lifted off Urmi's mind—a burden of long standing. She hardly knew what to do with this joy of freedom. She tore up and threw away the programme of study. She flung the ring out of the window to the beggar in the lane who was asking for alms.

"Will any hawker buy these fat books with their pencil annotations?" she asked.

"First let's hear what would happen, if no one bought them."

"The ghost of the dead and buried days may reside in them and may come and stand by my bed at dead of night, pointing its dread finger at me."

"If there be any such fear, I'll buy the books right away, without waiting for any hawker."

"What will you do with them?"

"Perform their last rites according to the Hindu *Shastras*. I would go as far as Gaya to consecrate their ashes, if that would set your mind at rest."

"No, that would be going too far."

"Very well, I'll build a pyramid in a corner of my library to lodge their mummy."

"But let me tell you, you can't go to your work today."

"Not at all?"

"Not at all."

"What am I to do instead?"

"Let's get into a car and just vanish."

"Go and get your sister's permission."

"I'll tell her after we return—though I'll get a good scolding. But then it won't matter."

"Right! I too am willing to stand your sister's scolding. I'll sweep you along at the rate of forty-five miles an hour, and won't mind bursting a tyre or running over a couple of our own species, even if it takes us as far as the jail—provided you promise thrice that at the end of our chariot-drive you will return to our house."

"Agreed, agreed, agreed!"

After the drive they returned to the Bhowanipore house, but the excitement of forty-five miles an hour still ran hot in their blood and would not subside. This turbulence of blood made them blind to all sense of responsibility, fear or shame.

For some days Sasanka's work fell into a state of complete disorder. He knew that what he was doing was not right and that the price of neglect might prove to be very heavy. At night he was haunted in bed by fearsome apprehensions in which all ominous possibilities seemed greatly exaggerated. But next day he was once again "heedless of his trust", like the Yaksa of *Meghaduta.*

Alcohol taken once has to be taken again to drown the regret.

Sasanka

Thus time passed. The eyes were frenzied, the mind infatuated. Urmi took long to realize what was happening to her, but one day she was rudely awakened to the reality. For some unknown reason Urmi was afraid of Mathur-dada and had always avoided him. One day Mathur came to her sister's room in the morning and stayed there till noon. Soon after, Sarmila sent for Urmi and with an expression at once calm and stern said to her: "Do you realize what havoc you have caused by distracting him from his work day after day?"

"Why, what has happened, Didi?" asked Urmi frightened.

"Mathur-dada has just informed me that your brother-in-law has grossly neglected his duties, leaving everything to Jawaharlal who has been helping himself to the building materials with both hands. It has come to light that large godowns have been so badly roofed that the rain pours through them as through a sieve, damaging the goods stored inside. Owing to the high reputation of our firm, the clients did not have the construction tested. And now we are faced not only with the loss of our firm's reputation but with considerable financial loss as well. Mathur-dada is severing the partnership."

Urmi's heart sank, her face grew ashen. In a moment, as by a lightning flash, her heart's hidden secret was revealed to her. She realized now the full measure of intoxication which had unconsciously robbed her of her senses, of her power of discrimination. She had looked upon Sasanka's work as a sort of rival who must be thwarted, and from whose clutches she was ever impatient to snatch him away, to have him all to herself. Many a time when Sasanka was bathing, she had thoughtlessly dismissed visitors on business with a curt, "He can't see anybody now,"—only because she was afraid lest Sasanka should again after his bath get engrossed in work and Urmi's day be rendered fruitless for want of his leisure. The terrible picture of her infatuation rose full and clear before her eyes. Instantly she flung herself at her sister's feet and began to repeat in hoarse and broken tones: "Kick me away from your house, drive me away from your presence, now, this very minute!"

The sister had made up her mind on no account to forgive Urmi, but now her heart melted. Gently caressing Urmi's head she said: "Don't worry. Some way out of the difficulty shall be found."

Urmi rose. "Why should you bear all the loss?" she cried. "I too have some means."

"Are you crazy?" broke in Sarmila. "Do you suppose I'm such a pauper as that? I have requested Mathur-dada not to make a fuss over this matter. I'll make up the loss. And now listen, see that your brother-in-law does not come to know that I know anything about it."

Urmi again fell at her sister's feet. "Forgive me, Didi, please forgive me!" she cried, beating her head.

"Who is to forgive whom, sister?" weariedly murmured Sarmila wiping her tears. "Life is so perplexing! We are baffled in our hopes, cheated of our loves."

After this incident Urmi did not leave her sister's side even for a moment, personally attending to every one of her needs, ministering medicine, serving food, helping her bathe, putting her to sleep. Once more she took to her books, poring over them, seated by her sister's bed. She dared not trust herself or Sasanka any more.

The result was that Sasanka took to visiting the sickroom. Only a male can be so clumsy in his infatuation as not to notice that his wife could plainly see through the motive of his frequent visits. Each time he bustled in Urmi blushed hot with shame. He invited Urmi to a football match to see the Mohun Bagan team play; the temptation did not work. He then brought the newspaper where in the advertisement column he had underlined Charlie Chaplin's name, but that also bore no fruit. When Urmi was less remote Sasanka did make an effort to attend to his work, but now even that was impossible.

However painful to her the sight of this unfortunate man, suffering so uselessly, Sarmila at first drew a secret pleasure from it. But she gradually noticed that his suffering was gaining on him, his face drying up, the black marks deepening under his eyes. It was obvious that with Urmi absent from the dining table, he did not relish his food and was slowly starving himself. The recent flood of gaiety that had inundated the house had suddenly ebbed, carrying away with it even the easy and peaceful tenor of their former days.

Once Sasanka had been indifferent to his appearance. He used to have his hair cropped so short as almost to render the service of a comb superfluous. After many vehement attempts at remonstrating, Sarmila had in the end given him up as hopeless. But lately Urmi's brief verdict couched in the form of a loud laugh had not been without effect. For the first time in his life Sasanka had begun to apply scented hairoils to the new growth of hair on his head. But nowadays his heart's wretchedness was so pitifully obvious in the unkempt state of his hair that it was no longer possible to make fun of it, open or secret. Love's tenderness proving stronger than its bitterness, Sarmila was torn with pity for him and contempt at her own callousness; the torment of her illness was intensified.

There was to be military tattoo on the Maidan of the troops stationed at the Fort. Timidly Sasanka inquired: "Will you come, Urmi? I have booked good seats." Before Urmi could reply, Sarmila said: "Of course she'll go. She's dying for a little outing."

Thus encouraged, Sasanka proposed after a couple of days: "Circus?" Urmi seemed only too eager. And then, "Botanical Gardens?" She hesitated, unwilling to leave her sister's side for so long. But the sister now advocated Sasanka's cause. Drudging with the masons the whole long day, getting messed all over with dust and sand—it was enough to drive one crazy. His health would break down if he didn't go out for a little fresh air. This plea was deemed sufficient to justify a trip as far as Rajganj.

'He cannot afford to lose her, for whose sake he does not mind risking the ruin of his work,' said Sarmila to herself.

Though no one ever told him in so many words, it seemed to Sasanka that what he was doing had the silent approval of all around him. He had convinced himself that Sarmila was in no way unhappy, that on the contrary she felt happy in watching the happiness of this pair. This might have been impossible in the case of an ordinary woman, but then Sarmila was no ordinary woman. During the days of his government service, an artist had made a pencil sketch of his wife, which had till now remained buried in his portfolio. He now took it out and had it expensively framed by a European firm and hung it on the wall in his office, facing his desk. The gardener filled the vase in front with fresh flowers every day.

At last a day came when Sasanka, taking Urmi round the garden to see the sunflowers in bloom, suddenly seized her hand and confessed: "Surely you know that I love you. As for your sister, she is a veritable goddess. I worship her as

I could worship none else in this life. She is no creature of this earth, so infinitely superior is she to us."

Her sister had repeatedly confided to Urmi that her greatest consolation was that Urmi would be there to fill her place. Painful, no doubt, it was to imagine another woman in her place; on the other hand, she could not bear the thought of Sasanka dragging on a forlorn, wretched existence, without a woman to look after his comfort. She had also said that if he was thwarted in love, it would react even more ruinously on his business. Once the hunger of his heart was appeased, his work would resume its old order.

Sasanka's mind was in a delirium of exhilaration. He felt transported to a fairyland where all sense of responsibility faded in a stupor of happiness. Nowadays he observed the sanctity of the Sunday as a holiday with the scrupulous adherence of a Christian. One day he came and told Sarmila: "I've secured the steam-launch for the day from the Jute Sahibs. Tomorrow being Sunday, I propose to take Urmi to Diamond Harbour. We'll leave before day-break and return before dusk."

Something seemed to wring the very veins of Sarmila's heart; her forehead was wrinkled with pain. Sasanka noticed nothing.

"What about the food?" she mildly inquired.

"I've ordered it at a hotel."

There was a time when she had looked after such details. Then Sasanka had been indifferent. Now it all seemed changed, topsy-turvy.

"All right. You may go," she said. No sooner had the words left her mouth than Sasanka turned and hurriedly left, without caring to waste a moment. A desire to sob aloud overpowered Sarmila. She hid her face in the pillow and murmured over and over again: "Why am I lingering?"

The next day, Sunday, was the anniversary of their wedding day, a day whose observance had never suffered a breach so far. This time, too, lying in her bed, she had planned all the arrangements, unknown to her husband. Nothing much. She would have made him put on the red *Banaras dhoti* he had worn at his wedding, herself clad in her wedding *sari*. She would have put a garland round his neck and made him sit and eat in front of her. Incense burning in the room, the gramophone in the adjoining room playing the familiar wedding music of the *sanai*—that was all. Every year on this day Sasanka had surprised her with some charming gift. This time too she had felt sure that he had brought something to give her on the morrow.

But everything had turned bitter today. All alone in the room, she kept on murmuring: "False, false, all is false. What's the use of this farce!"

She had no sleep that night. Early in the morning she heard the car drive away from the gate. She broke into sobs. "Thou art but a myth, Lord!" she cried.

From now on Sarmila's condition grew steadily and speedily worse. One day when the disease showed very grave symptoms, she sent for her husband. It was evening, the light in the room was faint. She motioned to the nurse to leave them alone. She made her husband sit beside her and, taking his hand in hers, said: "I have looked upon you as the Heaven-sent boon of my life. God did not grant me the power to prove worthy of you. I have done the best I could. For my many shortcomings I beg your forgiveness."

Silencing Sasanka, who was about to say something, she continued: "No, don't interrupt me. I leave Urmi to your care. She is my own sister; in her you will find me, and much else besides that you could not find in me. No, please keep still, don't say anything. That I have brought about your happiness before dying is to me the fulfilment of my good fortune."

From outside the nurse called: "The doctor has come."

"Please bring him in," answered Sarmila.
The conversation stopped.

Sarmila's maternal uncle was an enthusiastic patron of all sorts of unorthodox systems of healing. Recently he had become attached to a Sannyasi. When the doctors gave up Sarmila's case as hopeless, he insisted that the prescription of his Himalaya-returned Sannyasi should be given a trial. The medicine consisted of a powder made of a Tibetan root, to be taken with plenty of milk. Sasanka, who could never stand quacks, objected, but Sarmila pleaded: "It'll do no good, of course. But at any rate it'll please Uncle."

But the medicine did bear fruit. Her breathing trouble subsided and she no longer spat blood. Gradually, after a fortnight's treatment she was able to sit up. The doctors explained it by saying that sometimes the imminence of death provokes so desperate a reaction in the body that the life is saved. However that might be, Sarmila's life was saved.

'How embarrassing!' thought Sarmila. 'What's to be done? Will life saved prove in the end a greater calamity than death?'

Urmi was busy packing. Her term of stay had drawn to its end. Sarmila went up to her.

"You can't leave," she said.

"Why, what do you mean?"

"I mean—is it so rare in our Hindu society for sisters to be co-wives?"

"Hush—for shame!"

"Afraid of a scandal? Are people's tongues of greater consequence than the voice of Fate?"

She sent for Sasanka and told him: "Let's migrate to Nepal. You were once offered job at the Royal Court there. You may get it now if you try. No one will malign us there."

Without giving any one time to oppose her suggestion, Sarmila began to make preparations for departure. Morose and downcast, Urmi went about the house as though she would have liked to hide herself. Sasanka said to her: "If you abandon me now, you may well imagine what will happen to me."

"I'm unable to think, to decide for myself," replied Urmi. "Whatever you two decide, I'll accept."

The preparations took some days. When the day of departure drew near, Urmi said: "Please wait a week longer, while I go and consult uncle on a matter of business."

She left.

In her absence Mathur came to Sarmila looking very glum, and said: "You are going away at the right moment. After my last conversation with you, I arrived at a settlement with Sasanka of our mutual business relations, dividing the business without sharing liabilities. Lately Sasanka has been going through the accounts with a view to winding up his own share of the business and it has come to light that not only has all your money been used up but it seems that this house too may have to be sold, to meet the liability."

"Did it never strike him that the crash was so imminent?" asked Sarmila.

"Some crashes," explained Mathur, "like the crash of lightning, are difficult to predict. They strike without a moment's warning. He was aware of his losses and could have repaired them in time, if the silly notion had not possessed him of resorting to quick expedients to restore his losses. Without consulting me he began to speculate in coal. The result was that he was in the end obliged to sell off in a falling market the goods bought when the market was soaring. Now he has suddenly discovered that all he had has blown up like a rocket, leaving behind nothing but ashes. If now by God's grace he gets a job in Nepal, it may still be all right."

Sarmila was not afraid of poverty. On the contrary she knew that in the house of a needy husband her place would be all the more assured, for she was confident that she knew how to soften the rigours of want. Her ornaments would go a long way to keep off the starkness of poverty for some time. Urmi's portion too would be at the disposal of her husband if he married her—a faint suggestion of this thought did peep into her mind. But merely to exist is not enough. The fortune which her husband had built up so long by his own prowess, for whose sake she had, day after day, voluntarily suppressed many a claim of her heart, this embodiment of the joint dream of their lives now vanished like a mirage—the humiliation of it made her crumble into dust. She wished that death had spared her this dishonour.

"I have resigned myself to my fate," she said to herself, "but will he reconcile himself to the inexorable emptiness of poverty and dishonour? Will it not plant the bitterness of regret in his heart? He may find it hard one day to forgive her whose infatuation brought this all about; the very food served by her will taste like poison in his mouth. Choked with shame by the stench of his own sottishness, he will only find fault with the alcohol. And if in the end he is driven to dependence on Urmi's income, the bitterness of his humiliation will turn every moment of her life into a hell."

In the process of clearing his accounts with Mathur, Sasanka suddenly discovered that every penny of Sarmila's had been lost in his business, and that, without telling him anything about it, she had paid up the debt to Mathur. He recalled how, when he had resigned his Government post, he had built up his business with her money. Now again, leaving the ruin of his business behind, he was entering the harness of service, with the load of that same debt to Sarmila on his back. How would he ever repay the debt with the meagre income of a salaried post?

In about ten days' time they would be leaving for Nepal. That night he had not a wink of sleep. Before the day broke, he flung himself out of bed and bringing his fist down on the dressing table with all his might, cried out: "I will not go to Nepal." He swore: "Here in Calcutta we will stay on, the two of us along with Urmi—facing the full malicious glare of frowning, scowling society. And here in this very Calcutta I will build up once again the ruined edifice of my business."

Sarmila was busy making a list of articles to be taken on the journey or to be left behind. Suddenly she heard her name called out, and ran to her husband, throwing the list down. Apprehensive of some sudden calamity she asked with a trembling heart, "Why, what's the matter?"

"I will not go to Nepal," came the reply. "I will defy society and stick it out here."

"Why, what has happened?" she inquired.

"Work," he replied.

Work! The same old word! Her heart began to beat fast.

"Don't think I am a coward, Sarmi. Could you imagine me so degraded as to run away from my responsibility?"

Drawing closer, Sarmila took his hand in hers.

"Do make your meaning clear," she said.

"Don't conceal the fact from me," cried Sasanka, "that I am once again in your debt."

"All right, I won't," submitted Sarmila.

"From this very day," went on Sasanka, "I'll begin discharging the debt—as I did once before. Mark my words. I'll recover and drag up again what I have flung away into the abyss. Trust me again as you once gave me your trust."

Sarmila's head sank on her husband's breast.

"Let me also have your full trust," she murmured. "Teach me, train me, mould me so that I may become worthy of sharing your task."

From outside came the cry: "Letter!" Two letters came in, written in Urmi's hand. One of them was addressed to Sasanka: "I am on my way to Bombay *en route* for Europe. I shall carry out father's wishes and return a doctor in about six or seven years' time. In the meantime the havoc I have caused in your home will have had time to repair itself. Don't worry about me. I can't help worrying about you."

The other letter was for Sarmila.

"Didi, a thousand *pranaams* at your feet. Forgive me the wrong I have done you unwittingly. If no wrong has been done—then that very knowledge will make me happy. I dare not hope for any greater happiness, nor indeed do I know for certain wherein lies happiness. If happiness is not in store for me, let it be so. Let me only not err."

Glossary

Annapurna	:	A name of the goddess Durga, conceived in the act of giving food to Shiva, her consort, and to the whole world. Sasankamauli is also one of the names of Shiva.
Da	:	Short for *Dada,* a term applied to elder brothers, elder cousins as well as (as in this case) to elder brother-in-law.
Debottar	:	Property endowed for religious purposes; *Shebait,* its trustee.
Di	:	Short for *Didi,* a term applied to elder sisters and elder cousins.
Gaya	:	The holy city in Bihar where the Hindus go to perform the last rites of the dead.
Kaka	:	Father's younger brother or cousin.
Kalapahar	:	A Bengali Brahmin who renounced his religion and became a general under Muslim rulers and earned great notoriety as an iconoclast (16th century).
Khuki	:	A pet name for girls in Bengal.

Luchi-sthan	:	An untranslatable word. *Luchi* is a kind of fried pancake much favoured by Bengalis; *sthan* means place; *luchisthan* meaning a place which provides good food or material well-being. *Beluchisthan* (*be* meaning without), used as an antonym of *luchisthan*, is a pun on the word Baluchistan, the arid, rocky region to the north-west of India.
Makar	:	Fabulous marine animal described in Indian mythology as the mount of the goddess Ganga (Ganges); hence auspicious. The mouth of this animal appears as a decorative motif in Indian ornaments.
Mashi	:	Mother's sister. In Bengal servants usually address the mistress as *Mother*. The mistress's sister is hence referred to as *Mashi*.
Meghaduta	:	*The Cloud-Messenger,* the famous poem by Kalidasa.
Meghnadbadh Kavya	:	An epic in blank verse by Michael Madhusudan Dutta, the great predecessor of Tagore.
Pakhwaj	:	A kind of double drum.
Pranaam	:	The Hindu way of saluting one's elders is to touch their feet with one's hand and then to lift the hand to one's forehead.
Punjabi	:	A kind of upper garment worn by men; *Dhoti* is a lower garment.
Vidyut-lata	:	*Lit.* Lightning-creeper. *Nirad* literally means a cloud.

SĀDHANĀ

Preface

Perhaps it is well for me to explain that the subject-matter of the papers published in this book has not been philosophically treated, nor has it been approached from the scholar's point of view. The writer has been brought up in a family where texts of the Upanishads are used in daily worship; and he has had before him the example of his father, who lived his long life in the closest communion with God, while not neglecting his duties to the world, or allowing his keen interest in all human affairs to suffer any abatement. So in these papers, it may be hoped, western readers will have an opportunity of coming into touch with the ancient spirit of India as revealed in our sacred texts and manifested in the life of to-day.

All the great utterances of man have to be judged not by the letter but by the spirit—the spirit which unfolds itself with the growth of life in history. We get to know the real meaning of Christianity by observing its living aspect at the present moment—however different that may be, even in important respects, from the Christianity of earlier periods.

For western scholars the great religious scriptures of India seem to possess merely a retrospective and archaeological interest; but to us they are of living importance, and we cannot help thinking that they lose their significance when exhibited in labelled cases—mummied specimens of human thought and aspiration, preserved for all time in the wrappings of erudition. The meaning of the living words that come out of the experiences of great hearts can never be exhausted by any one system of logical interpretation. They have to be endlessly explained by the commentaries of individual lives, and they gain an added mystery in each new revelation. To me the verses of the Upanishads and the teachings of Buddha have ever been things of the spirit, and therefore endowed with boundless vital growth; and I have used them, both in my own life and in my preaching, as being instinct with individual meaning for me, as for others, and awaiting for their confirmation, my own special testimony, which must have its value because of its individuality.

I should add perhaps that these papers embody in a connected form, suited to this publication, ideas which have been culled from several of the Bengali discourses which I am in the habit of giving to my students in my school at Bolpur (in Bengal); and I have used here and there translations of passages from these done by my friends, Babu Satish Chandra Roy and Babu Ajit Kumar Chakravarti. The last paper of this series, 'Realization in Action', has been translated from my Bengali discourse on 'Karma-yoga' by my nephew, Babu Surendra Nath Tagore.

I take this opportunity of expressing my gratitude to Professor James H. Woods, of Harvard University, for his generous appreciation which encouraged me to complete this series of papers and read most of them before the Harvard University. And I offer my thanks to Mr. Ernest Rhys for his kindness in helping me with suggestions and revisions, and in going through the proofs.

A word may be added about the pronouncing of Sādhanā: the accent falls decisively on the first ā, which has the broad sound of the letter.

The Relation of the Individual
to the Universe

The civilization of ancient Greece was nurtured within city walls. In fact, all the modern civilizations have their cradles of brick and mortar.

These walls leave their mark deep in the minds of men. They set up a principle of "divide and rule" in our mental outlook, which begets in us a habit of securing all our conquests by fortifying them and separating them from one another. We divide nation and nation, knowledge and knowledge, man and nature. It breeds in us a strong suspicion of whatever is beyond the barriers we have built, and everything has to fight hard for its entrance into our recognition.

When the first Aryan invaders appeared in India it was a vast land of forests, and the new-comers rapidly took advantage of them. These forests afforded them shelter from the fierce heat of the sun and the ravages of tropical storms, pastures for cattle, fuel for sacrificial fire, and materials for building cottages. And the different Aryan clans with their patriarchal heads settled in the different forest tracts which had some special advantage of natural protection, and food and water in plenty.

Thus in India it was in the forests that our civilization had its birth, and it took a distinct character from this origin and environment. It was surrounded by the vast life of nature, was fed and clothed by her, and had the closest and most constant intercourse with her varying aspects. Such a life, it may be thought, tends to have the effect of dulling human intelligence and dwarfing the incentives to progress by lowering the standards of existence. But in ancient India we find that the circumstances of forest life did not overcome man's mind, and did not enfeeble the current of his energies, but only gave to it a particular direction. Having been in constant contact with the living growth of nature, his mind was free from the desire to extend his dominion by erecting boundary walls around his acquisitions. His aim was not to acquire but to realise, to enlarge his consciousness by growing with and growing into his surroundings. He felt that truth is all-comprehensive, that there is no such thing as absolute isolation in existence, and the only way of attaining truth is through the interpenetration of our being into all objects. To realise this great harmony between man's spirit and the spirit of the world was the endeavour of the forest-dwelling sages of ancient India.

In later days there came a time when these primeval forests gave way to cultivated fields, and wealthy cities sprang up on all sides. Mighty kingdoms were established, which had communications with all the great powers of the world. But even in the heyday of its material prosperity the heart of India ever looked back with adoration upon the early ideal of strenuous self-realization, and the dignity of the simple life of the forest hermitage, and drew its best inspiration from the wisdom stored there.

The west seems to take a pride in thinking that it is subduing nature; as if we are living in a hostile world where we have to wrest everything we want from an unwilling and alien arrangement of things. This sentiment is the product of the city-wall habit and training of mind. For in the city life man naturally directs the concentrated light of his mental vision upon his own life and works, and this creates an artificial dissociation between himself and the Universal Nature within whose bosom he lies.

But in India the point of view was different; it included the world with the man as one great truth. India put all her emphasis on the harmony that exists between the individual and the universal. She felt we could have no communication whatever with our surroundings if they were absolutely foreign to us. Man's complaint against nature is that he has to acquire most of his necessaries by his own efforts. Yes, but his efforts are not in vain; he is reaping success every day, and that shows there is a rational connection between him and nature, for we never can make anything our own except that which is truly related to us.

We can look upon a road from two different points of view. One regards it as dividing us from the object of our desire; in that case we count every step of our journey over it as something attained by force in the face of obstruction. The other sees it as the road which leads us to our destination; and as such it is part of our goal. It is already the beginning of our attainment, and by journeying over it we can only gain that which in itself it offers to us. This last point of view is that of India with regard to nature. For her, the great fact is that we are in harmony with nature; that man can think because his thoughts are in harmony with things; that he can use the forces of nature for his own purpose only because his power is in harmony with the power which is universal, and that in the long run his purpose never can knock against the purpose which works through nature.

In the west the prevalent feeling is that nature belongs exclusively to inanimate things and to beasts, that there is a sudden unaccountable break where human-nature begins. According to it, everything that is low in the scale of beings is merely nature, and whatever has the stamp of perfection on it, intellectual or moral, is human-nature. It is like dividing the bud and the blossom into two separate categories, and putting their grace to the credit of two different and antithetical principles. But the Indian mind never has any hesitation in acknowledging its kinship with nature, its unbroken relation with all.

The fundamental unity of creation was not simply a philosophical speculation for India; it was her life-object to realise this great harmony in feeling and in action. With meditation and service, with a regulation of her life, she cultivated her consciousness in such a way that everything had a spiritual meaning to her. The earth, water and light, fruits and flowers, to her were not merely physical phenomena to be turned to use and then left aside. They were necessary to her in the attainment of her ideal of perfection, as every note is necessary to the completeness of the symphony. India intuitively felt that the essential fact of this world has a vital meaning for us; we have to be fully alive to it and establish a conscious relation with it, not merely impelled by scientific curiosity or greed of material advantage, but realising it in the spirit of sympathy, with a large feeling of joy and peace.

The man of science knows, in one aspect, that the world is not merely what it appears to be to our senses; he knows that earth and water are really the play of forces that manifest themselves to us as earth and water—how, we can but partially apprehend. Likewise the man who has his spiritual eyes open knows that the ultimate truth about earth and water lies in our apprehension of the eternal will which works in time and takes shape in the forces we realise under those aspects. This is not mere knowledge, as science is, but it is a perception of the soul by the soul. This does not lead us to power, as knowledge does, but it gives us joy, which is the product of the union of kindred things. The man whose acquaintance with the world does not lead him deeper than science leads him, will never understand what it is that the man with the spiritual vision finds in these natural phenomena. The water does not merely cleanse his limbs, but it purifies his heart; for it touches his soul. The earth does not merely hold his body, but it gladdens his mind; for its contact is more than a physical contact—it is a living presence. When a man does not realise his kinship with the world, he lives in a prison-house whose walls are alien to him. When he meets the eternal spirit in all objects, then is he emancipated for then he discovers the fullest significance of the world into which he is born; then he finds himself in perfect truth, and his harmony with the all is established. In India men are enjoined to be fully awake to the fact that they are in the closest relation to things around them, body and soul, and that they are to hail the morning sun, the flowing water, the fruitful earth, as the manifestation of the same living truth which holds them in its embrace. Thus the text of our everyday meditation is the Gayatri, a verse which is considered to be the epitome of all the Vedas. By its help we try to realise the essential unity of the world with the conscious soul of man; we learn to perceive the unity held together by the one Eternal Spirit, whose power creates the earth, the sky, and the stars, and at the same time irradiates our minds with the light of a consciousness that moves and exists in unbroken continuity with the outer world.

It is not true that India has tried to ignore differences of value in different things, for she knows that would make life impossible. The sense of the superiority of man in the scale of creation has not been absent from her mind. But she has had her own idea as to that in which his superiority really consists. It is not in the power of possession but in the power of union. Therefore India chose her places of pilgrimage wherever there was in nature some special grandeur or beauty, so that her mind could come out of its world of narrow necessities and realise its place in the infinite. This was the reason why in India a whole people who once were meat-eaters gave up taking animal food to cultivate the sentiment of universal sympathy for life, an event unique in the history of mankind.

India knew that when by physical and mental barriers we violently detach ourselves from the inexhaustible life of nature; when we become merely man, not man-in-the-universe, we create bewildering problems, and having shut off the source of their solution, we try all kinds of artificial methods each of which brings its own crop of interminable difficulties. When man leaves his resting-place in universal nature, when he walks on the single rope of humanity, it means either a dance or a fall for him, he has ceaselessly to strain every nerve and muscle to keep his balance at each step, and then, in the intervals of his weariness, he fulminates against Providence and feels a secret pride and satisfaction in thinking that he has been unfairly dealt with by the whole scheme of things.

But this cannot go on for ever. Man must realise the wholeness of his existence, his place in the infinite; he must know that hard as he may strive he can never create his honey within the cells of his hive, for the perennial supply of his life food is outside their walls. He must know that when man shuts himself out from the vitalising and purifying touch of the infinite, and falls back upon himself for his sustenance and his healing, then he goads himself into madness, tears himself into shreds, and eats his own substance. Deprived of the background of the whole, his poverty loses its one great quality, which is simplicity, and becomes squalid and shamefaced. His wealth is no longer magnanimous; it grows merely extravagant. His appetites do not minister to his life, keeping to the limits of their purpose; they become an end in themselves and set fire to his life and play the fiddle in the lurid light of the conflagration. Then it is that in our self-expression we try to startle and not to attract; in art we strive for originality and lose sight of truth which is old and yet ever new; in literature we miss the complete view of man which is simple and yet great. Man appears instead as a psychological problem, or as the embodiment of a passion that is intense because abnormal, being exhibited in the glare of a fiercely emphatic artificial light. When man's consciousness is restricted only to the immediate vicinity of his human self, the deeper roots of his nature do not find their permanent soil, his spirit is ever on the brink of starvation, and in the place of healthful strength he substitutes rounds of stimulation. Then it is that man misses his inner perspective and measures his greatness by its bulk and not by its vital link with the infinite, judges his activity by its movement and not by the repose of perfection—the repose which is in the starry heavens, in the ever-flowing rhythmic dance of creation.

The first invasion of India has its exact parallel in the invasion of America by the European settlers. They also were confronted with primeval forests and a fierce struggle with aboriginal races. But this struggle between man and man, and man and nature lasted till the very end; they never came to any terms. In India the forests which were the habitation of barbarians became the sanctuary of sages, but in America these great living cathedrals of nature had no deeper significance to man. They brought wealth and power to him, and perhaps at times they ministered to his enjoyment of beauty, and inspired a solitary poet. They never acquired a sacred association in the hearts of men as the site of some great spiritual reconcilement where man's soul had its meeting-place with the soul of the world.

I do not for a moment wish to suggest that things should have been otherwise. It would be an utter waste of opportunities if history were to repeat itself exactly in the same manner in every place. It is best for the commerce of the spirit that people differently situated should bring their different produces into the market of humanity, each of which is complementary and necessary to the others. All that I wish to say is that India at the outset of her career met with a special combination of circumstances which was not lost upon her. She had, according to her opportunities, thought and pondered, striven and suffered, dived into the depths of existence, and achieved something which surely cannot be without its value to people whose evolution in history took a different way altogether. Man for his perfect growth requires all the living elements that constitute his complex life; that is why his food has to be cultivated in different fields and brought from different sources.

Civilization is a kind of mould that each nation is busy making for itself to shape its men and women according to its best ideal. All its institutions, its legislature, its standard of approbation and condemnation, its conscious and unconscious teachings tend toward that object. The modern civilization of the west, by all its organised efforts, is trying to turn out men perfect in physical, intellectual, and moral efficiency. There the vast energies of the nations are employed in extending man's power over his surroundings, and people are combining and straining every faculty to possess and to turn to account all that they can lay their hands upon, to overcome every obstacle on their path of conquest. They are ever disciplining themselves to fight nature and other races; their armaments are getting more and more stupendous every day; their machines, their appliances, their organisations go on multiplying at an amazing rate. This is a splendid achievement, no doubt, and a wonderful manifestation of man's masterfulness, which knows no obstacle and has for its object the supremacy of himself over everything else.

The ancient civilization of India had its own ideal of perfection towards which its efforts were directed. Its aim was not attaining power, and it neglected to cultivate to the utmost its capacities, and to organize men for defensive and offensive purposes, for co-operation in the acquisition of wealth and for military and political ascendancy. The ideal that India tried to realise led her best men to the isolation of a contemplative life, and the treasures that she gained for mankind by penetrating into the mysteries of reality cost her dear in the sphere of worldly success. Yet, this also was a sublime achievement,—it was a supreme manifestation of that human aspiration which knows no limit, and which has for its object nothing less than the realization of the Infinite.

There were the virtuous, the wise, the courageous; there were the statesmen, kings and emperors of India; but whom amongst all these classes did she look up to and choose to be the representative of men? They were the rishis. What were the rishis? *They who having attained the supreme soul in knowledge were filled with wisdom, and having found him in union with the soul were in perfect harmony with the inner self; they having realised him in the heart were free from all selfish desires, and having experienced him in all the activities of the world, had attained calmness. The rishis were they who having reached the supreme God from all sides had found abiding peace, had become united with all, had entered into the life of the Universe.*[1]

Thus the state of realising our relationship with all, of entering into everything through union with God, was considered in India to be the ultimate end and fulfilment of humanity.

Man can destroy and plunder, earn and accumulate, invent and discover, but he is great because his soul comprehends

---

1. Samprāpyainam rishayo jñānatriptāh
   Kritātmānō vītarāgāh praçantāh
   tē sarvagam sarvatah prāpya dhīrāh
   Yuktātmānah sarvamēvāviçanti.

all. It is dire destruction for him when he envelopes his soul in a dead shell of callous habits, and when a blind fury of works whirls round him like an eddying dust storm, shutting out the horizon. That indeed kills the very spirit of his being, which is the spirit of comprehension. Essentially man is not a slave either of himself or of the world; but he is a lover. His freedom and fulfilment is in love, which is another name for perfect comprehension. By this power of comprehension, this permeation of his being, he is united with the all-pervading Spirit, who is also the breath of his soul. Where a man tries to raise himself to eminence by pushing and jostling all others, to achieve a distinction by which he prides himself to be more than everybody else, there he is alienated from that Spirit. This is why the Upanishads describe those who have attained the goal of human life as *"peaceful"*[2] and as *"at-one-with-God,"*[3] meaning that they are in perfect harmony with man and nature, and therefore in undisturbed union with God.

We have a glimpse of the same truth in the teachings of Jesus when he says, "It is easier for a camel to pass through the eye of a needle than for a rich man to enter the kingdom of Heaven"—which implies that whatever we treasure for ourselves separates us from others; our possessions are our limitations. He who is bent upon accumulating riches is unable, with his ego continually bulging, to pass through the gates of comprehension of the spiritual world, which is the world of perfect harmony; he is shut up within the narrow walls of his limited acquisitions.

Hence the spirit of the teachings of the Upanishads is: In order to find him you must embrace all. In the pursuit of wealth you really give up everything to gain a few things, and that is not the way to attain him who is completeness.

---

2. Praçantāh.
3. Yuktāmānah.

Some modern philosophers of Europe, who are directly or indirectly indebted to the Upanishads, far from realising their debt, maintain that the Brahma of India is a mere abstraction, a negation of all that is in the world. In a word, that the Infinite Being is to be found nowhere except in metaphysics. It may be, that such a doctrine has been and still is prevalent with a section of our countrymen. But this is certainly not in accord with the pervading spirit of the Indian mind. Instead, it is the practice of realising and affirming the presence of the infinite in all things which has been its constant inspiration. We are enjoined to see *whatever there is in the world as being enveloped by God.*[4]

I bow to God over and over again who is in fire and in water, who permeates the whole world, who is in the annual crops as well as in the perennial trees.[5] Can this be God abstracted from the world? Instead, it signifies not merely seeing him in all things, but saluting him, in all the objects of the world. The attitude of the God-conscious man of the Upanishad towards the universe is one of a deep feeling of adoration. His object of worship is present everywhere. It is the one living truth that makes all realities true. This truth is not only of knowledge but of devotion. "*Namonamah,*"—we bow to him everywhere, and over and over again. It is recognized in the outburst of the Rishi, who addresses the whole world in a sudden ecstasy of joy: *Listen to me, ye sons of the immortal spirit, ye who live in the heavenly abode, I have known the Supreme Person whose light shines forth from beyond the darkness.*[6] Do we not find the

---

4. Içāvāsyamidam sarvam yat kiñcha jagatyāñ jagat.
5. Yo dāvō'gnau y'ōpsu yō viçvambhuvanamāviāça ya ōshadhishu yō vanaspatishu tasmai dēvāya namōnamah.
6. Crinvantu viçve amritasya putrā ā ye divya dhāmāni tasthuh vedāhametam purusham mahāntam āditya varnam tamasah parastāt.

overwhelming delight of a direct and positive experience
where there is not the least trace of vagueness or passivity?
Buddha, who developed the practical side of the teaching
of the Upanishads, preached the same message when he said,
With everything, whether it is above or below, remote or near,
visible or invisible, thou shalt preserve a relation of unlimited
love without any animosity or without a desire to kill. To live
in such a consciousness while standing or walking, sitting or
lying down till you are asleep, is Brahma vihāra, or, in other
words, is living and moving and having your joy in the spirit
of Brahma.

What is that spirit? The Upanishad says, *The being who*
is in his essence the light and life of all, who is world-conscious,
is Brahma.[7] To feel all, to be conscious of everything, is his
spirit. We are immersed in his consciousness body and soul.
It is through his consciousness that the sun attracts the earth;
it is through his consciousness that the light-waves are being
transmitted from planet to planet.

Not only in space, but *this light and life, this all-feeling*
being is in our souls.[8] He is all-conscious in space, or the world
of extension; and he is all-conscious in soul, or the world of
intension.

Thus to attain our world-consciousness, we have to unite
our feeling with this all-pervasive infinite feeling. In fact, the
only true human progress is coincident with this widening of
the range of feeling. All our poetry, philosophy, science, art,
and religion are serving to extend the scope of our
consciousness towards higher and larger spheres. Man does
not acquire rights through occupation of larger space, nor

7. Yaçchāyamasminnākāçē tājōmayō'mritamayah purushah
   sarvānubhūh.
8. Yaçchāyamasminnātmani tējōmayō'mritamayah purushah
   sarvānubhūh.

through external conduct, but his rights extend only so far as he is real, and his reality is measured by the scope of his consciousness.

We have, however, to pay a price for this attainment of the freedom of consciousness. What is the price? It is to give one's self away. Our soul can realise itself truly only by denying itself. The Upanishad says, *Thou shalt gain by giving away,*[9] *Thou shalt not covet.*[10] In the Gita we are advised to work disinterestedly, abandoning all lust for the result. Many outsiders conclude from this teaching that the conception of the world as something unreal lies at the root of the so-called disinterestedness preached in India. But the reverse is the truth.

The man who aims at his own aggrandizement underrates everything else. Compared with himself the rest of the world is unreal. Thus in order to be fully conscious of the reality of all, man has to be free himself from the bonds of personal desires. This discipline we have to go through to prepare ourselves for our social duties—for sharing the burdens of our fellow-beings. Every endeavour to attain a larger life requires of man "to gain by giving away, and not to be greedy." And thus to expand gradually the consciousness of one's unity with all is the striving of humanity.

The Infinite in India was not a thin nonentity, void of all content. The Rishis of India asserted emphatically, "To know him in this life is to be true; not to know him in this life is the desolation of death."[11] How to know him then? "By realising him in each and all."[12] Not only in nature, but in

---

9. Tyaktāna bhuñjīthāh.
10. Mā gridhah.
11. Iha chēt avēdit atha satyamasti, nachēt iha avēdit mahatī vinashtih.
12. Bhūtēshu bhūtēshu vichintya.

the family, in society, and in the state, the more we realise the World-conscious in all, the better for us. Failing to realise this, we turn our faces to destruction.

It fills me with great joy and a high hope for the future of humanity when I realise that there was a time in the remote past when our poet-prophets stood under the lavish sunshine of an Indian sky and greeted the world with the glad recognition of kindred. It was not an anthropomorphic hallucination. It was not seeing man reflected everywhere in grotesquely exaggerated images, and witnessing the human drama acted on a gigantic scale in nature's arena of flitting lights and shadows. On the contrary, it meant crossing the limiting barriers of the individual, to become more than man, to become one with the All. It was not a mere play of the imagination, but it was the liberation of consciousness from all the mystifications and exaggerations of the self. These ancient seers felt in the serene depth of their mind that the same energy, which vibrates and passes into the endless forms of the world, manifests itself in our inner being as consciousness; and there is no break in unity. For these seers there was no gap in their luminous vision of perfection. They never acknowledged even death itself as creating a chasm in the field of reality. They said, *His reflection is death as well as immortality.*[13] They did not recognize any essential opposition between life and death, and they said with absolute assurance, "It is life that is death."[14] They saluted with the same serenity of gladness "life in its aspect of appearing and in its aspect of departure"—*That which is past is hidden in life, and that which is to come.*[15] They knew that mere

13. Yasya chhāyāmritam yasya mrityuh.
14. Prāṇo mrityuh.
15. Namō astu āyatē namō astu parāyatē. Prāṇē ha bhūtam bhavyañcha.

appearance and disappearance are on the surface like waves on the sea, but life which is permanent knows no decay or diminution. *Everything has sprung from immortal life and is vibrating with life,*[16] for *life is immense.*[17] This is the noble heritage from our forefathers waiting to be claimed by us as our own, this ideal of the supreme freedom of consciousness. It is not merely intellectual or emotional, it has an ethical basis, and it must be translated into action. In the Upanishads it is said, *The supreme being is all-pervading, therefore he is the innate good in all.*[18] To be truly united in knowledge, love, and service with all beings, and thus to realise one's self in the all-pervading God is the essence of goodness, and this is the keynote of the teachings of the Upanishads: *Life is immense!*[19]

---

16. Yadidan kiñcha praöa ejati nihsritam.
17. Prāṇo virāt.
18. Sarvavyāpī sa bhagavān tasmāt sarvagatah çivah.
19. Prāṇo virāt.

Soul Consciousness

We have seen that it was the aspiration of ancient India to live and move and have its joy in Brahma, the all-conscious and all-pervading Spirit, by extending its field of consciousness over all the world. But that, it may be urged, is an impossible task for man to achieve. If this extension of consciousness be an outward process, then it is endless; it is like attempting to cross the ocean after ladling out its water. By beginning to try to realise all, one has to end by realising nothing.

But, in reality, it is not so absurd as it sounds. Man has every day to solve this problem of enlarging his region and adjusting his burdens. His burdens are many, too numerous for him to carry, but he knows that by adopting a system he can lighten the weight of his load. Whenever they feel too complicated and unwieldy, he knows it is because he has not been able to hit upon the system which would have set everything in place and distributed the weight evenly. This search for system is really a search for unity, for synthesis; it is our attempt to harmonise the heterogeneous complexity of outward materials by an inner adjustment. In the search we gradually become aware that to find out the One is to possess the All; that there, indeed, is our last and highest privilege. It is based on the law of that unity which is, if we only know it, our abiding strength. Its living principle is the power that is in truth; the truth of that unity which comprehends multiplicity. Facts are many, but the truth is one. The animal intelligence knows facts, the human mind has power to apprehend truth. The apple falls from the tree, the rain descends upon the earth—you can go on burdening your memory with such facts and never come to an end. But once you get hold of the law of gravitation you can dispense with the necessity of collecting facts *ad infinitum.* You have got at one truth which governs numberless facts. This discovery of a truth is pure joy to man—it is a liberation of his mind. For, a mere fact is like a blind lane, it leads only to itself—it has no beyond. But a truth opens up a whole horizon, it leads us to the infinite. That is the reason why, when a man like Darwin discovers some simple general truth about Biology, it does not stop there, but like a lamp shedding its light far beyond the object for which it was lighted, it illumines the whole region of human life and thought, transcending its original purpose. Thus we find that truth, while investing all facts, is not a mere aggregate of facts—it surpasses them on all sides and points to the infinite reality.

As in the region of knowledge so in that of consciousness, man must clearly realise some central truth which will give him an outlook over the widest possible field. And that is the object which the Upanishad has in view when it says, *Know thine own Soul.* Or, in other words, realise the one great principle of unity that there is in every man.

All our egoistic impulses, our selfish desires, obscure our true vision of the soul. For they only indicate our own narrow self. When we are conscious of our soul, we perceive the inner being that transcends our ego and has its deeper affinity with the All.

Children, when they begin to learn each separate letter of the alphabet, find no pleasure in it, because they miss the real purpose of the lesson; in fact, while letters claim our attention only in themselves and as isolated things, they fatigue us. They become a source of joy to us only when they combine into words and sentences and convey an idea.

Likewise, our soul when detached and imprisoned within the narrow limits of a self loses its significance. For its very essence is unity. It can only find out its truth by unifying itself with others, and only then it has its joy. Man was troubled and he lived in a state of fear so long as he had not discovered the uniformity of law in nature; till then the world was alien to him. The law that he discovered is nothing but the perception of harmony that prevails between reason, which is the soul of man, and the workings of the world. This is the bond of union through which man is related to the world in which he lives, and he feels an exceeding joy when he finds this out, for then he realises himself in his surroundings. To understand anything is to find in it something which is our own, and it is the discovery of ourselves outside us which makes us glad. This relation of understanding is partial, but the relation of love is complete. In love the sense of difference is obliterated and the human soul fulfils its purpose in perfection, transcending the limits of itself and reaching across the threshold of the infinite. Therefore love is the highest bliss that man can attain to, for through it alone he truly knows that he is more than himself, and that he is at one with the All.

This principle of unity which man has in his soul is ever active, establishing relations far and wide through literature, art, and science, society, statecraft, and religion. Our great Revealers are they who make manifest the true meaning of the soul by giving up self for the love of mankind. They face calumny and persecution, deprivation and death in their service of love. They live the life of the soul, not of the self, and thus they prove to us the ultimate truth of humanity. We call them *Mahātmās,* "the men of the great soul."

It is said in one of the Upanishads: *It is not that thou lovest thy son because thou desirest him, but thou lovest thy son because thou desirest thine own soul.*[1] The meaning of this is, that whomsoever we love, in him we find our own soul in the highest sense. The final truth of our existence lies in this. *Paramātmā,* the supreme soul, is in me, as well as in my son, and my joy in my son is the realization of this truth. It has become quite a commonplace fact, yet it is wonderful to think upon, that the joys and sorrows of our loved ones are joys and sorrows to us—nay, they are more. Why so? Because in them we have grown larger, in them we have touched that great truth which comprehends the whole universe.

It very often happens that our love for our children, our friends, or other loved ones, debars us from the further realization of our soul. It enlarges our scope of consciousness, no doubt, yet it sets a limit to its freest expansion. Nevertheless it is the first step, and all the wonder lies in this first step itself. It shows to us the true nature of our soul. From it we know, for certain, that our highest joy is in the losing of our egoistic self and in the uniting with others. This love gives us a new power and insight and beauty of mind to the extent of the limits we set around it, but ceases to do so if those limits lose their elasticity, and militate against the spirit of love altogether; then our friendships become exclusive, our families selfish and inhospitable, our nations insular and aggressively inimical to other races. It is like putting a burning light within a sealed enclosure, which shines brightly till the poisonous gases accumulate and smother the flame. Nevertheless it has proved its truth before it dies, and made known the joy of freedom from the grip of the darkness, blind and empty and cold.

---

1. Na vā are putrasya kāmāya putrah priyō bhavati, ātmanastu kāmāya putrah priyō priyō bhavati.

According to the Upanishads, the key to cosmic consciousness, to God-consciousness, is in the consciousness of the soul. To know our soul apart from the self is the first step towards the realization of the supreme deliverance. We must know with absolute certainty that essentially we are spirit. This we can do by winning mastery over self, by rising above all pride and greed and fear, by knowing that worldly losses and physical death can take nothing away from the truth and the greatness of our soul. The chick knows when it breaks through the self-centred isolation of its egg that the hard shell which covered it so long was not really a part of its life. That shell is a dead thing, it has no growth, it affords no glimpse whatever of the vast beyond that lies outside it. However pleasantly perfect and rounded it may be, it must be given a blow to, it must be burst through and thereby the freedom of light and air be won, and the complete purpose of bird life be achieved. In Sanskrit, the bird has been called the twice-born: so too the man is named, who has gone through the ceremony of the discipline of self-restraint and high thinking for a period of at least twelve years; who has come out simple in wants, pure in heart, and ready to take up all the responsibilities of life in a disinterested largeness of spirit. He is considered to have had his rebirth from the blind envelopment of self to the freedom of soul life; to have come into living relation with his surroundings; to have become at one with the All.

I have already warned my hearers, and must once more warn them against the idea that the teachers of India preached a renunciation of the world and of self which leads only to the blank emptiness of negation. Their aim was the realization of the soul, or, in other words, gaining the world in perfect truth. When Jesus said, "Blessed are the meek, for they shall inherit the earth," he meant this. He proclaimed the truth that when man gets rid of his pride of self then he comes into his true inheritance. No more has he to fight his way into his position in the world; it is secure for him everywhere by the immortal right of his soul. Pride of self interferes with the proper function of the soul which is to realise itself by perfecting its union with the world and the world's God.

In his sermon to Sádhu Simha, Buddha says, *It is true, Simha, that I denounce activities, but only the activities that lead to the evil in words, thoughts, or deeds. It is true, Simha, that I preach extinction, but only the extinction of pride, lust, evil thought, and ignorance, not that of forgiveness, love, charity, and truth.*

The doctrine of deliverance that Buddha preached was the freedom from the thraldom of *avidyā. Avidyā* is the ignorance that darkens our consciousness, and tends to limit it within the boundaries of our personal self. It is this *avidyā,* this ignorance, this limiting of consciousness that creates the hard separateness of the ego, and thus becomes the source of all pride and greed and cruelty incidental to self-seeking. When a man sleeps he is shut up within the narrow activities of his physical life. He lives, but he knows not the varied relations of his life to his surroundings,—therefore he knows not himself. So when a man lives the life of *Avidya* he is confined within his own self. It is a spiritual sleep; his consciousness is not fully awake to the highest reality that surrounds him, therefore he knows not the reality of his own soul. When he attains *Bodhi, i.e.* the awakenment from the sleep of self to the perfection of consciousness, he becomes Buddha.

Once I met two ascetics of a certain religious sect in a village of Bengal. 'Can you tell me,' I asked them, 'wherein lies the special features of your religion?' One of them hesitated for a moment and answered, 'It is difficult to define that.' The other said, 'No, it is quite simple. We hold that we have first of all to know our own soul under the guidance of our spiritual teacher, and when we have done that we can find him, who is the Supreme Soul, within us.' 'Why don't you preach your doctrine to all the people of the world?' I asked. 'Whoever feels thirsty will of himself come to the river,' was his reply. 'But then, do you find it so? Are they coming?' The man gave a gentle smile, and with an assurance which had not the least tinge of impatience or anxiety, he said, 'They must come, one and all.'

Yes, he is right, this simple ascetic of rural Bengal. Man is indeed abroad to satisfy needs which are more to him than food and clothing. He is out to find himself. Man's history is the history of his journey to the unknown in quest of the realization of his immortal self—his soul. Through the rise and fall of empires; through the building up gigantic piles of wealth and the ruthless scattering of them upon the dust; through the creation of vast bodies of symbols that give shape to his dreams and aspirations, and the casting of them away like the playthings of an outworn infancy; through his forging of magic keys with which to unlock the mysteries of creation, and through his throwing away of this labour of ages to go back to his workshop and work up afresh some new form; yes, through it all man is marching from epoch to epoch towards the fullest realization of his soul,—the soul which is greater than the things man accumulates, the deeds he accomplishes, the theories he builds, the soul whose onward course is never checked by death or dissolution. Man's mistakes and failures have by no means been trifling or small, they have strewn his path with colossal ruins; his sufferings have been immense, like birth-pangs for a giant child; they are the prelude of a fulfilment whose scope is infinite. Man has gone through and is still undergoing martyrdoms in various ways, and his institutions are the altars he has built whereto he brings his daily sacrifices, marvellous in kind and stupendous in quantity. All this would be absolutely unmeaning and unbearable if all along he did not feel that deepest joy of the soul within him, which tries its divine strength by suffering and proves its exhaustless riches by renunciation. Yes, they are coming, the pilgrims, one and all—coming to their true inheritance of the world; they are ever broadening their consciousness, ever seeking a higher and higher unity, ever approaching nearer to one central Truth which is all-comprehensive.

Man's poverty is abysmal, his wants are endless till he becomes truly conscious of his soul. Till then, the world to him is in a state of continual flux—a phantasm that is and is not. For a man who has realised his soul there is a determinate centre of the universe around which all else can find its proper place, and from thence only can he draw and enjoy the blessedness of a harmonious life.

There was a time when the earth was only a nebulous mass whose particles were scattered far apart through the expanding force of heat; when she had not yet attained her definiteness of form and had neither beauty nor purpose, but only heat and motion. Gradually, when her vapours were condensed into a unified rounded whole through a force that strove to bring all straggling matters under the control of a centre, she occupied her proper place among the planets of the solar system, like an emerald pendant in a necklace of diamonds. So with our soul. When the heat and motion of blind impulses and passions distract it on all sides, we can neither give nor receive anything truly. But when we find our centre in our soul by the power of self-restraint, by the force that harmonises all warring elements and unifies those that are apart, then all our isolated impressions reduce themselves to wisdom, and all our momentary impulses of heart find their completion in love; then all the petty details of our life reveal an infinite purpose, and all our thoughts and deeds unite themselves inseparably in an internal harmony.

The Upanishads say with great emphasis, *Know thou the One, the Soul.*[2] *It is the bridge leading to the immortal being.*[3]

This is the ultimate end of man, to find the *One* which is in him; which is his truth, which is his soul; the key with which he opens the gate of the spiritual life, the heavenly kingdom. His desires are many, and madly they run after the varied objects of the world, for therein they have their life and fulfilment. But that which is *one* in him is ever seeking for unity—unity in knowledge, unity in love, unity in purposes of will; its highest joy is when it reaches the infinite one within its eternal unity. Hence the saying of the Upanishad, *Only those of tranquil minds, and none else, can attain abiding joy, by realising within their souls the Being who manifests one essence in a multiplicity of forms.*[4]

Through all the diversities of the world the one in us is threading its course towards the one in all; this is its nature and this is its joy. But by that devious path it could never reach its goal if it had not a light of its own by which it could catch in a flash the sight of what it was seeking. The vision of the Supreme One in our own soul is a direct and immediate intuition, not based on any ratiocination or demonstration at all. Our eyes naturally see an object as a whole, not by breaking it up into parts, but by bringing all the parts together into a unity with ourselves. So with the intuition of our Soul-consciousness, which naturally and totally realises its unity in the Supreme One.

Says the Upanishad: *This deity who is manifesting himself in the activities of the universe always dwells in the heart of*

---

2. Tamēvaikam jānātha ātmānam.
3. Amritasyaisha sētuh.
4. Ekam rūpam bahudhā ya karōti ** tam ātmastham yē anupaçyanti dhīrāh, tēshām sukham çāçvatam nētarēshām.

man as the supreme soul. Those who realise him through the immediate perception of the heart attain immortality.[5]

He is *Vishvakarma;* that is, in a multiplicity of forms and forces lies his outward manifestation in nature; but his inner manifestation in our soul is that which exists in unity. Our pursuit of truth in the domain of nature therefore is through analysis and the gradual methods of science, but our apprehension of truth in our soul is immediate and through direct intuition. We cannot attain the supreme soul by successive additions of knowledge acquired bit by bit even through all eternity, because he is one, he is not made up of parts; we can only know him as heart of our hearts and soul of our soul; we can only know him in the love and joy we feel when we give up our self and stand before him face to face.

The deepest and the most earnest prayer that has ever risen from the human heart has been uttered in our ancient tongue: *O thou self-revealing one, reveal thyself in me.*[6] We are in misery because we are creatures of self—the self that is unyielding and narrow, that reflects no light, that is blind to the infinite. Our self is loud with its own discordant clamour— it is not the tuned harp whose chords vibrate with the music of the eternal. Sighs of discontent and weariness of failure, idle regrets for the past and anxieties for the future are troubling our shallow hearts because we have not found our souls, and the self-revealing spirit has not been manifest within us. Hence our cry, *O thou awful one, save me with thy smile of grace ever and evermore.*[7] It is a stifling shroud of death, this self-gratification, this insatiable greed, this pride of possession, this

---

5. Esha dēvō vishvakarmā mahātmā sadā janānām hridayē sannivishtah. Hridā manīsha manasābhiklriptō ya ētad viduramritāstē bhavanti.
6. Ávirāvīrmayādhi.
7. Rudra yat tē dakshinam mukham tēna mām pāhi nityam.

insolent alienation of heart. *Rudra, O thou awful are, rend this dark cover in twain and let the saving beam of thy smile of grace strike through this night of gloom and waken my soul. From unreality lead me to the real, from darkness to the light, from death to immortality.*[8] But how can one hope to have this prayer granted? For infinite is the distance that lies between truth and untruth, between death and deathlessness. Yet this measureless gulf is bridged in a moment when the self-revealing one reveals himself in the soul. There the miracle happens, for there is the meeting-ground of the finite and infinite. *Father, completely sweep away all my sins!*[9] For in sin man takes part with the finite against the infinite that is in him. It is the defeat of his soul by his self. It is a perilously losing game, in which man stakes his all to gain a part. Sin is the blurring of truth which clouds the purity of our consciousness. In sin we lust after pleasures, not because they are truly desirable, but because the red light of our passion makes them appear desirable; we long for things not because they are great in themselves, but because our greed exaggerates them and makes them appear great. These exaggerations, these falsifications of the perspective of things, break the harmony of our life at every step; we lose the true standard of values and are distracted by the false claims of the varied interests of life contending with one another. It is this failure to bring all the elements of his nature under the unity and control of the Supreme One that makes man feel the pang of his separation from God and gives rise to the earnest prayer, *O God, O Father, completely sweep away all our sins. Give into us that which is good,*[10] the good which is the daily

---

8. Asatōmā sadgamaya, tamasōmā jyōtirgamaya, mrityōrmā mritangamaya.
9. Vishvānidāva savitar duritāni parāsuva.
10. Yad bhadram tanna āsuva.

bread of our souls. In our pleasures we are confined to ourselves, in the good we are freed and we belong to all. As the child in its mother's womb gets its sustenance through the union of its life with the larger life of its mother, so our soul is nourished only through the good which is the recognition of its inner kinship, the channel of its communication with the infinite by which it is surrounded and fed. Hence it is said, "Blessed are they which do hunger and thirst after righteousness: for they shall be filled." For righteousness is the divine food of the soul; nothing but this can untruth and unrighteousness hold its reign; and things can come to such a pass that we may cry out in our anguish, "Such utter lawlessness could never prevail if there were a God!" Indeed, God has stood aside from our self, where his watchful patience knows no bounds, and where he never forces open the doors if shut against him. For this self of ours has to attain its ultimate meaning, which is the soul, not through the compulsion of God's power but through love, and thus become united with God in freedom.

He whose spirit has been made one with God stands before man as the supreme flower of humanity. There man finds in truth what he is; for there the *Avih* is revealed to him in the soul of man as the most perfect revelation for him of God; for there we see the union of the supreme will with our will, our love with the love everlasting.

Therefore, in our country he who truly loves God receives such homage from men as would be considered almost sacrilegious in the west. We see in him God's wish fulfilled, the most difficult of all obstacles to his revealment removed, and God's own perfect joy fully blossoming in humanity. Through him we find the whole world of man overspread with a divine homeliness. His life, burning with God's love, makes all our earthly love resplendent. All the intimate associations of our life, all its experience of pleasure and pain, group themselves around this display of the divine love, and form the drama that we witness in him. The touch of an infinite mystery passes over the trivial and the familiar, making it break out into ineffable music. The trees and the stars and the blue hills appear to us as symbols aching with a meaning which can never be uttered in words. We seem to watch the Master in the very act of creation of a new world when a man's soul draws her heavy curtain of self aside, when her veil is lifted and she is face to face with her eternal lover.

But what is this state? It is like a morning of spring, varied in its life and beauty, yet one and entire. When a man's life rescued from distractions finds its unity in the soul, then the consciousness of the infinite becomes at once direct and natural to it as the light is to the flame. All the conflicts and contradictions of life are reconciled; knowledge, love, and action harmonized; pleasure and pain become one in beauty; enjoyment and renunciation equal in goodness; the breach between the finite and the infinite fills with love and overflows; every moment carries its message of the eternal: the formless appears to us in the form of the flower, of the fruit; the boundless takes us up in his arms as a father and walks by our side as a friend. It is only the soul, the one in man which by its very nature can overcome all limits, and finds its affinity with the Supreme One. While yet we have not attained the internal harmony, and the wholeness of our being, our life remains a life of habits. The world still appears to us as a machine, to be mastered where it is useful, to be guarded against where it is dangerous, and never to be known in its full fellowship with us alike in its physical nature and in its spiritual life and beauty.

The Problem of Evil

The question why there is evil in existence is the same as why there is imperfection, or, in other words, why there is creation at all. We must take it for granted that it could not be otherwise; that creation must be imperfect, must be gradual, and that it is futile to ask the question, Why are we?

But this is the real question we ought to ask: Is this imperfection the final truth, is evil absolute and ultimate? The river has its boundaries, its banks, but is a river all banks? or are the banks the final facts about the river? Do not these obstructions themselves give its water an onward motion? The towing rope binds a boat, but is the bondage its meaning? Does it not at the same time draw the boat forward?

The current of the world has its boundaries, otherwise it could have no existence, but its purpose is not shown in the boundaries which restrain it, but in its movement, which is towards perfection. The wonder is not that there should be obstacles and sufferings in this world, but that there should be law and order, beauty and joy, goodness and love. The idea of God that man has in his being is the wonder of all wonders. He has felt in the depths of his life that what appears as imperfect is the manifestation of the perfect; just as a man who has an ear for music realises the perfection of a song, while in fact he is only listening to a succession of notes. Man has found out the great paradox that what is limited is not imprisoned within its limits; it is ever moving, and therewith shedding its finitude every moment. In fact, imperfection is not a negation of perfectness; finitude is not contradictory to infinity: they are but completeness manifested in parts, infinite revealed within bounds.

Pain, which is the feeling of our finiteness, is not a fixture in our life. It is not an end in self, as joy is. To meet with it is to know that it has no part in the true permanence of creation. It is what error is in our intellectual life. To go through the history of the development of science is to go through the maze of mistakes it made current at different times. Yet no one really believes that science is the one perfect mode of disseminating mistakes. The progressive ascertainment of truth is the important thing to remember in the history of science, not its innumerable mistakes. Error, by its nature, cannot be stationary; it cannot remain with truth; like a tramp, it must quit its lodging as soon as it fails to pay its score to the full.

As in intellectual error, so in evil of any other form, its essence is impermanence, for it cannot accord with the whole. Every moment it is being corrected by the totality of things and keeps changing its aspect. We exaggerate its importance by imagining it as at a standstill. Could we collect the statistics of the immense amount of death and putrefaction happening every moment in this earth, they would appal us. But evil is ever moving; with all its incalculable immensity it does not effectually clog the current of our life; and we find that the earth, water, and air remain sweet and pure for living beings. All such statistics consist of our attempts to represent statically what is in motion; and in the process things assume a weight in our mind which they have not in reality. For this reason a man, who by his profession is concerned with any particular aspect of life, is apt to magnify its proportions; in laying undue stress upon facts he loses his hold upon truth. A detective may have the opportunity of studying crimes in detail, but he loses his sense of their relative place in the whole social economy. When science collects facts to illustrate the struggle for existence that is going on in the animal kingdom, it raises a picture in our minds of "nature red in tooth and claw." But in these mental pictures we give a fixity to colours and forms which are really evanescent. It is like calculating the weight of the air on each square inch of our body to prove that it must be crushingly heavy for us. With every weight, however, there is an adjustment, and we lightly bear our burden. With the struggle for existence in nature there is reciprocity. There is the love for children and for comrades; there is the sacrifice of self, which springs from love; and this love is the positive element in life.

If we kept the search-light of our observation turned upon the fact of death, the world would appear to us like a huge charnel-house; but in the world of life the thought of death has, we find, the least possible hold upon our minds. Not because it is the least apparent, but because it is the negative aspect of life; just as, in spite of the fact that we shut our eyelids every second, it is the openings of the eyes that count. Life as a whole never takes death seriously. It laughs, dances and plays, it builds, hoards and loves in death's face. Only when we detach one individual fact of death do we see its blankness and become dismayed. We lose sight of the wholeness of a life of which death is part. It is like looking at a piece of cloth through a microscope. It appears like a net; we gaze at the big holes and shiver in imagination. But the truth is, death is not the ultimate reality. It looks black, as the sky looks blue; but it does not blacken existence, just as the sky does not leave its stain upon the wings of the bird.

When we watch a child trying to walk, we see its countless failures; its successes are but few. If we had to limit our observation within a narrow space of time, the sight would be cruel. But we find that in spite of its repeated failures there is an impetus of joy in the child which sustains it in its seemingly impossible task. We see it does not think of its falls so much as of its power to keep its balance though for only a moment.

Like these accidents in a child's attempts to walk, we meet with sufferings in various forms in our life every day, showing the imperfections in our knowledge and our available power, and in the application of our will. But if these revealed our weakness to us only, we should die of utter depression. When we select for observation a limited area of our activities, our individual failures and miseries loom large in our minds; but our life leads us instinctively to take a wider view. It gives us an ideal of perfection which ever carries us beyond our present limitations. Within us we have a hope which always walks in front of our present narrow experiences; it is the undying faith in the infinite in us; it will never accept any of our disabilities as a permanent fact; it sets no limit to its own scope; it dares to assert that man has oneness with God; and its wild dreams become true every day.

We see the truth when we set our mind towards the infinite. The ideal of truth is not in the narrow present, not in our immediate sensations, but in the consciousness of the whole which gives us a taste of what we *should* have in what we *do* have. Consciously or unconsciously we have in our life this feeling of Truth which is ever larger than its appearance; for our life is facing the infinite, and it is in movement. Its aspiration is therefore infinitely more than its achievement, and as it goes on it finds that no realization of truth ever leaves it stranded on the desert of finality, but carries it to a region beyond. Evil cannot altogether arrest the course of life on the highway and rob it of its possessions. For the evil has to pass on, it has to grow into good; it cannot stand and give battle to the All. If the least evil could stop anywhere indefinitely, it would sink deep and cut into the very roots of existence. As it is, man does not really believe in evil, just as he cannot believe that violin strings have been purposely made to create the exquisite torture of discordant notes, though by the aid of statistics is can be mathematically proved that the probability of discord is far greater than that of harmony, and for one who can play the violin there are thousands who cannot. The potentiality of perfection outweighs actual contradictions. No doubt there have been people who asserted existence to be an absolute evil, but man can never take them seriously. Their pessimism is a mere pose, either intellectual or sentimental, but life itself is optimistic: it wants to go on. Pessimism is a form of mental dipsomania, it disdains healthy nourishment, indulges in the strong drink of denunciation, and creates an artificial dejection which thirsts for a stronger draught. If existence were an evil, it would wait for no philosopher to prove it. It is like convicting a man of suicide, while all the time he stands before you in the flesh. Existence itself is here to prove that it cannot be an evil.

An imperfection which is not all imperfection, but which has perfection for its ideal, must go through a perpetual realization. Thus, it is the function of our intellect to realise the truth through untruths, and knowledge is nothing but the continually burning up of error to set free the light of truth. Our will, our character, has to attain perfection by continually overcoming evils, either inside or outside us, or both; our physical life is consuming bodily materials every moment to maintain the life fire; and our moral life too has its fuel to burn. This life process is going on—we know it, we have felt it; and we have a faith which no individual instances to the contrary can shake, that the direction of humanity is from evil to good. For we feel that good is the positive element in man's nature, and in every age and every clime what man values most is his ideal of goodness. We have known the good, we have loved it, and we have paid our highest reverence to men who have shown in their lives what goodness is.

The question will be asked, What is goodness; what does our moral nature mean? My answer is, that when a man begins to have an extended vision of his true self, when he realises that he is much more than at present he seems to be, he begins to get conscious of his moral nature. Then he grows aware of that which he is yet to be, and the state not yet experienced by him becomes more real than that under his direct experience. Necessarily, his perspective of life changes, and his will takes the place of his wishes. For will is the supreme wish of the larger life, the life whose greater portion is out of our present reach, whose objects are not for the most part before our sight. Then comes the conflict of our lesser man with our greater man, of our wishes with our will, of the desire for things affecting our senses with the purpose that is within our heart. Then we begin to distinguish between what we immediately desire and what is good. For good is that which is desirable for our greater self. Thus the sense of goodness comes out of a truer view of our life, which is the connected view of the wholeness of the field of life, and which takes into account not only what is present before us but what is not, and perhaps never humanly can be. Man, who is provident, feels for that life of his which is not yet existent, feels much more for that than for the life that is with him; therefore he is ready to sacrifice his present inclination for the unrealised future. In this he becomes great, for he realises truth. Even to be efficiently selfish a man has to recognize this truth, and has to curb his immediate impulses—in other words, has to be moral. For our moral faculty is the faculty by which we know that life is not made up of fragments, purposeless and discontinuous. This moral sense of man not only gives him the power to see that the self has a continuity in time, but it also enables him to see that he is not true when he is only restricted to his own self. He is more in truth than he is in fact. He truly belongs to individuals who are not included in his own individuality, and whom he is never even likely to know. As he has a feeling for his future self which is outside his present consciousness, so he has a feeling for his greater self which is outside the limits of his personality. There is no man who has not this feeling to some extent, who has never sacrificed his selfish desire for the sake of some other person, who has never felt a pleasure in undergoing some loss or trouble because it pleased somebody else. It is a truth that man is not a detached being, that he has a universal aspect; and when he recognizes this, he becomes great. Even the most evilly-disposed selfishness has to recognize this when he seeks the power to do evil; for it cannot ignore truth and yet be strong. So in order to claim the aid of truth, selfishness has to be unselfish to some extent. A band of robbers must be moral in order to hold together as a band; they may rob the whole world but not each other. To make an immoral intention successful, some of its weapons must be moral. In fact, very often it is our very moral strength which gives us most effectively the power to do evil, to exploit other individuals for our own benefit, to rob other people of their just rights. The life of an animal is unmoral, for it is aware only of an immediate present; the life of a man can be immoral, but that only means that it must have a moral basis. What is immoral is imperfectly moral just as what is false is true to a small extent, or it cannot be false. Not to see is to be blind, but to see wrongly is to see only in an imperfect manner. Man's selfishness is a beginning to see some connection, some purpose in life; and to act in accordance with its dictates requires self-restraint and regulation of conduct. A selfish man willingly undergoes troubles for the sake of the self, he suffers hardship and privation without a murmur, simply because he knows that what is pain and trouble, looked at from the point of view of a short space of time, is just the opposite when seen in a larger perspective. Thus what is a loss to the smaller man is a gain to the greater, and *vice versa*.

To the man who lives for an idea, for his country, for the good of humanity, life has an extended meaning, and to that extent pain becomes important to him. To live the life of goodness is to live the life of all. Pleasure is for one's own self, but goodness is concerned with the happiness of all humanity and for all time. From the point of view of the good, pleasure and pain appear in a different meaning; so much so, that pleasure may be shunned, and pain be courted in its place, and death itself be made welcome as giving a higher value to life. From these higher standpoints of a man's life, the standpoints of the good, pleasure and pain lose their absolute value. Martyrs prove it in history, and we prove it every day in our life in our little martyrdoms. When we take a pitcherful of water from the sea it has its weight, but when we take a dip into the sea itself a thousand pitchersful of water flow above our head, and we do not feel their weight. We have to carry the pitcher of self with our strength; and so, while on the plane of selfishness pleasure and pain have their full weight, on the moral plane they are so much lightened that the man who has reached it appears to us almost super-human in his patience under crushing trials, and his forbearance in the face of malignant persecution.

To live in perfect goodness is to realise one's life in the infinite. This is the most comprehensive view of life which we can have by our inherent power of the moral vision of the wholeness of life. And the teaching of Buddha is to cultivate this moral power to the highest extent, to know that our field of activities is not bound to the plane of our narrow self. This is the vision of the heavenly kingdom of Christ. When we attain to that universal life, which is the moral life, we become free from bonds of pleasure and pain, and the place vacated by our self becomes filled with an unspeakable joy which springs from measureless love. In this state the soul's activity is all the more heightened, only its motive power is not from desires, but in its own joy. This is the *Karmayoga* of the Gita, the way to become one with the infinite activity by the exercise of the activity of disinterested goodness.

When Buddha meditated upon the way of releasing mankind from the grip of misery he came to this truth: that when man attains his highest end by merging the individual in the universal, he becomes free from the thraldom of pain. Let us consider this point more fully.

A student of mine once related to me his adventure in a storm, and complained that all the time he was troubled with the feeling that this great commotion in nature behaved to him as if he were no more than a mere handful of dust. That he was a distinct personality with a will of his own had not the least influence upon what was happening.

I said, "If consideration for our individuality could sway nature from her path, then it would be the individuals who would suffer most."

But he persisted in his doubt, saying that there was this fact which could not be ignored—the feeling that I am. The "I" in us seeks for a relation which is individual to it.

I replied that the relation of the "I" is with something which is "not-I." So we must have a medium which is common to both, and we must be absolutely certain that it is the same to the "I" as it is to the "not-I".

This is what needs repeating here. We have to keep in mind that our individuality by its nature is impelled to seek for the universal. Our body can only die if it tries to eat its own substance, and our eye loses the meaning of its function if it can only see itself.

Just as we find that the stronger the imagination the less is it merely imaginary and the more is it in harmony with truth, so we see the more vigorous our individuality the more does it widen towards the universal. For the greatness of a personality is not in itself but in its content, which is universal, just as the depth of a lake is judged not by the size of its cavity but by the depth of its water.

So, if it is a truth that the yearning of our nature is for reality, and that our personality cannot be happy with a fantastic universe of its own creation, then it is clearly best for it that our will can only deal with things by following their law, and cannot do with them just as it pleases. This unyielding sureness of reality sometimes crosses our will, and very often leads us to disaster, just as the firmness of the earth invariably hurts the falling child who is learning to walk. Nevertheless it is the same firmness that hurts him which makes his walking possible. Once, while passing under a bridge, the mast of my boat got stuck in one of its girders. If only for a moment the mast would have bent an inch or two, or the bridge raised its back like a yawning cat, or the river given in, it would have been all right with me. But they took no notice of my helplessness. That is the very reason why I could make use of the river, and sail upon it with the help of the mast, and that is why, when its current was inconvenient, I could rely upon the bridge. Things are what they are, and we have to know them if we would deal with them, and knowledge of them is possible because our wish is not their law. This knowledge is a joy to us, for the knowledge is one of the channels of our relation with the things outside us; it is making them our own, and thus widening the limit of our self.

At every step we have to take into account others than ourselves. For only in death are we alone. A poet is a true poet when he can make his personal idea joyful to all men, which he could not do if he had not a medium common to all his audience. This common language has its own law which the poet must discover and follow, by doing which he becomes true and attains poetical immortality.

We see then that man's individuality is not his highest truth; there is that in him which is universal. If he were made to live in a world where his own self was the only factor to consider, then that would be the worst prison imaginable to him, for man's deepest joy is in growing greater and greater by more and more union with the all. This, as we have seen, would be an impossibility if there were no law common to all. Only by discovering the law and following it, do we become great, do we realise the universal; while, so long as our individual desires are at conflict with the universal law, we suffer pain and are futile.

There was a time when we prayed for special concessions, we expected that the laws of nature should be held in abeyance for our own convenience. But now we know better. We know that law cannot be set aside, and in this knowledge we have become strong. For this law is not something apart from us; it is our own. The universal power which is manifested in the universal law is one with our own power. It will thwart us where we are small, where we are against the current of things; but it will help us where we are great, where we are in unison with the all. Thus, through the help of science, as we come to know more of the laws of nature, we gain in power; we tend to attain a universal body. Our organ of sight, our organ of locomotion, our physical strength becomes world-wide; steam and electricity become our nerve and muscle. Thus we find that, just as throughout our bodily organization there is a principle of relation by virtue of which we can call the entire body our own, and can use it as such, so all through the universe there is that principle of uninterrupted relation by virtue of which we can call the whole world our extended body and use it accordingly. And in this age of science it is our endeavour fully to establish our claim to our world-self. We know all our poverty and sufferings are owing to our inability to realise this legitimate claim of ours. Really, there is no limit to our powers, for we are not outside the universal power which is the expression of universal law. We are on our way, to overcome disease and death, to conquer pain and poverty; for through scientific knowledge we are ever on our way to realise the universal in its physical aspect. And as we make progress we find pain, disease, and poverty of power are not absolute, but that it is only the want of adjustment of our individual self to our universal self which gives rise to them.

It is the same with our spiritual life. When the individual man in us chafes against the lawful rule of the universal man we become morally small, and we must suffer. In such a condition our successes are our greatest failures, and the very fulfilment of our desires leaves us poorer. We hanker after special gains for ourselves, we want to enjoy privileges which none else can share with us. But everything that is absolutely special must keep up a perpetual warfare with what is general. In such a state of civil war man always lives behind barricades, and in any civilization which is selfish our homes are not real homes, but artificial barriers around us. Yet we complain that we are not happy, as if there were something inherent in the nature of things to make us miserable. The universal spirit is waiting to crown us with happiness, but our individual spirit would not accept it. It is our life of the self that causes conflicts and complications everywhere, upsets the normal balance of society and gives rise to miseries of all kinds. It brings things to such a pass that to maintain order we have to create artificial coercions and organized forms of tyranny, and tolerate infernal institutions is our midst, whereby at every moment humanity is humiliated.

We have seen that in order to be powerful we have to submit to the laws of the universal forces, and to realise in practice that they are our own. So, in order to be happy, we have to submit our individual will to the sovereignty of the universal will, and to feel in truth that it is our own will. When we reach that state wherein the adjustment of the finite in us to the infinite is made perfect, then pain itself becomes a valuable asset. It becomes a measuring rod with which to gauge the true value of our joy.

The most important lesson that man can learn from his life is not that there is pain in this world, but that it depends upon him to turn it into good account, that it is possible for him to transmute it into joy. That lesson has not been lost altogether to us, and there is no man living who would willingly be deprived of his right to suffer pain, for that is his right to be a man. One day the wife of a poor labourer complained bitterly to me that her eldest boy was going to be sent away to a rich relative's house for part of the year. It was the implied kind intention of trying to relieve her of her trouble that gave her the shock, for a mother's trouble is a mother's own by her inalienable right of love, and she was not going to surrender it to any dictates of expediency. Man's freedom is never in being saved troubles, but it is the freedom to take trouble for his own good, to make the trouble an element in his joy. It can be made so only when we realise that our individual self is not the highest meaning of our being, that in us we have the world-man who is immortal, who is not afraid of death or sufferings, and who looks upon pain as only the other side of joy. He who has realised this knows that it is pain which is our true wealth as imperfect beings, and has made us great and worthy to take our seat with the perfect. He knows that we are not beggars; that it is the hard coin which must be paid for everything valuable in this life, for our power, our wisdom, our love; that in pain is symbolised the infinite possibility of perfection, the eternal unfolding of joy; and the man who loses all pleasure in accepting pain sinks down and down to the lowest depth of penury and degradation. It is only when we invoke the aid of pain for our self-gratification that she becomes evil and takes her vengeance for the insult done to her by hurling us into misery. For she is the vestal virgin consecrated to the service of the immortal perfection, and when she takes her true place before the altar of the infinite she casts off her dark veil and bares her face to the beholder as a revelation of supreme joy.

The Problem of Self

At one pole of my being I am one with stocks and stones. There I have to acknowledge the rule of universal law. That is where the foundation of my existence lies, deep down below. Its strength lies in its being held firm in the clasp of the comprehensive world, and in the fullness of its community with all things.

But at the other pole of my being I am separate from all. There I have broken through the cordon of equality and stand alone as an individual. I am absolutely unique, I am I, I am incomparable. The whole weight of the universe cannot crush out this individuality of mine. I maintain it in spite of the tremendous gravitation of all things. It is small in appearance but great in reality. For it holds its own against the forces that would rob it of its distinction and make it one with the dust.

This is the superstructure of the self which rises from the indeterminate depth and darkness of its foundation into the open, proud of its isolation, proud of having given shape to a single individual idea of the architect's which has no duplicate in the whole universe. If this individuality be demolished then though no material be lost, not an atom destroyed the creative joy which was crystallised therein is gone. We are absolutely bankrupt if we are deprived of this speciality, this individuality, which is the only thing we can call our own; and which, if lost, is also a loss to the whole world. It is most valuable because it is not universal. And therefore only through it can we gain the universe more truly than if we were lying within its breast unconscious of our distinctiveness. The universal is ever seeking its consummation in the unique. And the desire we have to keep our uniqueness intact is really the desire of the universe acting in us. It is our joy of the infinite in us that gives us our joy in ourselves.

That this separateness of self is considered by man as his most precious possession is proved by the sufferings he undergoes and the sins he commits for its sake. But the consciousness of separation has come from the eating of the fruit of knowledge. It has led man to shame and crime and death; yet it is dearer to him than any paradise where the self lies, securely slumbering in perfect innocence in the womb of mother nature.

It is a constant striving and suffering for us to maintain the separateness of this self of ours. And in fact it is this suffering which measures its value. One side of the value is sacrifice, which represents how much the cost has been. The other side of it is the attainment, which represents how much has been gained. If the self meant nothing to us but pain and sacrifice, it could have no value for us, and on no account would we willingly undergo such sacrifice. In such case there could be no doubt at all that the highest object of humanity would be the annihilation of self.

But if there is a corresponding gain, if it does not end in a void but in a fullness, then it is clear that its negative qualities, its very sufferings and sacrifices, make it all the more precious. That it is so has been proved by those who have realised the positive significance of self, and have accepted its responsibilities with eagerness and undergone sacrifices without flinching.

With the foregoing introduction it will be easy for me to answer the question once asked by one of my audience as to whether the annihilation of self was not been held by India as the supreme goal of humanity?

In the first place we must keep in mind the fact that man is never literal in the expression of his ideas, except in matters most trivial. Very often man's words are not a language at all, but merely a local gesture of the dumb. They may indicate, but do not express his thoughts. The more vital his thoughts the more have his words to be explained by the context of his life. Those who seek to know his meaning by the aid of the dictionary only technically reach the house, for they are stopped by the outside wall and find no entrance to the hall. This is the reason why the teachings of our greater prophets give rise to endless disputations when we try to understand them by following their words and not by realising them in our own lives. The men who are cursed with the gift of the literal mind are the unfortunate ones who are always busy with the nets and neglect the fishing.

It is not only in Buddhism and the Indian religion but in Christianity too, that the ideal of selflessness is preached with all fervour. In the last the symbol of death has been used for expressing the idea of man's deliverance from the life which is not true. This is the same as Nirvāna, the symbol of the extinction of the lamp.

In the typical thought of India it is held that the true deliverance of man is the deliverance from avidyā, from ignorance. It is not in destroying anything that is positive and real, for that cannot be possible, but that which is negative, which obstructs our vision of truth. When this obstruction, which is ignorance, is removed, then only is the eye lid drawn up which is no loss to the eye.

It is our ignorance which makes us think that our self, as self, is real, that it has its complete meaning in itself. When we take that wrong view of self then we try to live in such a manner as to make self the ultimate object of our life. Then are we doomed to disappointment like the man who tries to reach his destination by firmly clutching the dust of the road. Our self has no means of holding us, for its own nature is to pass on; and by clinging to this thread of self which is passing through the loom of life we cannot make it serve the purpose of the cloth into which it is being woven. When a man, with elaborate care, arranges for an enjoyment of the self, he lights a fire but has no dough to make his bread with; the fire flares up and consumes itself to extinction, like an unnatural beast that eats its own progeny and dies.

In an unknown language the words are tyrannically prominent. They stop us but say nothing. To be rescued from this fetter of words we must rid ourselves of the *avidyā*, our ignorance, and then our mind will find its freedom in the inner idea. But it could be foolish to say that our ignorance of the language can be dispelled only by the destruction of the words. No, when the perfect knowledge comes, every word remains in its place, only they do not bind us to themselves, but let us pass through them and lead us to the idea which is emancipation.

Thus it is only *avidyā* which makes the self our fetter by making us think that it is an end in itself, and by preventing our seeing that it contains the idea that transcends its limits. That is why the wise man comes and says, "Set yourselves free from the *avidyā;* know your true soul and be saved from the grasp of the self which imprisons you."

We gain our freedom when we attain our truest nature. The man who is an artist finds his artistic freedom when he finds his ideal of art. Then is he freed from laborious attempts at imitation, from the goadings of popular approbation. It is the function of religion not to destroy our nature but to fulfil it.

The Sanskrit word *dharma* which is usually translated into English as religion has a deeper meaning in our language.

Dharma is the innermost nature, the essence, the implicit truth, of all things. *Dharma* is the ultimate purpose that is working in our self. When any wrong is done we say that *dharma* is violated, meaning that the lie has been given to our true nature.

But this *dharma*, which is the truth in us, is not apparent, because it is inherent. So much so, that it has been held that sinfulness is the nature of man, and only by the special grace of God can a particular person be saved. This is like saying that the nature of the seed is to remain enfolded within its shell, and it is only by some special miracle that it can be grown into a tree. But do we not know that the *appearance* of the seed contradicts its true nature. When you submit it to chemical analysis you may find in it carbon and protein and a good many other things, but not the idea of a branching tree. Only when the tree begins to take shape do you come to see its *dharma*, and then you can affirm without doubt that the seed which has been wasted and allowed to rot in the grounds has been thwarted in its *dharma*, in the fulfilment of its true nature. In the history of humanity we have known the living seed in us to sprout. We have seen the great purpose in us taking shape in the lives of our greatest men, and have felt certain that though there are numerous individual lives that seem ineffectual, still it is not their *dharma* to remain barren; but it is for them to burst their cover and transform themselves into a vigorous spiritual shoot, growing up into the air and light, and branching out in all directions.

The freedom of the seed is in the attainment of its *dharma*, its nature and destiny of becoming a tree; it is the non-accomplishment which is its prison. The sacrifice by which a thing attains its fulfilment is not a sacrifice which ends in death; it is the casting-off of bonds which wins freedom.

When we know the highest ideal of freedom which a man has, we know his *dharma*, the essence of his nature, the real meaning of his self. At first sight it seems that man counts that as freedom by which he gets unbounded opportunities of self-gratification and self-aggrandizement. But surely this is not borne out by history. Our revelatory men have always been those who have lived the life of self-sacrifice. The higher nature in man always seeks for something which transcends itself and yet is its deepest truth; which claims all its sacrifice, yet makes this sacrifice its own recompense. This is man's *dharma,* man's religion, and man's self is the vessel which is to carry this sacrifice to the altar.

We can look at our self in its two different aspects. The self which displays itself, and the self which transcends itself and thereby reveals its own meaning. To display itself it tries to be big, to stand upon the pedestal of its accumulations, and to retain everything to itself. To reveal itself it gives up everything it has, thus becoming perfect like a flower that has blossomed out from the bud, pouring from its chalice of beauty all its sweetness.

The lamp contains its oil, which it holds securely in its close grasp and guards from the least loss. Thus is it separate from all other objects around it and is miserly. But when lighted it finds its meaning at once; its relation with all things far and near is established, and it freely sacrifices its fund of oil to feed the flame.

Such a lamp is our self. So long as it hoards its possessions it keeps itself dark, its conduct contradicts its true purpose. When it finds illumination it forgets itself in a moment, holds the light high, and serves it with everything it has; for therein is its revelation. This revelation is the freedom which Buddha preached. He asked the lamp to give up its oil. But purposeless giving up is a still darker poverty which he never could have meant. The lamp must give up its oil to the light and thus set free the purpose it has in its hoarding. This is emancipation. The path Buddha pointed out was not merely the practice of self-abnegation, but the widening of love. And therein lies the true meaning of Buddha's preaching.

When we find that the state of *Nirvāna* preached by Buddha is through love, then we know for certain that *Nirvāna* is the highest culmination of love. For love is an end unto itself. Everything else raises the question "Why?" in our mind, and we require a reason for it. But when we say, "I love," then there is no room for the "why"; it is the final answer in itself.

Doubtless, even selfishness impels one to give away. But the selfish man does it on compulsion. That is like plucking fruit when it is unripe; you have to tear it from the tree and bruise the branch. But when a man loves, giving becomes a matter of joy to him, like the tree's surrender of the ripe fruit. All our belongings assume a weight by the ceaseless gravitation of our selfish desires; we cannot easily cast them away from us. They seem to belong to our very nature, stick to us as a second skin, and we bleed as we detach them. But when we are possessed by love, its force acts in the opposite direction. The things that closely adhered to us lose their adhesion and weight, and we find that they are not of us. Far from being a loss to give them away, we find in that the fulfilment of our nature.

Thus we find in perfect love the freedom of our self. That only which is done for love is done freely, however much pain it may cause. Therefore working for love is freedom in action. This is the meaning of the teaching of disinterested work in the Gīta.

The Gīta says action we must have, for only in action do we manifest our nature. But this manifestation is not perfect so long as our action is not free. In fact, our nature is obscured by work done by the compulsion of want or fear. The mother reveals herself in the service of her children, so our true freedom is not the freedom *from* action but freedom *in* action, which can only be attained in the work of love.

God's manifestation is in his work of creation, and it is said in the Upanishad, *Knowledge, power, and action are of his nature,*[1] they are not imposed upon him from outside. Therefore his work is his freedom, and in his creation he realises himself. The same thing is said elsewhere in other words: *From joy does spring all this creation, by joy is it maintained, towards joy does it progress, and into joy does it enter.*[2] This means that God's creation has not its source in any necessity; it comes from his fullness of joy; it is his love that creates, therefore in creation is his own revealment.

The artist who has a joy in the fullness of his artistic idea objectifies its and thus gains it more fully by holding it afar. It is joy which detaches ourselves from us, and then gives it form in creations of love in order to make it more perfectly our own. Hence there must be this separation, not a separation of repulsion but a separation of love. Repulsion has only the one element, the element of severance. But love has two, the element of severance, which is only an appearance, and the element of union which is the ultimate truth. Just as when the father tosses his child up from his arms it has the appearance of rejection but its truth is quite the reverse.

So we must know that the meaning of our self is not to be found in its separateness from God and others, but in the ceaseless realization of *yoga*, of union; not on the side of the canvas where it is blank, but on the side where the picture is being painted.

This is the reason why the separateness of our self has been described by our philosophers as *māyā*, as an illusion, because it has no intrinsic reality of its own. It looks perilous; it raises its isolation to a giddy height and casts a black

---

1. 'Svābhāvikī jnāna bala kriyācha.'
2. Ānandādhyēva khalvimāni bhūtāni jāyantē, ānandēna jātāni jīvanti, ānandamprayantyabhisamvicanti.

shadow upon the fair face of existence; from the outside it has an aspect of a sudden disruption, rebellious and destructive; it is proud, domineering and wayward, it is ready to rob the world of all its wealth to gratify its craving of a moment; to pluck with a reckless, cruel hand all the plumes from the divine bird of beauty to deck its ugliness for a day; indeed man's legend has it that it bears the black mark of disobedience stamped on its forehead for ever; but still all this is *māyā*, envelopment of *avidyā* it is the mist, it is not the sun; it is the black smoke that presages the fire of love.

Imagine some savage who, in his ignorance, thinks that it is the paper of the banknote that has the magic, by virtue of which the possessor of it gets all he wants. He piles up the papers, hides them, handles them in all sorts of absurd ways, and then at last, wearied by his efforts, comes to the sad conclusion that they are absolutely worthless, only fit to be thrown into the fire. But the wise man knows that the paper of the banknote is all *māyā*, and until it is given up to the bank it is futile. It is only *avidyā*, our ignorance, that makes us believe that the separateness of our self like the paper of the banknote is precious in itself, and by acting on this belief our self is rendered valueless. It is only when the *avidyā* is removed that this very self comes to us with a wealth which is priceless. For *He manifests Himself in deathless forms which His joy assumes.*[3] These forms are separate from Him, and the value that these forms have is only what his joy has imparted to them. When we transfer back these forms into that original joy, which is love, then we cash them in the bank and we find their truth.

When pure necessity drives man to his work it takes an accidental and contingent character, it becomes a mere

---

3. Ānandarūpamamritam yadvibhāti.

makeshift arrangement; it is deserted and left in ruins when necessity changes its course. But when his work is the outcome of joy, the forms that it takes have the elements of immortality. The immortal in man imparts to it its own quality of permanence.

Our self, as a form of God's joy, is deathless. For his joy is *amritam*, eternal. This it is in us which makes us sceptical of death, even when the fact of death cannot be doubted. In reconcilement of this contradiction in us we come to the truth that in the dualism of death and life there is a harmony. We know that the life of a soul, which is finite in its expression and infinite in its principle, must go through the portals of death in its journey to realise the infinite. It is death which is monistic, it has no life in it. But life is dualistic; it has an appearance as well as truth; and death is that appearance, that *māyā,* which is an inseparable companion to life. Our self to live must go through a continual change and growth of form, which may be termed a continual death and a continual life going on at the same time. It is really courting death when we refuse to accept death; when we wish to give the form of the self some fixed changelessness; when the self feels no impulse which urges it to grow out of itself; when it treats its limits as final and acts accordingly. Then comes our teacher's call to die to this death; not a call to annihilation but so eternal life. It is the extinction of the lamp in the morning light; not the abolition of the sun. It is really asking us consciously to give effect to the innermost wish that we have in the depths of our nature.

We have a dual set of desires in our being, which it should be our endeavour to bring into a harmony. In the region of our physical nature we have one set of which we are conscious always. We wish to enjoy our food and drink, we hanker after bodily pleasure and comfort. These desires are self-centred; they are solely concerned with their respective impulses. The wishes of our palate often run counter to what our stomach can allow. But we have another set, which is the desire of our physical system as a whole, of which we are usually unconscious. It is the wish for health. This is always doing its work, mending and repairing, making new adjustments in cases of accident, and skilfully restoring the balance wherever disturbed. It has no concern with the fulfilment of our immediate bodily desires, but it goes beyond the present time. It is the principle of our physical wholeness, it links our life with its past and its future and maintains the unity of its parts. He who is wise knows it, and makes his other physical wishes harmonise with it.

We have a greater body which is the social body. Society is an organism, of which we as parts have our individual wishes. We want our own pleasure and licence. We want to pay less and gain more than anybody else. This causes scramblings and fights. But there is that other wish in us which does its work in the depths of the social being. It is the wish for the welfare of the society. It transcends the limits of the present and the personal. It is on the side of the infinite.

He who is wise tries to harmonise the wishes that seek for self-gratification with the wish for the social good, and only thus can he realise his higher self.

In its finite aspect the self is conscious of its separateness, and there it is ruthless in its attempt to have more distinction than all others. But in its infinite aspect its wish is to gain that harmony which leads to its perfection and not its mere aggrandizement.

The emancipation of our physical nature is in attaining health, of our social being in attaining goodness, and of our self in attaining love. This last is what Buddha describes as extinction—the extinction of selfishness. This is the function of love, and it does not lead to darkness but to illumination.

This is the attainment of *bodhi*, or the true awakening; it is the revealing in us of the infinite joy by the light of love. The passage of our self is through its selfhood, which is independent, to its attainment of soul, which is harmonious. This harmony can never be reached through compulsion. So our will, in the history of its growth, must come through independence and rebellion to the ultimate completion. We must have the possibility of the negative form of freedom, which is licence, before we can attain the positive freedom, which is love.

This negative freedom, the freedom of self-will, can turn its back upon its highest realization, but it cannot cut itself away from it altogether, for then it will lose its own meaning. Our self-will has freedom up to a certain extent; it can know what it is to break away from the path, but it cannot continue in that direction indefinitely. For we are finite on our negative side. We must come to an end in our evil doing, in our career of discord. For evil is not infinite, and discord cannot be an end in itself. Our will has freedom in order that it may find out that its true course is towards goodness and love. For goodness and love are infinite, and only in the infinite is the perfect realization of freedom possible. So our will can be free not towards the limitations of our self, not where it is *māyā* and negation, but towards the unlimited, where is truth and love. Our freedom cannot go against its own principle of freedom and yet be free; it cannot commit suicide and yet live. We cannot say that we should have infinite freedom to fetter ourselves, for the fettering ends the freedom.

So in the freedom of our will, we have the same dualism of appearance and truth—our self-will is only the appearance of freedom and love is the truth. When we try to make this appearance independent of truth, then our attempt brings misery and proves its own futility in the end. Everything has this dualism of *māyā* and *satyam,* appearance and truth.

Words are *māyā* where they are merely sounds and finite, they are *satyam* where they are ideas and infinite. Our self is *māyā* where it is merely individual and finite, where it considers its separateness as absolute; it is *satyam* where it recognizes its essence in the universal and infinite, in the supreme self, in *paramātman*. This is what Christ means when he says, "Before Abraham was I am." This is the eternal *I am* that speaks through the *I am* that is in me. The individual *I am* attains its perfect end when it realises its freedom of harmony in the infinite *I am*. Then is its *mukti*, its deliverance from the thraldom of *māyā*, of appearance which springs from *avidyā*, from ignorance; its emancipation in *çāntam çivam advaitam*, in the perfect repose in truth, in the perfect activity in goodness, and in the perfect union in love.

Not only in our self but also in nature is there this separateness from God, which has been described as *māyā* by our philosophers, because the separateness does not exist by itself, it does not limit God's infinity from outside. It is his own will that has imposed limits to itself, just as the chess-player restricts his will with regard to the moving of the chessmen. The player willingly enters into definite relations with each particular piece and realises the joy of his power by these very restrictions. It is not that he cannot move the chessmen just as he pleases, but if he does so then there can be no play. If God assumes his role of omnipotence, then his creation is at an end and his power loses all its meaning. For power to be a power must act within limits. God's water must be water, his earth can never be other than earth. The law that has made them water and earth is his own law by which he has separated the play from the player, for therein the joy of the player consists.

As by the limits of law nature is separated from God, so it is the limits of its egoism which separates the self from him. He has willingly set limits to his will, and has given us mastery over the little world of our own. It is like a father's settling upon his son some allowance within the limit of which he is free to do what he likes. Though it remains a portion of the father's own property, yet he frees it from the operation of his own will. The reason of it is that the will, which is love's will and therefore free, can have its joy only in a union with another free will. The tyrant who must have slaves looks upon them as instruments of his purpose. It is the consciousness of his own necessity which makes him crush the will out of them to make his self-interest absolutely secure. This self-interest cannot brook the least freedom in others, because it is not itself free. The tyrant is really dependent on his slaves, and therefore he tries to make them completely useful by making them subservient to his own will. But a lover must have two wills for the realization of his love, because the consummation of love is in harmony, the harmony between freedom and freedom. So God's love from which our self has taken form has made it separate from God; and it is God's love which again establishes a reconciliation and unites God with our self through the separation. That is why our self has to go through endless renewals. For in its career of separateness it cannot go on for ever. Separateness is the finitude where it finds its barriers to come back again and again to its infinite source. Our self has ceaselessly to cast off its age, repeatedly shed its limits in oblivion and death, in order to realise its immortal youth. Its personality must merge in the universal time after time, in fact pass through it every moment, ever to refresh its individual life. It must follow the eternal rhythm and touch the fundamental unity at every step, and thus maintain its separation balanced in beauty and strength.

The play of life and death we see everywhere—this transmutation of the old into the new. The day comes to us every morning, naked and white, fresh as a flower. But we know it is old. It is age itself. It is that very ancient day which took up the newborn earth in its arms, covered it with its white mantle of light, and sent it forth on its pilgrimage among the stars.

Yet its feet are untired and its eyes undimmed. It carries the golden amulet of ageless eternity, at whose touch all wrinkles vanish from the forehead of creation. In the very core of the world's heart stands immortal youth. Death and decay cast over its face momentary shadows and pass on; they leave no marks of their steps—and truth remains fresh and young.

This old, old day of our earth is born again and again every morning. It comes back to the original refrain of its music. If its march were the march of an infinite straight line, if it had not the awful pause of its plunge in the abysmal darkness and its repeated rebirth in the life of the endless beginning, then it would gradually soil and bury truth with its dust and spread ceaseless aching over the earth under its heavy tread. Then every moment would leave its load of weariness behind, and decrepitude would reign supreme on its throne of eternal dirt.

But every morning the day is reborn among the newly-blossomed flowers with the same message retold and the same assurance renewed that death eternally dies, that the waves of turmoil are on the surface, and that the sea of tranquillity is fathomless. The curtain of night is drawn aside and truth emerges without a speck of dust on its garment, without a furrow of age on its lineaments.

We see that he who is before everything else is the same to-day. Every note of the song of creation comes fresh from his voice. The universe is not a mere echo, reverberating from sky to sky, like a homeless wanderer—the echo of an old song sung once for all in the dim beginning of things and then left orphaned. Every moment it comes from the heart of the master, it is breathed in his breath.

And that is the reason why it overspreads the sky like a thought taking shape in a poem, and never has to break into pieces with the burden of its own accumulating weight. Hence the surprise of endless variations, the advent of the unaccountable, the ceaseless procession of individuals, each of whom is without a parallel in creation. As at the first so to the last, the beginning never ends—the world is ever old and ever new.

It is for our self to know that it must be born anew every moment of its life. It must break through all illusions that encase it in their crust to make it appear old, burdening it with death.

For life is immortal youthfulness, and it hates age that tries to clog its movements—age that belongs not to life in truth, but follows it as the shadow follows the lamp.

Our life, like a river, strikes its banks not to find itself closed in by them, but to realise anew every moment that it has its unending opening towards the sea. It is as a poem that strikes its metre at every step not to be silenced by its rigid regulations, but to give expression every moment to the inner freedom of its harmony.

The boundary walls of our individuality thrust us back within our limits, on the one hand, and thus lead us, on the other, to the unlimited. Only when we try to make these limits infinite are we launched into an impossible contradiction and court miserable failure.

This is the cause which leads to the great revolutions in human history. Whenever the part, spurning the whole, tries to run a separate course of its own, the great pull of the all gives it a violent wrench, stops it suddenly, and brings it to the dust. Whenever the individual tries to dam the ever-flowing current of the world-force and imprison it within the area of his particular use, it brings on disaster. However powerful a king may be, he cannot raise his standard of rebellion against the infinite source of strength, which is unity, and yet remain powerful.

It has been said, *By unrighteousness men prosper, gain what they desire, and triumph over their enemies, but at the end they are cut off at the root and suffer extinction.*[4] Our roots must go deep down into the universal if we would attain the greatness of personality.

It is the end of our self to seek that union. It must bend its head low in love and meekness and take its stand where great and small all meet. It has to gain by its loss and rise by its surrender. His games would be a horror to the child if he could not come back to his mother, and our pride of personality will be a curse to us if we cannot give it up in love. We must know that it is only the revelation of the Infinite which is endlessly new and eternally beautiful in us and gives the only meaning to our self.

---

4. Adharmēnaidhatē tāvat tatō bhadrāni pacyati tatah sapatnān jayati samūlastu vinaçyati.

Realization in Love

We come now to the eternal problem of the coexistence of the infinite and the finite, of the supreme being and our soul. There is the sublime paradox that lies at the root of existence. We never can go round it, because we never can stand outside the problem and weigh it against any other possible alternative. But the problem exists in logic only; in reality it does not offer us any difficulty at all. Logically speaking, the distance between two points, however near, may be said to be infinite, because it is infinitely divisible. But we *do* cross the infinite at every step, and meet the eternal in every second. Therefore some of our philosophers say there is no such thing as finitude; it is but a *māyā*, an illusion. The real is the infinite, and it is only *māyā*, the unreality, which causes the appearance of the finite. But the word *māyā* is a mere name, it is no explanation. It is merely saying that with truth there is this appearance which is the opposite of truth; but how they come to exist at one and the same time is incomprehensible.

We have what we call in Sanskrit *dvandva*, a series of opposites in creation; such as, positive pole and the negative, the centripetal force and the centrifugal, attraction and repulsion. These are also mere names, they are no explanations. They are only different ways of asserting that the world in its essence is a reconciliation of pairs of opposing forces.

These forces, like the left and the the right hands of the creator, are acting in absolute harmony, yet acting from opposite directions.

There is a bond of harmony between our two eyes, which makes them act in unison. Likewise there is an unbreakable continuity of relation in the physical world between heat and cold, light and darkness, motion and rest, as between the bass and treble notes of a piano. That is why these opposites do not bring confusion in the universe, but harmony. If creation were but a chaos, we should have to imagine the two opposing principles as trying to get the better of each other. But the universe is not under martial law, arbitrary and provisional. Here we find no force which can run amok, or go on indefinitely in its wild road, like an exiled outlaw, breaking all harmony with its surroundings; each force, on the contrary, has to come back in a curved line to its equilibrium. Waves rise, each to its individual height in a seeming attitude of unrelenting competition, but only up to a certain point; and thus we know of the great repose of the sea to which they are all related, and to which they must all return in a rhythm which is marvellously beautiful.

In fact, these undulations and vibrations, these risings and fallings, are not due to the erratic contortions of disparate bodies, they are a rhythmic dance. Rhythm never can be born of the haphazard struggle of combat. Its underlying principle must be unity, not opposition.

This principle of unity is the mystery of all mysteries. The existence of a duality at once raises a question in our minds, and we seek its solution in the One. When at last we find a relation between these two, and thereby see them as one in essence, we feel that we have come to the truth. And then we give utterance to this most startling of all paradoxes, that the One appears as many, that the appearance is the opposite of truth and yet is inseparably related to it.

Curiously enough, there are men who lose that feeling of mystery, which is at the root of all our delights, when they discover the uniformity of law among the diversity of nature. As if gravitation is not more of a mystery than the fall of an apple, as if the evolution from one scale of being to the other is not something which is even more shy of explanation than a succession of creations. The trouble is that we very often stop at such a law as if it were the final end of our search, and then we find that it does not even begin to emancipate our spirit. It only gives satisfaction to our intellect, and as it does not appeal to our whole being it only deadens in us the sense of the infinite.

A great poem, when analysed, is a set of detached sounds. The reader who finds out the meaning, which is the inner medium that connects these outer sounds, discovers a perfect law all through, which is never violated in the least; the law of the evolution of ideas, the law of the music and the form.

But law in itself is a limit. It only shows that whatever is can never be otherwise. When a man is exclusively occupied with the search for the links of causality, his mind succumbs to the tyranny of law in escaping from the tyranny of facts. In learning a language, when from mere words we reach the laws of words we have gained a great deal. But if we stop at that point, and only concern ourselves with the marvels of the formation of a language, seeking the hidden reason of all its apparent caprices, we do not reach the end—for grammar is not literature, prosody is not a poem.

When we come to literature we find that though it conforms to rules of grammar it is yet a thing of joy, it is freedom itself. The beauty of a poem is bound by strict laws, yet it transcends them. The laws are its wings, they do not keep it weighed down, they carry it to freedom. Its form is in law but its spirit is in beauty. Law is the first step towards freedom, and beauty is the complete liberation which stands on the pedestal of law.

Beauty harmonises in itself the limit and the beyond, the law and the liberty.

In the world-poem, the discovery of the law of its rhythms, the measurement of its expansion and contraction, movement and pause, the pursuit of its evolution of forms and characters, are true achievements of the mind; but we cannot stop there. It is like a railway station; but the station platform is not our home. Only he has attained the final truth who knows that the whole world is a creation of joy.

This leads me to think how mysterious the relation of the human heart with nature must be. In the outer world of activity nature has one aspect, but in our hearts, in the inner world, it presents an altogether different picture.

Take an instance—the flower of a plant. However fine and dainty it may look, it is pressed to do a great service, and its colours and forms are all suited to its work. It must bring forth the fruits, or the continuity of plant life will be broken and the earth will be turned into a desert ere long. The colour and the smell of the flower are all for some purpose therefore; no sooner is it fertilised by the bee, and the time of its fruition arrives, than it sheds its exquisite petals and a cruel economy compels it to give up its sweet perfume. It has no time to flaunt its finery, for it is busy beyond measure. Viewed from without, necessity seems to be the only factor in nature for which everything works and moves. There the bud develops into the flower, the flower into the fruit, the fruit into the seed, the seed into a new plant again, and so forth, the chain of activity running on unbroken. Should there crop up any disturbance or impediment, no excuse would be accepted, and the unfortunate thing thus choked in its movement would at once be labelled as rejected, and be bound to die and disappear post-haste. In the great office of nature there are innumerable departments with endless work going on, and the fine flower that you behold there, gaudily attired and scented like a dandy, is by no means what it appears to be, but rather, is like a labourer toiling in sun and shower, who has to submit a clear account of his work and has and no breathing space to enjoy himself in playful frolic.

But when this same flower enters the heart of men its aspect of busy practicality is gone, and it becomes the very emblem of leisure and repose. The same object that is the embodiment of endless activity without is the perfect expression of beauty and peace within.

Science here warns us that we are mistaken, that the purpose of a flower is nothing but what is outwardly manifested, and that the relation of beauty and sweetness which we think it bears to us is all our own making, gratuitous and imaginary.

But our heart replies that we are not in the least mistaken. In the sphere of nature the flower carries with it a certificate which recommends it as having immense capacity for doing useful work, but it brings an altogether different letter of introduction when it knocks at the door of our hearts. Beauty becomes its only qualification. At one place it comes as a slave, and at another as a free thing. How, then, should we give credit to its first recommendation and disbelieve the second one? That the flower has got its being in the unbroken chain of causation is true beyond doubt; but that is an outer truth. The inner truth is: *Verily from the everlasting joy do all objects have their birth.*[1]

A flower, therefore, has not its only function in nature, but has another great function to exercise in the mind of man. And what is that function? In nature its work is that of a servant who has to make his appearance at appointed times, but in the heart of man it comes like a messenger from the King. In the Rāmāyana, when Sītā, forcibly separated

---

1. Ānandādhyēva khalvimāni bhūtāni jāyantā.

from her husband, was bewailing her evil fate in Ravana's golden palace, she was met by a messenger who brought with him a ring of her beloved Rāmchandra himself. The very sight of it convinced Sītā of the truth of the tidings he bore. She was at once reassured that he came indeed from her beloved one, who had not forgotten her and was at hand to rescue her.

Such a messenger is a flower from our great lover. Surrounded with the pomp and pageantry of worldliness, which may be likened to Ravana's golden city, we still live in exile, while the insolent spirit of worldly prosperity tempts us with allurements and claims us as its bride. In the meantime the flower comes across with a message from the other shore, and whispers in our ears, "I am come. He has sent me. I am a messenger of the beautiful, the one whose soul is the bliss of love. This island of isolation has been bridged over by him, and he has not forgotten thee, and will rescue thee even now. He will draw thee unto him and make thee his own. This illusion will not hold thee in thraldom for ever."

If we happen to be awake then, we question him: "How are we to know that thou art come from him indeed?" The messenger says, "Look! I have this ring from him. How lovely are its hues and charms!"

Ah, doubtless it is his—indeed, it is our wedding ring. Now all else passes into oblivion, only this sweet symbol of the touch of the eternal love fills us with a deep longing. We realise that the palace of gold where we are has nothing to do with us—our deliverance is outside it—and there our love has its fruition and our life its fulfilment.

What to the bee in nature is merely colour and scent, and the marks or spots which show the right track to the honey, is to the human heart beauty and untrammelled by necessity. They bring a love-letter to the heart written in many-coloured inks.

I was telling you, therefore, that however busy our active nature outwardly may be, she has a secret chamber within the heart where she comes and goes freely, without any design whatsoever. There the fire of her workshop is transformed into lamps of a festival, the noise of her factory is heard like music. The iron chain of cause and effect sounds heavily outside in nature, but in the human heart its unalloyed delight seems to sound, as it were, like the golden strings of a harp.

It indeed seems to be wonderful that nature has these two aspects at one and the same time, and so antithetical—one being of thraldom and the other of freedom. In the same form, sound, colour, and taste two contrary notes are heard, one of necessity and the other of joy. Outwardly nature is busy and restless, inwardly she is all silence and peace. She has toil on one side and leisure on the other. You see her bondage only when you see her from without, but within her heart is a limitless beauty.

Our seer says, "From joy are born all creatures, by joy they are sustained, towards joy they progress, and into joy they enter."

Not that he ignores law, or that his contemplation of this infinite joy is born of the intoxication produced by an indulgence in abstract thought. He fully recognises the inexorable laws of nature, and says, "Fire burns for fear of him (*i.e.* by his law); the sun shines by fear of him; and for fear of him the wind, the clouds, and death perform their offices." It is a reign of iron rule, ready to punish the least transgression. Yet the poet chants the glad song, "From joy are born all creatures, by joy they are sustained, towards joy they progress, and into joy they enter."

The immortal being manifests himself in joy-form.[2] His manifestation in creation is out of his fulness of joy. It is the

2. Ānandarūpamamritam yad vibhāti.

nature of this abounding joy to realise itself in form which is law. The joy, which is without form, must create, must translate itself into forms. The joy of the singer is expressed in the form of a song, that of the poet in the form of a poem. Man in his rôle of a creator is ever creating forms, and they come out of his abounding joy.

This joy, whose other name is love, must by in very nature have duality for its realization. When the singer has his inspiration he makes himself into two; he has within him his other self as the hearer, and the outside audience is merely an extension of this other self of his. The lover seeks his own other self in his beloved. It is the joy that creates this separation, in order to realise through obstacles the union.

The *amritam*, the immortal bliss, has made himself into two. Our soul is the loved one, it is his other self. We are separate; but if this separation were absolute, then there would have been absolute misery and unmitigated evil in this world. Then from untruth we never could reach truth, and from sin we never could hope to attain purity of heart; then all opposites would ever remain opposite, and we could never find a medium through which our differences could ever tend to meet. Then we could have no language, no understanding, no blending of hearts, no co-operation in life. But on the contrary, we find that the separateness of objects is in a fluid state. Their individualities are ever changing, they are meeting and merging into each other, till science itself is turning into metaphysics, matter losing its boundaries, and the definition of life becoming more and more indefinite.

Yes, our individual soul has been separated from the supreme soul, but this has not been from alienation but from the fulness of love. It is for that reason that untruths, sufferings, and evils are not at a standstill; the human soul can defy them, can overcome them, nay, can altogether transform them into new power and beauty.

The singer is translating his song into singing, joy into forms, and the hearer has to translate back the singing into the original joy; then the communion between the singer and the hearer is complete. The infinite joy is manifesting itself in manifold forms, taking upon itself the bondage of law, and we fulfil our destiny when we go back from forms to joy, from law to the love, when we untie the knot of the finite and hark back to the infinite.

The human soul is on its journey from the law to love, from discipline to liberation, from the moral plane to the spiritual. Buddha preached the discipline of self-restraint and moral life; it is a complete acceptance of law. But this bondage of law cannot be an end by itself; by mastering it thoroughly we acquire the means of getting beyond it. It is going back to Brahma, to the infinite love, which is manifesting itself through the finite forms of law. Buddha names it *Brahma-vihāra*, the joy of living in Brahma. He who wants to reach this stage, according to Buddha, 'shall deceive none, entertain no hatred for anybody, and never wish to injure through anger. He shall have measureless love for all creatures, even as a mother has for her only child, whom she protects with her own life. Up above, below, and all around him he shall extend his love, which is without bounds and obstacles, and which is free from all cruelty and antagonism. While standing, sitting, walking, lying down, till he falls asleep, he shall keep his mind active in this exercise of universal goodwill.'

Want of love is a degree of callousness; for love is the perfection of consciousness. We do not love because we do not comprehend, or rather we do not comprehend because we do not love. For love is the ultimate meaning of everything around us. It is not a mere sentiment; it is truth; it is the joy that is at the root of all creation. It is the white light of pure consciousness that emanates from Brahma. So, to be one with this *sarvānubhūh*, this all-feeling being who is in the external sky, as well as in our inner soul, we must attain to that summit of consciousness, which is love: *Who could have breathed or moved if the sky were not filled with joy, with love?*[3] It is through the heightening of our consciousness into love, and extending it all over the world, that we can attain *Brahma-vihāra,* communion with this infinite joy.

Love spontaneously gives itself in endless gifts. But these gifts lose their fullest significance if through them we do not reach that love, which is the giver. To do that, we must have love in our own heart. He who has no love in him values the gifts of his lover only according to their usefulness. But utility is temporary and partial. It can never occupy our whole being; what is useful only touches us at the point where we have some want. When the want is satisfied, utility becomes a burden if it still persists. On the other hand, a mere token is of permanent worth to us when we have love in our heart. For it is not for any special use. It is an end in itself; it is for our whole being and therefore can never tire us.

The question is, In what manner do we accept this world, which is a perfect gift of joy? Have we been able to receive it in our heart where we keep enshrined things that are of deathless value to us? We are frantically busy making use of the forces of the universe to gain more and more power; we feed and we clothe ourselves from its stores, we scramble for its riches, and it becomes for us a field of fierce competition. But were we born for this, to extend our proprietary rights over this world and make of it a marketable commodity? When our whole mind is bent only upon making use of this world it loses for us its true value. We make it cheap by our sordid desires; and thus to the end of our days we only try to feed upon it and miss its truth, just like the

---

3. Ko hyēvānyāt kah prānyāt yadēsha ākāça ānandō na syāt.

greedy child who tears leaves from a precious book and tries to swallow them.

In the lands where cannibalism is prevalent man looks upon man as his food. In such a country civilization can never thrive, for there man loses his higher value and is made common indeed. But there are other kinds of cannibalism, perhaps not so gross, but not less heinous, for which one need not travel far. In countries higher in the scale of civilization we find sometimes man looked upon as a mere body, and he is bought and sold in the market by the price of his flesh only. And sometimes he gets his sole value from being useful; he is made into a machine, and is traded upon by the man of money to acquire for him more money. Thus our lust, our greed, our love of comfort result in cheapening man to his lowest value. It is self-deception on a large scale. Our desires blind us to the *truth* that there is in man, and this is the greatest wrong done by ourselves to our own soul. It deadens our consciousness, and is but a gradual method of spiritual suicide. It produces ugly sores in the body of civilization, gives rise to its hovels and brothels, its vindictive penal codes, its cruel prison systems, its organised method of exploiting foreign races to the extent of permanently injuring them by depriving them of the discipline of self-government and means of self-defence.

Of course man is useful to man, because his body is a marvellous machine and his mind an organ of wonderful efficiency. But he is a spirit as well, and this spirit is truly known only by love. When we define a man by the market value of the service we can expect of him, we know him imperfectly. With this limited knowledge of him it becomes easy for us to be unjust to him and to entertain feelings of triumphant self-congratulation when, on account of some cruel advantage on our side, we can get out of him much more than we have paid for. But when we know him as a spirit we know him as our own. We at once feel that cruelty to him is cruelty to ourselves, to make him small is stealing from our own humanity, and in seeking to make use of him solely for personal profit we merely gain in money or comfort what we pay for in truth.

One day I was out in a boat on the Ganges. It was a beautiful evening in autumn. The sun had just set; the silence of the sky was full to the brim with ineffable peace and beauty. The vast expanse of water was without a ripple, mirroring all the changing shades of the sunset glow. Miles and miles of a desolate sandbank lay like a huge amphibious reptile of some antediluvian age, with its scales glistening in shining colours. As our boat was silently gliding by the precipitous river-bank, riddled with the nest-holes of a colony of birds, suddenly a big fish leapt up to the surface of the water and then disappeared, displaying on its vanishing figure all the colours of the evening sky. It drew aside for a moment the many-coloured screen behind which there was a silent world full of the joy of life. It came up from the depths of its mysterious dwelling with a beautiful dancing motion and added its own music to the silent symphony of the dying day. I felt as if I had a friendly greeting from an alien world in its own language, and it touched my heart with a flash of gladness. Then suddenly the man at the helm exclaimed with a distinct note of regret, "Ah, what a big fish!" It at once brought before his vision the picture of the fish caught and made ready for his supper. He could only look at the fish through his desire, and thus missed the whole truth of its existence. But man is not entirely an animal. He aspires to a spiritual vision, which is the vision of the whole truth. This gives him the highest delight, because it reveals to him the deepest harmony that exists between him and his surroundings. It is our desires that limit the scope of our self-realization, hinder our extension of consciousness, and give rise to sin, which is the innermost barrier that keeps us apart from our God, setting up disunion and the arrogance of exclusiveness. For sin is not one mere action, but it is an attitude of life which takes for granted that our goal is finite, that our self is the ultimate truth, and that we are not all essentially one but exist each for his own separate individual existence.

So I repeat we never can have a true view of man unless we have a love for him. Civilization must be judged and prized, not by the amount of power it has developed, but by how much it has evolved and given expression to, by its laws and institutions, the love of humanity. The first question and the last which it has to answer is, Whether and how far it recognises man more as a spirit than as a machine? Whenever some ancient civilization fell into decay and died, it was owing to causes which produced callousness of heart and led to the cheapening of man's worth; when either the state or some powerful group of men began to look upon the people as a mere instrument of their power; when, by compelling weaker races to slavery and trying to keep them down by every means, man struck at the foundation of his greatness, his own love of freedom and fair-play. Civilization can never sustain itself upon cannibalism of any form. For that by which alone man is true can only be nourished by love and justice.

As with man, so with this universe. When we look at the world through the veil of our desires we make it small and narrow, and fail to perceive its full truth. Of course it is obvious that the world serves us and fulfils our needs, but our relation to it does not end there. We are bound to it with a deeper and truer bond than that of necessity. Our soul is drawn to it; our love of life is really our wish to continue our relation with this great world. This relation is one of love. We are glad that we are in it; we are attached to it with numberless threads, which extend from this earth to the stars. Man foolishly tries to prove his superiority by imagining his radical separateness from what he calls his physical world, which, in his blind fanaticism, he sometimes goes to the extent of ignoring altogether, holding it as his direst enemy. Yet the more his knowledge progresses, the more it becomes difficult for man to establish this separateness, and all the imaginary boundaries he had set up around himself vanish one after another. Every time we lose some of our badges of absolute distinction by which we conferred upon our humanity the right to hold itself apart from its surroundings, it gives us a shock of humiliation. But we have to submit to this. If we set up our pride on the path of our self-realization to create divisions and disunion, then it must sooner or later come under the wheels of truth and be ground to dust. No, we are not burdened with some monstrous superiority, unmeaning in its singular abruptness. It would be utterly degrading for us to live in a world immeasurably less than ourselves in the quality of soul, just as it would be repulsive and degrading to be surrounded and served by a host of slaves, day and night, from birth to the moment of death. On the contrary, this world is our compeer, nay, we are one with it.

Through our progress in science the wholeness of the world and our oneness with it is becoming clearer to our mind. When this perception of the perfection of unity is not merely intellectual, when it opens out our whole being into a luminous consciousness of the all, then it becomes a radiant joy, an overspreading love. Our spirit finds its larger self in the whole world, and is filled with an absolute certainty that it is immortal. It dies a hundred times in its enclosures of self; for separateness is doomed to die, it cannot be made eternal. But it never can die where it is one with the all, for there is its truth, its joy. When a man feels the rhythmic throb of the soul-life of the whole world in his own soul, then is he free. Then he enters into the secret courting that goes on between this beautiful world-bride, view with the veil of the many-coloured finiteness and the *paramatmam,* the bridegroom, in his spotless white. Then he knows that he is the partaker in this gorgeous love festival, and he is the honoured guest at the feast of immortality. Then he understands the meaning of the seer-poet who sings, "From love the world is born, by love it is sustained, towards love it moves, and into love it enters."

In love all the contradictions of existence merge themselves and are lost. Only in love are unity and duality not at variance. Love must be one and two at the same time.

Only love is motion and rest in one. Our heart ever changes its place till it finds love, and then it has its rest. But this rest itself is an intense form of activity where utter quiescence and unceasing energy meet at the same point in love.

In love, loss and gain are harmonised. In its balance-sheet, credit and debit accounts are in the same column, and gifts are added to gains. In this wonderful festival of creation, this great ceremony of self-sacrifice of God, the lover constantly gives himself up to gain himself in love. Indeed, love is what brings together and inseparably connects both the act of abandoning and that of receiving.

In love at one of its poles you find the personal, and at the other the impersonal. At one you have the positive assertion—Here I am; at the other the equally strong denial— I am not. Without this ego what is love? And again, with only this ego how can love be possible?

Bondage and liberation are not antagonistic in love. For love is most free and at the same time most bound. If God were absolutely free there would be no creation. The infinite being has assumed unto himself the mystery of finitude. And in him who is love the finite and the infinite are made one.

Similarly, when we talk about the relative values of freedom and non-freedom, it becomes a mere play of words. It is not that we desire freedom alone, we want thraldom as well. It is the high function of love to welcome all limitations and to transcend them. For nothing is more independent than love, and where else, again, shall we find so much of dependence? In love, thraldom is as glorious as freedom.

The *Vaishnava* religion has boldly declared that God has bound himself to man, and in that consists the greatest glory of human existence. In the spell of the wonderful rhythm of the finite he fetters himself at every step, and thus gives his love out in music in his most perfect lyrics of beauty. Beauty is his wooing of our heart; it can have no other purpose. It tells us everywhere that the display of power is not the ultimate meaning of creation; wherever there is a bit of colour, a note of song, a grace of form, there comes the call for our love. Hunger compels us to obey its behests, but hunger is not the last word for a man. There have been men who have deliberately defied its commands to show that the human soul is not to be led by the pressure of wants and threat of pain. In fact, to live the life of man we have to resist its demands every day, the least of us as well as the greatest. But, on the other hand, there is a beauty in the world, which never insults our freedom, never raises even its little finger to make us acknowledge its sovereignty. We can absolutely ignore it and suffer no penalty in consequence. It is a call to us, but not a command. It seeks for love in us, and love can never be had by compulsion. Compulsion is not indeed the final appeal to man, but joy is. And joy is everywhere; it is in the earth's green covering of grass; in the blue serenity of the sky; in the reckless exuberance of spring; in the severe abstinence of grey winter; in the living flesh that animates our bodily frame; in the perfect poise of the human figure, noble and upright; in living; in the exercise of all our powers; in the acquisition of knowledge; in fighting evils; in dying for gains we never can share. Joy is there everywhere; it is superfluous, unnecessary; nay, it very often contradicts the most peremptory behests of necessity. It exists to show that the bonds of law can only be explained by love; they are like body and soul. Joy is the realization of the truth of oneness, the oneness of our soul with the world and of the world-soul with the supreme lover.

Realization in Action

It is only those who have known that joy expresses itself through law who have learnt to transcend the law. Not that the bonds of law have ceased to exist for them—but that the bonds have become to them as the form of freedom incarnate. The freed soul delights in accepting bonds, and does not seek to evade any of them, for in each does it feel the manifestation of an infinite energy whose joy is in creation.

As a matter of fact, where there are no bonds, where there is the madness of licence, the soul ceases to be free. There is its hurt; there is its separation from the infinite, its agony of sin. Wherever at the call of temptation the soul falls away from the bondage of law, then, like a child deprived of the support of its mother's arms, it cries out, *Smite me not!*[1] "Bind me," it prays, "oh, bind me in the bonds of thy law; bind me within and without; hold me tight; let me in the clasp of law be bound up together with thy joy; protect me by thy firm hold from the deadly laxity of sin."

As some, under the idea that law is the opposite of joy, mistake intoxication for joy, so there are many in our country who imagine action to be opposed to freedom. They think that activity being in the material plane is a restriction of the free spirit of the soul. But we must remember that as joy

---

1. Mā mā himsīh.

expresses itself in law, so the soul finds its freedom in action. It is because joy cannot find expression in itself alone that it desires the law which is outside. Likewise it is because the soul cannot find freedom within itself that it wants external action. The soul of man is ever freeing itself from it own folds by its activity; had it been otherwise it could not have done any voluntary work.

The more man acts and makes actual what was latent in him, the nearer does he bring the distant Yet-to-be. In that actualisation man is ever making himself more and yet more distinct, and seeing himself clearly under newer and newer aspects in the midst of his varied activities, in the state, in society. This vision makes for freedom.

Freedom is not in darkness, nor in vagueness. There is no bondage so fearful as that of obscurity. It is to escape from this obscurity that the seed struggles to sprout, the bud to blossom. It is to rid itself of this envelope of vagueness that the ideas in our mind are constantly seeking opportunities to take on outward form. In the same way our soul, in order to release itself from the mist of indistinctness and come out into the open, is continually creating for itself fresh fields of action, and is busy contriving new forms of activity, even such as are not needful for the purposes of its earthly life. And why? Because it wants freedom. It wants to see itself, to realise itself.

When man cuts down the pestilential jungle and makes unto himself a garden, the beauty that he thus sets free from within its enclosure of ugliness is the beauty of his own soul: without giving it this freedom outside, he cannot make it free within. When he implants law and order in the midst of the waywardness of society, the good which he sets free from the obstruction of the bad is the goodness of his own soul: without being thus made free outside it cannot find freedom within. Thus is man continually engaged in setting free in action his powers, his beauty, his goodness, his very soul. And the more he succeeds in so doing, the greater does he see himself to be, the broader becomes the field of his knowledge of self.

The Upanishad says: *In the midst of activity alone wilt thou desire to live a hundred years.*[2] It is the saying of those who had amply tasted the joy of the soul. Those who have fully realised the soul have never talked in mournful accents of the sorrowfulness of life or of the bondage of action. They are not like the weakling flower whose stem-hold is so light that it drops away before attaining fruition. They hold on to life with all their might and say, "never will we let go till the fruit is ripe." They desire in their joy to express themselves strenuously in their life and in their work. Pain and sorrow dismay them not, they are not bowed down to the dust by the weight of their own heart. With the erect head of the victorious hero they march through life seeing themselves and showing themselves in increasing resplendence of soul through both joys and sorrows. The joy of their life keeps step with the joy of that energy which is playing at building and breaking throughout the universe. The joy of the sunlight, the joy of the free air, mingling with the joy of their lives, makes one sweet harmony reign within and without. It is they who say, *In the midst of activity alone wilt thou desire to live a hundred years.*

This joy of life, this joy of work, in man is absolutely true. It is no use saying that it is a delusion of ours; that unless we cast it away we cannot enter upon the path of self-realization. It will never do the least good to attempt the realization of the infinite apart from the world of action.

It is not the truth that man is active on compulsion. If there is compulsion on one side, on the other there is pleasure;

---

2. Kurvannēvēha karmāni jijīvishet çatam samāh.

on the one hand action is spurred on by want, on the other it hies to its natural fulfilment. That is why, as man's civilizations advance, he increases his obligations and the work that he willingly creates for himself. One would have thought that nature had given him quite enough to do to keep him busy, in fact that it was working him to death with the lash of hunger and thirst,—but no. Man does not think that sufficient; he cannot rest content with only doing the work that nature prescribes for him in common with the birds and beasts. He needs must surpass all, even in activity. No creature has to work so hard as man; he has been impelled to contrive for himself a vast field of action in society; and in this field he is for ever building up and pulling down, making and unmaking laws, piling up heaps of material, and incessantly thinking, seeking and suffering. In this field he has fought his mightiest battles, gained continual new life, made death glorious, and, far from evading troubles, has willingly and continually taken up the burden of fresh trouble. He has discovered the truth that he is not complete in the cage of his immediate surroundings, that he is greater than his present, and that while to stand still in one place may be comforting, the arrest of life destroys his true function and the real purpose of his existence.

This *mahatī vinashtih—this great destruction* he cannot bear, and accordingly he toils and suffers in order that he may gain in stature by transcending his present, in order to become that which he yet is not. In this travail is man's glory, and it is because he knows it, that he has not sought to circumscribe his field of action, but is constantly occupied in extending the bounds. Sometimes he wanders so far that his work tends to lose its meaning, and his rushings to and fro create fearful eddies round different centres—eddies of self-interest, of pride of power. Still, so long as the strength of the current is not lost, there is no fear; the obstructions and the dead accumulations of his activity are dissipated and carried away; the impetus corrects its own mistakes. Only when the soul sleeps in stagnation do its enemies gain overmastering strength, and these obstructions become too clogging to be fought through. Hence have we been warned by our teachers that to work we must live, to live we must work; that life and activity are inseparably connected.

It is the very characteristic of life that it is not complete within itself; it must come out. Its truth is in the commerce of the inside and the outside. In order to live, the body must maintain its various relations with the outside light and air— not only to gain life-force, but also to manifest it. Consider how fully employed the body is with its own inside activities; its heart-beat must not stop for a second, its stomach, its brain, must be ceaselessly working. Yet this is not enough; the body is outwardly restless all the while. Its life leads it to an endless dance of work and play outside; it cannot be satisfied with the circulations of its internal economy, and only finds the fulfilment of joy in its outward excursions.

The same with the soul. It cannot live on its own internal feelings and imaginings. It is ever in need of external objects; not only to feed its inner consciousness but to apply itself in action, not only to receive but also to give.

The real truth is, we cannot live if we divide him who is truth itself into two parts. We must abide in him within as well as without. In whichever aspect we deny him we deceive ourselves and incur a loss. *Brahma has not left me, let me not leave Brahma.*[3] If we say that we would realise him in introspection alone and leave him out of our external activity, that we would enjoy him by the love in our heart, but not worship him by outward ministrations; or if we say the opposite, and overweight ourselves on one side in the

---

3. Māham brahma nirākuryyām mā mā brahma nirākarōt.

journey of our life's quest, we shall alike totter to our downfall. .

In the great western continent we see that the soul of man is mainly concerned with extending itself outwards; the open field of the exercise of power is its field. Its partiality is entirely for the world of extension, and it would leave aside— nay, hardly believe in—that field of inner consciousness which is the field of fulfilment. It has gone so far in this that the perfection of fulfilment seems to exist for it nowhere. Its science has always talked of the never-ending evolution of the world. Its metaphysics has now begun to talk of the evolution of God himself. They will not admit that he *is,* they would have it that he also is *becoming.*

They fail to realise that while the infinite is always greater than any assignable limit, it is also complete; that on the one hand Brahma is evolving, on the other he is perfection; that in the one aspect he is essence, in the other manifestation— both together at the same time, as is the song and the act of singing. This is like ignoring the consciousness of the singer and saying that only the singing is in progress, that there is no song. Doubtless we are directly aware only of the singing, and never at any one time of the song as a whole; but do we not all the time know that the complete song is in the soul of the singer?

It is because of this insistence on the doing and the becoming that we perceive in the west the intoxication of power. These men seem to have determined to despoil and grasp everything by force. They would always obstinately be doing and never be done—they would not allow to death its natural place in the scheme of things—they know not the beauty of completion.

In our country the danger comes from the opposite side. Our partiality is for the internal world. We would cast aside with contumely the field of power and of extension. We would realise Brahma in meditation only in his aspect of completeness, we have determined not to see him in the commerce of the universe in his aspect of evolution. That is why in our seekers we so often find the intoxication of the spirit and its consequent degradation. Their faith would acknowledge no bondage of law, their imagination soars unrestricted, their conduct disdains to offer any explanation to reason. Their intellect, in its vain attempts to see Brahma inseparable from his creation, works itself stone-dry, and their heart, seeking to confine him within its own outpourings, swoons in a drunken ecstasy of emotion. They have not even kept within reach any standard whereby they can measure the loss of strength and character which manhood sustains by thus ignoring the bonds of law and the claims of action in the external universe.

But true spirituality, as taught in our sacred lore, is calmly balanced in strength, in the correlation of the within and the without. The truth has its law, it has its joy. On one side of it is being chanted the *Bhayādasyāgnistapati*,[4] on the other the *Ānandādhyeva khalvimāni bhūtāni jāyante*.[5] Freedom is impossible of attainment without submission to law, for Brahma is in one aspect bound by his truth, in the other free in his joy.

As for ourselves, it is only when we wholly submit to the bonds of truth that we fully gain the joy of freedom. And how? As does the string that is bound to the harp. When the harp is truly strung, when there is not the slightest laxity in the strength of the bond, then only does music result; and the string transcending itself in its melody finds and every chord its true freedom. It is because it is bound by such hard and fast rules on the one side that it can find this range of

---

4. "For fear of him the fire doth burn," etc.
5. "From Joy are born all created things," etc.

freedom in music on the other. While the string was not true, it was indeed merely bound; but a loosening of its bondage would not have been the way to freedom, which it can only fully achieve by being bound tighter and tighter till it has attained the true pitch.

The bass and treble strings of our duty are only bonds so long as we cannot maintain them steadfastly attuned according to the law of truth; and we cannot call by the name of freedom the loosening of them into the nothingness of inaction. That is why I would say that the true striving in the quest of truth, of *dharma,* consists not in the neglect of action but in the effort to attune it closer and closer to the eternal harmony. The text of this striving should be, *Whatever works thou doest, consecrate them to Brahma.*[6] That is to say, the soul is to dedicate itself to Brahma through all its activities. This dedication is the song of the soul, in this is its freedom. Joy reigns when all work becomes the path to the union with Brahma; when the soul ceases to return constantly to its own desires; when in it our self-offering grows more and more intense. Then there is completion, then there is freedom, then, in this world, comes the kingdom of God.

Who is there that, sitting in his corner, would deride this grand self-expression of humanity in action, this incessant self-consecration? Who is there that thinks the union of God and man is to be found in some secluded enjoyment of his own imaginings, away from the sky-towering temple of the greatness of humanity, which the whole of mankind, in sunshine and storm, is toiling to erect through the ages? Who is there that thinks this secluded communion is the highest form of religion?

O thou distraught wanderer, thou *Sannyasin,* drunk in the wine of self-intoxication, dost thou not already hear the

---

6. Yadyat karma prakurvīta tadbrahmani samarpayet.

progress of the human soul along the highway traversing the wide fields of humanity—the thunder of its progress in the car of its achievements, which is destined to overpass the bounds that prevent its expansion into the universe? The very mountains are cleft asunder and give way before the march of its banners waving triumphantly in the heavens; as the mist before the rising sun, the tangled obscurities of material things vanish at its irresistible approach. Pain, disease, and disorder are at every step receding before its onset; the obstructions of ignorance are being thrust aside; the darkness of blindness is being pierced through; and behold, the promised land of wealth and health, of poetry and art, of knowledge and righteousness is gradually being revealed to view. Do you in your lethargy desire to say that this car of humanity, which is shaking the very earth with the triumph of its progress along the mighty vistas of history, has no charioteer leading it on to its fulfilment? Who is there who refuses to respond to his call to join in this triumphal progress? Who so foolish as to run away from the gladsome throng and seek him in the listlessness of inaction? Who so steeped in untruth as to dare to call all this untrue—this great world of men, this civilization of expanding humanity, this eternal effort of man, through depths of sorrow, through heights of gladness, through innumerable impediments within and without, to win victory for his powers? He who can think of this immensity of achievement as an immense fraud, can he truly believe in God who is the truth? He who thinks to reach God by running away from the world, when and where does he expect to meet him? How far can he fly—can he fly and fly, till he flies into nothingness itself? No, the coward who would fly can nowhere find him. We must be brave enough to be able to say: We are reaching him here in this very spot, now at this very moment. We must be able to assure ourselves that as in our actions we are realising ourselves, so in ourselves we are realising him who is the self of self. We must earn the right to say so unhesitatingly by clearing away with our own effort all obstruction, all disorder, all discords from our path of activity; we must be able to say, "In my work is my joy, and in that joy does the joy of my joy abide."

Whom does the Upanishad call *The chief among the knowers of Brahma?*[7] He is defined as *He whose joy is in Brahma, whose play is in Brahma, the active one.*[8] Joy without the play of joy is no joy at all—play without activity is no play. Activity is the play of joy. He whose joy is in Brahma, how can he live in inaction? For must he not by his activity provide that in which the joy of Brahma is to take form and manifest itself? That is why he who knows Brahma, who has his joy in Brahma, must also have all his activity in Brahma— his eating and drinking, his earning of livelihood and his beneficence. Just as the joy of the poet in his poem, of the artist in his art, of the brave man in the output of his courage, of the wise man in his discernment of truths, ever seeks expression in their several activities, so the joy of the knower of Brahma, in the whole of his everyday work, little and big, in truth, in beauty, in orderliness and in beneficence, seeks to give expression to the infinite.

Brahma himself gives expression to his joy in just the same way. *By his many-sided activity, which radiates in all directions, does he fulfil the inherent want of his different creatures.*[9] That inherent want is he himself, and so he is in so many ways, in so many forms, giving himself. He works, for without working how could he give himself? His joy is ever dedicating itself in the dedication which is his creation.

---

7. Brahmavidāmvaristhah.
8. Ātmakrīṛha ātmaratih kriyāvān.
9. Bahudhā, çakti yogāt varṇānanekān nihitārtho dadhāti.

In this very thing does our own true meaning lie, in this is our likeness to our father. We must also give up ourselves in many-sided variously aimed activity. In the Vedas he is called *the giver of himself, the giver of strength.*[10] He is not content with giving us himself, but he gives us strength that we may likewise give ourselves. That is why the seer of the Upanishad prays to him who is thus fulfilling our wants, *May he grant us the beneficent mind,*[11] may he fulfil that uttermost want of ours by granting us the beneficent mind. That is to say, it is not enough he alone should work to remove our want, but he should give us the desire and the strength to work with him in his activity and in the exercise of the good. Then, indeed, will our union with him alone be accomplished. The beneficent mind is that which shows us the want (*swārtha*) of another self to be the inherent want (*nihitārtha*) of our own self; that which shows that our joy consists in the varied aiming of our many-sided powers in the work of humanity. When we work under the guidance of this beneficent mind, then our activity is regulated, but does not become mechanical; it is action not goaded on by want, but stimulated by the satisfaction of the soul. Such activity ceases to be a blind imitation of that of the multitude, a cowardly following of the dictates of fashion. Therein we begin to see that *He is in the beginning and in the end of the universe,*[12] and likewise see that of our own work is he the fount and the inspiration, and at the end thereof is he, and therefore that all our activity is pervaded by peace and good and joy.

The Upanishad says: *Knowledge, power, and action are of his nature.*[13] It is because this naturalness has not yet been

---

10. Ātmadā baladā.
11. Sa no buddhya çubhayā samyunaktu.
12. Vichaitī chānte viçvamādau.
13. Svābhāvikī jnāna bala kriyā cha.

born in us that we tend to divide joy from work. Our day of work is not our day of joy—for that we require a holiday; for, miserable that we are, we cannot find our holiday in our work. The river finds its holiday in its onward flow, the fire in its outburst of flame, the scent of the flower in its permeation of the atmosphere; but in our everyday work there is no such holiday for us. It is because we do not let ourselves go, because we do not give ourselves joyously and entirely up to it, that our work overpowers us.

O giver of thyself! At the vision of thee as joy let our souls flame up to thee as the fire, flow on to thee as the river, permeate thy being as the fragrance of the flower. Give us strength to love, to love fully, our life in its joys and sorrows, in its gains and losses, in its rise and fall. Let us have strength enough fully to see and hear thy universe and to work with full vigour therein. Let us fully live the life thou hast given us, let us bravely take and bravely give. This is our prayer to thee. Let us once for all dislodge from our minds the feeble fancy that would make out thy joy to be a thing apart from action, thin, formless, and unsustained. Wherever the peasant tills the hard earth, there does thy joy gush out in the green of the corn, wherever man displaces the entangled forest, smooths the stony ground, and clears for himself a homestead, there does thy joy enfold it in orderliness and peace.

O worker of the universe! We would pray to thee to let the irresistible current of thy universal energy come like the impetuous south wind of spring, let it come rushing over the vast field of the life of man, let it bring the scent of many flowers, the murmurings of many woodlands, let it make sweet and vocal the lifelessness of our dried-up soul-life. Let our newly awakened powers cry out for unlimited fulfilment in leaf and flower and fruit.

The Realization of Beauty

Things in which we do not take joy are either a burden upon our minds to be got rid of at any cost; or they are useful, and therefore in temporary and partial relation to us, becoming burdensome when their utility is lost; or they are like wandering vagabonds, loitering for a moment on the outskirts of our recognition, and then passing on. A thing is only completely our own when it is a thing of joy to us.

The greater part of this world is to us as if it were nothing. But we cannot allow it to remain so, for thus it belittles our own self. The entire world is given to us, and all our powers have their final meaning in the faith that by their help we are to take possession of our patrimony.

But what is the function of our sense of beauty in this process of the extension of our consciousness? Is it there to separate truth into strong lights and shadows, and bring it before us in its uncompromising distinction of beauty and ugliness? If that were so, then we should have to admit that this sense of beauty creates a dissension in our universe and sets up a wall of hindrance across the highway of communication that leads from each individual thing to all things.

But that cannot be true. As long as our realization is incomplete a division necessarily remains between things known and unknown, pleasant and unpleasant. But in spite of the dictum of some philosophers man does not accept any arbitrary and absolute limit to his knowable world. Every day his science is penetrating into the region formerly marked in his map as unexplored or inexplorable. Our sense of beauty is similarly engaged in ever pushing on its conquests. Truth is everywhere, therefore everything is the object of our knowledge. Beauty is omnipresent, therefore everything is capable of giving us joy.

In the early days of his history man took everything as a phenomenon of life. His science of life began by creating a sharp distinction between life and non-life. But as it is proceeding farther and farther the line of demarcation between the animate and inanimate is growing more and more dim. In the beginning of our apprehension these sharp lines of contrast are helpful to us, but as our comprehension becomes clearer they gradually fade away.

The Upanishads have said that all things are created and sustained by an infinite joy. To realise this principle of creation we have to start with a division—the division into the beautiful and the non-beautiful. Then the apprehension of beauty has to come to us with a vigorous blow to awaken our consciousness from its primitive lethargy, and it attains its object by the urgency of the contrast. Therefore our first acquaintance with beauty is in her dress of motley colours, that affects us with its stripes and feathers, nay with its disfigurements. But as our acquaintance ripens, the apparent discords are resolved into modulations of rhythm. At first we detach beauty from its surroundings, we hold it apart from the rest, but at the end we realise its harmony with all. Then the music of beauty has no more need of exciting us with loud noise; it renounces violence, and appeals to our heart with the truth that it is meekness that inherits the earth.

In some stage of our growth, in some period of our history, we try to set up a special cult of beauty, and pare it down to a narrow circle, so as to make it a matter of pride for a chosen few. Then it breeds in its votaries affectations and exaggerations as it did with the Brahmins in the time of the decadence of Indian civilization, when the perception of the higher truth fell away and superstitions grew up unchecked.

In the history of aesthetics there also comes an age of emancipation when the recognition of beauty in things great and small becomes easy, and when we see it more in the unassuming harmony of common objects than in things startling in their singularity. So much so, that we have to go through the stages of reaction when in the representation of beauty we try to avoid everything that is obviously pleasing and that has been crowned by the sanction of convention. We are then tempted in defiance to exaggerate the commonness of commonplace things, thereby making them aggressively uncommon. To restore harmony we create the discords which are a feature of all reactions. We already see in the present age the sign of this aesthetic reaction, which proves that man has at last come to know that it is only the narrowness of perception which sharply divides the field of his aesthetic consciousness into ugliness and beauty. When he has the power to see things detached from self-interest and from the insistent claims of the lust of the senses, then alone can he have the true vision of the beauty that is everywhere. Then only can he see that what is unpleasant to us is not necessarily unbeautiful, but has its beauty in truth.

When we say that beauty is everywhere we do not mean that the word ugliness should be abolished from our language, just as it would be absurd to say that there is no such thing as untruth. Untruth there certainly is, not in the system of the universe, but in our power of comprehension, as its negative element. In the same manner there is ugliness in the distorted expression of beauty in our life and in our art which comes from our imperfect realization of Truth. To a certain extent we can set our life against the law of truth which is in us and which is in all, and likewise we can give rise to ugliness by going counter to the eternal law of harmony which is everywhere.

Through our sense of truth we realise law in creation, and through our sense of beauty we realise harmony in the universe. When we recognize the law in nature we extend our mastery over physical forces and become powerful; when we recognize the law in our moral nature we attain mastery over self and become free. In like manner the more we comprehend the harmony in the physical world the more our life shares the gladness of creation, and our expression of beauty in art becomes more truly catholic. As we become conscious of the harmony in our soul, our apprehension of the blissfulness of the spirit of the world becomes universal, and the expression of beauty in our life moves in goodness and love towards the infinite. This is the ultimate object of our existence, that we must ever know that 'beauty is truth, truth beauty'; we must realise the whole world in love, for love gives it birth, sustains it, and takes it back to its bosom. We must have that perfect emancipation of heart which gives us the power to stand at the innermost center of things and have the taste of that fullness of disinterested joy which belongs to Brahma.

Music is the purest form of art, and therefore the most direct expression of beauty, with a form and spirit which is one and simple, and least encumbered with anything extraneous. We seem to feel that the manifestation of the infinite in the finite forms of creation is music itself, silent and visible. The evening sky, tirelessly repeating the starry constellations, seems like a child struck with wonder at the mystery of its own first utterance, lisping the same word over and over again, and listening to it in unceasing joy. When in the rainy night of July the darkness is thick upon the meadows and the pattering rain draws veil upon veil over the stillness of the slumbering earth, this monotony of the rain patter seems to be the darkness of sound itself. The gloom of the dim and dense line of trees, the thorny bushes scattered in the bare heath like floating heads of swimmers with bedraggled hair, the smell of the damp grass and the wet earth, the spire of the temple rising above the undefined mass of blackness grouped around the village huts—everything seems like notes rising from the heart of the night, mingling and losing themselves in the one sound of ceaseless rain filling the sky.

Therefore the true poets, they who are seers,seek to express the universe in terms of music.

They rarely use symbols of painting to express the unfolding of forms, the mingling of endless lines and colours that goes on every moment on the canvas of the blue sky.

They have their reason. For the man who paints must have canvas, brush, and colour-box. The first touch of his brush is very far from the complete idea. And then when the work is finished and the artist is gone, the widowed picture stands alone, the incessant touches of love of the creative hand are withdrawn.

But the singer has everything within him. The notes come out from his very life. They are not materials gathered from outside. His idea and his expression are brother and sister; very often they are born as twins. In music the heart reveals itself immediately; it suffers not from any barrier of alien material.

Therefore though music has to wait for its completeness like any other art, yet at every step it gives out the beauty of the whole. As the material of expression even words are barriers, for their meaning has to be construed by thought. But music never has to depend upon any obvious meaning; it expresses what no words can ever express.

What is more, music and the musician are inseparable. When the singer departs, his singing dies with him; it is in eternal union with the life and joy of the master.

This world-song is never for a moment separated from its singer. It is not fashioned from any outward material. It is his joy itself talking never-ending form. It is the great heart sending the tremor of its thrill over the sky. There is a perfection in each individual strain of this music, which is the revelation of completion in the incomplete. No one of its notes is final, yet each reflects the infinite.

What does it matter if we fail to derive the exact meaning of this great harmony? Is it not like the hand meeting the string and drawing out at once all its tones at the touch? It is the language of beauty, the caress, that comes from the heart of the world and straightway reaches our heart.

Last night, in the silence which pervaded the darkness, I stood alone and heard the voice of the singer of eternal melodies. When I went to sleep I closed my eyes with this last thought in my mind, that even when I remain unconscious in slumber the dance of life will still go on in the hushed arena of my sleeping body, keeping step with the stars. The heart will throb, the blood will leap in the veins and the millions of living atoms of my body will vibrate in tune with the note of the harp-string that thrills at the touch of the master.

The Realization of the Infinite

The Upanishads say: "Man becomes true if in this life he can apprehend God; if not, it is the greatest calamity for him."

But what is the nature of this attainment of God? It is quite evident that the infinite is not like one object among many, to be definitely classified and kept among our possessions, to be used as an ally specially favouring us in our politics, warfare, money-making, or in social competitions. We cannot put our God in the same list with our summer-houses, motor-cars, or our credit at the bank, as so many people seem to want to do.

We must try to understand the true character of the desire that a man has when his soul longs for his God. Does it consist of his wish to make an addition, however valuable, to his belongings? Emphatically no! It is an endlessly wearisome task, this continual adding to our stores. In fact, when the soul seeks God she seeks her final escape from this incessant gathering and heaping and never coming to an end. It is not an additional object that she seeks, but it is the *nityo' nityānām*, the permanent in all that is impermanent, the *rasānām rasatamah*, the highest abiding joy unifying all enjoyments. Therefore when the Upanishads teach us to realise everything in Brahma, it is not to seek something extra, not to manufacture something new.

Know everything that there is in the universe as enveloped by God.[1] *Enjoy whatever is given by him and harbour not in your mind the greed for wealth which is not your own.*[2]

When you know that whatever there is is filled by him and whatever you have is his gift, then you realise the infinite in the finite, and the giver in the gifts. Then you know that all the facts of the reality have their only meaning in the manifestation of the one truth, and all your possessions have their only significance for you, not in themselves but in the relation they establish with the infinite.

So it cannot be said that we can find Brahma as we find other objects; there is no question of searching for him in one thing in preference to another, in one place instead of somewhere else. We do not have to run to the grocer's shop for our morning light; we open our eyes and there it is; so we need only give ourselves up to find that Brahma is everywhere.

This is the reason why Buddha admonished us to free ourselves from the confinement of the life of the self. If there were nothing else to take its place more positively perfect and satisfying, then such admonition would be absolutely unmeaning. No man can seriously consider the advice much less have any enthusiasm for it, of surrendering everything one has for gaining nothing whatever.

So our daily worship of God is not really the process of gradual acquisition of him, but the daily process of surrendering ourselves, removing all obstacles to union and extending our consciousness of him in devotion and service, in goodness and to love.

The Upanishads say: *Be lost altogether in Brahma like an arrow that has completely penetrated its target.* Thus to be

---

1. Īçāvāsyamidam sarvam yat kincha jagatyānjagat.
2. Tēna tyaktēna bhunjī hā mā gridhah kasyasviddhanam.

conscious of being absolutely enveloped by Brahma is not an act of mere concentration of mind. It must be the aim of the whole of our life. In all our thoughts and deeds we must be conscious of the infinite. Let the realization of this truth become easier every day of our life, that *none could live or move if the energy of the all-pervading joy did not fill the sky.*[3] In all our actions let us feel that impetus of the infinite energy and be glad.

It may be said that the infinite is beyond our attainment, so it is for us as if it were naught. Yes, if the word attainment implies any idea of possession, then it must be admitted that the infinite is unattainable. But we must keep in mind that the highest enjoyment of man is not in the having but in a getting, which is at the same time not getting. Our physical pleasures leave no margin for the unrealised. They, like the dead satellite of the earth, have but little atmosphere around them. When we take food and satisfy our hunger it is a complete act of possession. So long as the hunger is not satisfied it is a pleasure to eat. For then our enjoyment of eating touches at every point the infinite. But, when it attains completion, or in other words, when our desire for eating reaches the end of the stage of its non-realization, it reaches the end of its pleasure. In all our intellectual pleasures the margin is broader, the limit is far off. In all our deeper love getting and non-getting run ever parallel. In one of our Vaishöava lyrics the lover says to his beloved: "I feel as if I have gazed upon the beauty of thy face from my birth, yet my eyes are hungry still: as if I have kept thee pressed to my heart for millions of years, yet my heart is not satisfied."

This makes it clear that it is really the infinite whom we seek in our pleasures. Our desire for being wealthy is not a desire for a particular sum of money but it is indefinite, and

---

3. Ko hyevānyāt kaḥ prāṇyāt yadesha ākāça ānando na syāt.

the most fleeting of our enjoyments are but the momentary touches of the eternal. The tragedy of human life consists in our vain attempts to stretch the limits of things which can never become unlimited,—to reach the infinite by absurdly adding to the rungs of the ladder of the finite.

It is evident from this that the real desire of our soul is to get beyond all our possessions. Surrounded by things she can touch and feel, she cries, "I am weary of getting; ah, where is he who is never to be got?"

We see everywhere in the history of man that the spirit of renunciation is the deepest reality of the human soul. When the soul says of anything, "I do not want it, for I am above it," she gives utterance to the highest truth that is in her. When a girl's life outgrows her doll, when she realises that in every respect she is more than her doll is, then she throws it away. By the very act of possession we know that we are greater than the things we possess. It is a perfect misery to be kept bound up with things lesser than ourselves. This it is that Maitreyi felt when her husband gave her his property on the eve of leaving home. She asked him, "Would these material things help one to attain the highest?"—or, in other words, "Are they more than my soul to me?" When her husband answered, "They will make you rich in worldly possessions," she said at once, "Then what am I to do with these?" It is only when a man truly realises what his possessions are that he has no more illusions about them; then he knows his soul is far above these things and he becomes free from their bondage. Thus man truly realises his soul by outgrowing his possessions, and man's progress in the path of eternal is through a series of renunciations.

That we cannot absolutely possess the infinite being is not a mere intellectual proposition. It has to be experienced, and this experience is bliss. The bird, while taking its flight in the sky, experiences at every beat of its wings that the sky is boundless, that its wings can never carry it beyond. Therein lies its joy. In the cage the sky is limited; it may be quite enough for all the purposes of the bird's life, only it is not more than is necessary. The bird cannot rejoice within the limits of the necessary. It must feel that what it has is immeasurably more than it ever can want or comprehend, and then only can it be glad.

Thus our soul must soar in the infinite, and she must feel every moment that in the sense of not being able to come to the end of her attainment is her supreme joy, her final freedom.

Man's abiding happiness is not in getting anything but in giving himself up to what is greater than himself, to ideas which are larger than his individual life, the idea of his country, of humanity, of God. They make it easier for him to part with all that he has, not excepting his life. His existence is miserable and sordid till he finds some great idea which can truly claim his all, which can release him from all attachment to his belongings. Buddha and Jesus, and all our great prophets, represent such great ideas. They hold before us opportunities for surrendering our all. When they bring forth their divine alms-bowl we feel we cannot help giving, and we find that in giving is our truest joy and liberation, for it is uniting ourselves to that extent with the infinite.

Man is not complete; he is yet to be. In what he *is* he is small, and if we could conceive him stopping there for eternity we should have an idea of the most awful hell that man can imagine. In his *to be* he is infinite, there is his heaven, his deliverance. His *is* is occupied every moment with what it can get and have done with; his *to be* is hungering for something which is more than can be got, which he never can lose because he never has possessed.

The finite pole of our existence has its place in the world of necessity. There man goes about searching for food to live, clothing to get warmth. In this region—the region of nature—

it is his function to go get things. The natural man is occupied with enlarging his possessions.

But this act of getting is partial. It is limited to man's necessities. We can have a thing only to the extent of our requirements, just as a vessel can contain water only to the extent of its emptiness. Our relation to food is only in feeding, our relation to a house is only in habitation. We call it a benefit when a thing is fitted only to some particular want of ours. Thus to get is always to get partially, and never can be otherwise. So this craving for acquisition belongs to our finite self.

But that side of our existence whose direction is towards the infinite seeks not wealth, but freedom and joy. There the reign of necessity ceases, and there our function is not to get but to be. To be what? To be one with Brahma. For the region of the infinite is the region of unity. Therefore the Upanishads say: *If man apprehends God he becomes true.* Here it is becoming, it is not having more. Words do not gather bulk when you know their meaning; they become true by being one with the idea.

Though the West has accepted as its teacher him who boldly proclaimed his oneness with his Father, and who exhorted his followers to be perfect as God, it has never been reconciled to this idea of our unity with the infinite being. It condemns, as a piece of blasphemy, any implication of man's becoming God. This idea of absolute transcendence is certainly not that which Christ preached, nor perhaps the idea of the Christian mystics, but this seems to be the idea that has become popular in the Christian west.

But the highest wisdom in the East holds that it is not the function of our soul to *gain* God, to utilise him for any special material purpose. All that we can ever aspire to is to become more and more one with God. In the region of nature, which is the region of diversity, we grow by acquisition; in the spiritual world, which is the region of unity, we grow by losing ourselves, by uniting. Gaining a thing, as we have said, is by its nature partial, it is limited only to a particular want; but *being* is complete, it belongs to our wholeness, it springs not from any necessity but from our affinity with the infinite, which is the principle of perfection that we have in our soul.

Yes, we must become Brahma. We must not shrink from avowing this. Our existence is meaningless if we never can expect to realise the highest perfection that there is. If we have an aim and yet can never reach it, then it is no aim at all.

But can it then be said that there is no difference between Brahma and our individual soul? Of course the difference is obvious. Call it illusion or ignorance, or whatever name you may give it, it is there. You can offer explanations but you cannot explain it away. Even illusion is true as illusion.

Brahma is Brahma, he is the infinite ideal of perfection. But we are not what we truly are; we are ever to become true, ever to become Brahma. There is the eternal play of love in the relation between this being and the becoming; and in the depth of this mystery is the source of all truth and beauty that sustains the endless march of creation.

In the music of the rushing stream sounds the joyful assurance, "I shall become the sea." It is not a vain assumption; it is true humility, for it is the truth. The river has no other alternative. On both sides of its banks it has numerous fields and forests, villages and towns; it can serve them in various ways, cleanse them and feed them, carry their produce from place to place. But it can have only partial relations with these, and however long it may linger among them it remains separate; it never can become a town or a forest.

But it can and does become the sea. The lesser moving water has its affinity with the great motionless water of the ocean. It moves through the thousand objects on its onward course, and its motion finds its finality when it reaches the sea.

The river can become the sea, but she can never make the sea part and parcel of herself. If, by some chance, she has encircled some broad sheet of water and pretends that she has made the sea a part of herself, we at once know that it is not so, that her current is still seeking rest in the great ocean to which it can never set boundaries.

In the same manner, our soul can only become Brahma as the river can become the sea. Everything else she touches at one of her points, then leaves and moves on, but she never can leave Brahma and move beyond him. Once our soul realises her ultimate object of repose in Brahma, all her movements acquire a purpose. It is this ocean of infinite rest which gives significance to endless activities. It is this perfectness of being that lends to the imperfection of becoming that quality of beauty which finds its expression in all poetry, drama, and art.

There must be a complete idea that animates a poem. Every sentence of the poem touches that idea. When the reader realises that pervading idea, as he reads on, then the reading of the poem is full of joy to him. Then every part of the poem becomes radiantly significant by the light of the whole. But if the poem goes on interminably, never expressing the idea of the whole, only throwing off disconnected images, however beautiful, it becomes wearisome and unprofitable in the extreme. The progress of our soul is like a perfect poem. It has an infinite idea which once realised makes all movements full of meaning and joy. But if we detach its movements from that ultimate idea, if we do not see the infinite rest and only see the infinite motion, then existence appears to us a monstrous evil, impetuously rushing towards an unending aimlessness.

I remember in our childhood we had a teacher who used to make us learn by heart the whole book of Sanskrit grammar, which is written in symbols, without explaining their meaning to us. Day after day we went toiling on, but on towards what, we had not the least notion. So, as regards our lessons, we were in the position of the pessimist who only counts the breathless activities of the world, but cannot see the infinite repose of the perfection whence these activities are gaining their equilibrium every moment in absolute fitness and harmony. We lose all joy in thus contemplating existence, because we miss the truth. We see the gesticulations of the dancer, and we imagine these are directed by a ruthless tyranny of chance, while we are deaf to the eternal music which makes every one of these gestures inevitably spontaneous and beautiful. These motions are ever growing into that music of perfection, becoming one with it, dedicating to that melody at every step the multitudinous forms they go on creating.

And this is the truth of our soul, and this is her joy, that she must ever be growing into Brahma, that all her movements should be modulated by this ultimate idea, and all her creations should be given as offerings to the supreme spirit of perfection.

There is a remarkable saying in the Upanishads: *I think not that I know him well, or that I know him, or even that I know him not.*[4]

By the process of knowledge we can never know the infinite being. But if he is altogether beyond our reach, then he is absolutely nothing to us. The truth is that we know him not, yet we know him.

This has been explained in another saying of the Upanishads: *From Brahma words come back baffled, as well as the mind, but he who knows him by the joy of him is free from all fears.*[5]

Intellectual knowledge is partial, because our intellect is an instrument, it is only a part of us, it can give us information

---

4. Nāham manye suvedeti no na vedeti vedacha.
5. Yato vācho nivartante aprapya manasā saha ānandam brahmano vidvān na vibheti kutaçchana.

about things which can be divided and analysed, and whose properties can be classified, part by part. But Brahma is perfect, and knowledge which is partial can never be a knowledge of him.

But he can be known by joy, by love. For joy is knowledge in its completeness, it is knowing by our whole being. Intellect sets us apart from the things to be known, but love knows its object by fusion. Such knowledge is immediate and admits no doubt. It is the same as knowing our own selves, only more so.

Therefore, as the Upanishads say, mind can never know Brahma, words can never describe him; he can only be known by our soul, by her joy in him, by her love. Or, in other words, we can only come into relation with him by union—union of our whole being. We must be one with our Father, we must be perfect as he is.

But how can that be? There can be no grade in infinite perfection. We cannot grow more and more into Brahma. He is the absolute one, and there can be no more or less in him.

Indeed, the realization of the *paramātman*, the supreme soul, within our *antarātman*, our inner individual soul, is in a state of absolute completion. We cannot think of it as non-existent and depending on our limited powers for its gradual construction. If our relation with the divine were all a thing of our own making, how should we rely on it as true, and how should it lend us support?

Yes, we must know that within us we have that where space and time cease to rule and where the links of evolution are merged in unity. In that everlasting abode of the *ātman*, the soul, the revelation of the *paramātman*, the supreme soul, is already complete. Therefore the Upanishads say: *He who knows Brahman, the true, the all-conscious, and the infinite as hidden in the depths of the soul, which is the supreme sky (the inner sky of consciousness), enjoys all objects of desire in union with the all-knowing Brahman.*[6]

The union is already accomplished. The *paramātman*, the supreme soul, has himself chosen this soul of ours as his bride and the marriage has been completed. The solemn *mantram* has been uttered: *Let thy heart be even as my heart is.*[7] There is no room in this marriage for evolution to act the part of the master of ceremonies. The *eshah*, who cannot otherwise be described than as *This*, the nameless immediate presence, is ever here in our innermost being. *"This eshah, or This,* is the supreme end of the other this";[8] "this *This* is the supreme treasure of the other this";[9] "this *This* is the supreme dwelling of the other this";[10] "this *This* is the supreme joy of the other this."[11] Because the marriage of supreme love has been accomplished in timeless time. And now goes on the endless *līlā,* the play of love. He who has been gained in eternity is now being pursued in time and space, in joys and sorrows, in this world and in the worlds beyond. When the soul-bride understands this well, her heart is blissful and at rest. She knows that she, like a river, has attained the ocean of her fulfilment at one end of her being, and at the other end she is ever attaining it; at one end it is eternal rest and completion, at the other it is incessant movement and change. When she knows both ends as inseparably connected, then she knows the world as her own household by the right of knowing the master of the world as her own lord. Then all her services

---

6. Satyam jñānam anantam brahma yo veda nihitam guhāyām parame vyoman so⁰çnute sarvān kāmān saha brahmaṇa vipaāchita.
7. Yadetat hṛidayam mama tadastu hṛidayan tava.
8. Eshāsya paramā gatiḥ.
9. Eshāsya paramā sampat.
10. Eshāsya paramo lokah.
11. Eshāsya parama ānandah.

become services of love, all the troubles and tribulations of life come to her as trials triumphantly borne to prove the strength of her love, smilingly to win the wager from her lover. But so long as she remains obstinately in the dark, lifts not her veil, does not recognise her lover, and only knows the world dissociated from him, she serves as a handmaid here, where by right she might reign as a queen; she sways in doubt, and weeps in sorrow and dejection. *She passes from starvation to starvation, from trouble to trouble, and from fear to fear.*[12]

I can never forget that scrap of a song I once heard in the early dawn in the midst of the din of the crowd that had collected for a festival the night before: "Ferryman, take me across to the other shore!"

In the bustle of all our work there comes out this cry, "Take me across." The carter in India sings while driving his cart, "Take me across." The itinerant grocer deals out his goods to his customers and sings, "Take me across."

What is the meaning of this cry? We feel we have not reached our goal; and we know with all our striving and toiling we do not come to the end, we do not attain our object. Like a child dissatisfied with its dolls, our heart cries, "Not this, not this." But what is that other? Where is the further shore?

Is it something else than what we have? Is it somewhere else than where we are? Is it to take rest from all our works, to be relieved from all the responsibilities of life?

No, in the very heart of our activities we are seeking for our end. We are crying for the across, even where we stand. So, while our lips utter their prayer to be carried away, our busy hands are never idle.

In truth, thou ocean of joy, this shore and the other shore are one and the same in thee. When I call this my own, the

---

12. Daurbhikshāt vāti daurbhiksham klecāt klecam bhavāt bhayam.

other lies estranged; and missing the sense of that completeness which is in me, my heart incessantly cries out for the other. All my this, and that other, are waiting to be completely reconciled in thy love.

This "I" of mine toils hard, day and night, for a home which it knows as it own. Alas, there will be no end of its sufferings so long as it is not able to call this home thine. Till then it will struggle on, and its heart will ever cry, "Ferryman, lead me across." When this home of mine is made thine, that very moment is it taken across, even while its old walls enclose it. This "I" is restless. It is working for a gain which can never be assimilated with its spirit, which it never can hold and retain. In its efforts to clasp in its own arms that which is for all, it hurts others and is hurt in its turn, and cries, "Lead me across." But as soon as it is able to say, "All my work is thine," everything remains the same, only it is taken across.

Where can I meet thee unless in this my home made thine? Where can I join thee unless in this my work transformed into thy work? If leave my home I shall not reach thy home; if I cease my work I can never join thee in thy work. For thou dwellest in me and I in thee. Thou without me or I without thee are nothing.

Therefore, in the midst of our home and our work, the prayer rises, "Lead me across!" For here rolls the sea, and even here lies the other shore waiting to be reached—yes, here is this everlasting present, not distant, not anywhere else.

LETTERS TO A FRIEND

Preface[*]

The letters contained in this volume were written to me by Rabindranath Tagore during the years 1913–1922. Many of them were published in India, in the *Modern Review*, and also in book form, under the title *Letters from Abroad*. The present volume represents an entire revision and enlargement of that book, of which only a few copies reached England. The material has now been divided into chapters, with a brief explanatory summary of the circumstances in which the letters were written.

With the Poet's sanction, this volume has been dedicated to the memory of my own dear friend and fellow-worker at Santiniketan, William Winstanley Pearson. He accompanied me on journeys undertaken with Rabindranath Tagore in different parts of the world, and also was my companion when I travelled with him alone to South Africa, Australia, New Zealand and Fiji. He was with the Poet in Europe and America at the time when many of these letters were written, and is often referred to in them. His death, owing to a railway accident in Italy in 1923—just when he was at the height of his powers of service and love—has made the fellowship between East and West, for which Santiniketan stands, doubly sacred to us all. He had two homes, one in Manchester and

Note: Edited Version.

one at Santiniketan, both of them very dear to him. In each, his memory is still fresh after the lapse of years.

In conclusion, my special thanks are due to Muirhead Bone, Mukul Dey and William Rothenstein. They all shared with me the friendship of Willie Pearson, to whose memory this book is dedicated.

C.F. Andrews

October 1928

An Essay on the
Bengal Renaissance

I

The course taken by the Bengal Renaissance a hundred years ago was strangely similar to that of Western Europe in the sixteenth century. The result in the history of mankind is likely to be in certain respects the same also. For, just as Europe awoke to new life then, so Asia is awakening today.

In Europe, it was the shock of the Arab civilization and the Faith of Islam which startled the West out of the intellectual torpor of the Dark Ages. Then followed the recovery of the Greek and Latin Classics and a new interpretation of the Christian Scriptures, both to which, acting together, brought the full Reformation and Renaissance.

In Bengal, it was the shock of the Western civilization that startled the East into new life and helped forward its wonderful re-birth. Then followed the revival of the Sanskrit Classics and a reformation from within of the old religions. These two forces, acting together, made the Bengal Renaissance a living power in Asia. In Bengal itself, the literary and artistic movement came into greatest prominence. Rabindranath Tagore has been its crown.

II

Early in the nineteenth century, the burning question in Bengal was whether the spread of the English language should be encouraged or not. Macaulay's famous minute, written in 1835, fixed the English tongue as the medium for higher education. 'Never on earth,' writes Sir John Seeley, 'was a more momentous question discussed.' The phrase is an arresting one, and appears a palpable exaggeration until we understand the issues involved, not only for Bengal, but for every country in the East.

Macaulay won the victory. Nevertheless, some of his premises were unsound and his conclusions inaccurate. He poured contempt on the Sanskrit Classics; he treated Bengali literature as useless. In expressing these opinions he committed egregious blunders. Yet, strangely enough, in spite of his narrow outlook, his practical insight was not immediately at fault. The hour for the indigenous revival had not yet come. A full shock from without was needed, and the study of English gave the shock required.

But the new life which first appeared was not altogether healthy. It led immediately to a shaking of old customs and an unsettlement of religious convictions, carried often to a violent and unthinking extreme. The greatest disturbance of all was in the social sphere. A wholesale imitation of purely Western habits led to a painful confusion of ideas. It was a brilliant and precocious age, bubbling over with a new vitality; but wayward and unregulated, like a rudderless ship on a stormy sea.

III

The one outstanding personality, whose presence saved Bengal at this crisis, was the great Raja Ram Mohun Roy. Towering above his contemporaries, solitary and majestic, this extraordinary genius seems to have measured accurately the force of every new current as it flowed quickly past, and to have steered his own course with an almost unerring precision. As practical as Macaulay, he was no mere opportunist. He was a true prophet, and had the prophet's sacred fire of enthusiasm. On the literary side, he was one of the most ardent promoters of the new Western learning, and eagerly helped forward Macaulay's programme. But the best energies of his marvellously full life were directed to re-create in the heart of the Bengali people that true reverence for the Indian past which should lead to a revival of their own Sanskrit Classics. Above all, he did not despise his Bengali mother-tongue, but brought it back into full literary use.

<h2 style="text-align:center">IV</h2>

Debendranath Tagore, the father of Rabindranath, was the next outstanding figure in the Bengali literary revival. His work and influence lasted for more than half a century. If Ram Mohun Roy may be likened to the root of this tree of literature, planted deep in the soil, Debendranath Tagore may be compared to its strong and vigorous stem, and Rabindranath, his son, to its flower and fruit. Rarely in the history of literature can such a direct succession be traced.

Debendranath's religious character illuminated the age with a moral grandeur of its own. So impressive was his spiritual authority, that he received by universal consent the name of Maharshi, or great saint. During the floodtide of English fashion he held fast to the ancient moorings and strengthened every bond which kept his country close to its own historic past.

His autobiography, translated by his son, reveals the deep religious spirit of modern Bengal, along with its passion for intellectual truth. The Tagore family had already been attracted within the orbit of Raja Ram Mohun Roy, and the vivid memory of the great reformer was one of the strongest influences in moulding the life of Debendranath as he grew up from boyhood to youth.

By the middle of the nineteenth century, owing to these initial movements, a creative period in Bengali literary history had set in. It represented not merely an awakening of Bengal, but the beginning of a new era for the whole of Asia.

V

This Bengal Renaissance bears on its surface the marks of conflict between the new Western learning and the revived Sanskrit Classics. Toru Dutt, the fairest and frailest flower among the writers, composed her songs only in English; but the fragrance of the Sanskrit past pervades all her works and makes them a national possession. Michael Dutt began by writing English verse; but he abandoned this while his literary powers were still at their height, and composed his later poems in a wonderfully sonorous and majestic Bengali metre. He has been called the Milton of the Bengal revival. Bankim's novels carry back the mind at every turn to the romance writers in the West. We can almost feel behind them the zest with which young Bengal explored their newfound treasures.

But the strength of the period consisted in this, that the writers, amid all their passionate and devoted study of English, remained true to the ancient Indian ideal. They remembered the rock from whence they were hewn. They did not despise their own birthright. Not only the language, but also the subjects, of this new literature were brought more in touch with the people. The village life of Bengal, which had tended to fall into the background, gained a new appreciation. The mediaeval as well as the classical times were laid under contribution for subject-matter. The commanding ideal at last rose up before the minds of men, to build a truly national literature and art out of the living stones of indigenous poetry, music and song.

VI

Into this rich heritage of the past the young poet Rabindranath entered, and he has done more than anyone else to make this ideal a living inspiration in Bengal. A friend of mine has described to me the scene that took place when the aged novelist Bankim was being honoured and garlanded. The old man took the garland from off his own neck and placed it on that of a young writer who was seated at his feet—Rabindranath Tagore.

This act of Bankim has now been universally recognized as both generous and just. That which others were struggling to attain, in the midst of insuperable difficulties, Rabindranath has reached with the quick leap and joyful ease of supreme genius. The ideals of art, which were before only dimly discerned, he has seen with open vision. Moreover, in his later works he has carried still further the spiritual mission of his father, and he has clothed his own deepest religious thoughts with a raiment of simplicity and beauty.

His fame has come to the full in recent years, and his poetry has taken on a more prophetic tone. He has passed forward from the subjective period of unbounded delight in Nature, to enter into the mystery of the vast sorrow of the world; to share the heavy burden of the poor; to face death itself unmoved; to look for and attain the unclouded vision of God.

VII

In all this, Rabindranath has remained close to the heart of Bengal. Every day that I was with him, in 1912, his eyes seemed to be straining across the sea, to greet his boys at Santiniketan—longing also to be back among his village people at Shileida, among whom he was a father and a friend.

Is it not wonderful, therefore, that Bengal, from whose soil he seems to draw his deepest inspiration, should have been inspired in turn by his music and song with a high consciousness of its own destiny. He has given vital expression, at a supreme moment of history, to the rising hopes of his own people. In that country of music and art and song,

The prophetic soul of the wide world
Dreaming of things to come

has found at last its vision in and through his poems. The dreams which Bengal is now dreaming may not all come true.

The tumult and the shouting dies:
The captains and the kings depart,

in the pageant of literature as well as that of empire. But song and music are mighty instruments, when the spirit of a rising people is beating high with hope; and to-day, men, women, and even little children, are seeing through the eyes of Rabindranath the vision of "Golden Bengal."

That gracious vision is radiant and luminous. And, there is not unmixed with it a sacred sense of awe, that God has visited His people.

If this supreme power of music and literature to create a new spirit in a whole people seems somewhat unreal in the West, it must be remembered that India still retains, deep below the surface, her living faith in the Unseen.

An Essay on The Personality of Tagore

I

The temperament and character of Rabindranath Tagore may best be understood if I attempt to describe one memorable day in London, when he told me in outline the story of his own life in relation to his literary career.

He was lodging in the upper room of a house just outside the entrance to South Kensington Underground Station. The time was a morning in September 1912, and a thick London fog filled the air. He was still weak on account of a very serious illness, which had brought him to the West to undergo an operation, and his face looked pale and worn.

He first told me about his father—how all the household became still and hushed when he was present in the house, as if anxious not to disturb his meditations.

He spoke to me, also, about his mother, who had died when he was quite young. As he saw her face for the last time on earth, calm and beautiful in death, it awakened in him no childish terror, nor even wonder, all seemed so peaceful and natural. It was only later, as he grew older, that he learnt Death's inner meaning.

The account he gave me of his own life in early childhood was as follows:

I was very lonely—that was the chief feature of my childhood—I was very lonely. I saw my father seldom: he was away a great deal, but his presence pervaded the whole house and was one of the deepest influences on my life. I was kept in the charge of servants of the household after my mother died, and I used to sit, day after day, in front of the window and picture to myself what was going on in the outer world.

From the very first time that I can remember, I was passionately fond of Nature. Oh! it used to make me mad with joy when I saw the clouds come up in the sky one by one. I felt, even in those early days, that I was surrounded with a companionship very intense and very intimate, though I did not know how to name it. I had such an exceeding love for Nature, that I cannot think in what way to describe it to you; but she was a kind of loving companion, always with me, and always revealing to me some fresh beauty.

This was how he pictured his childhood to me on that foggy day in London, and a passage in his *Reminiscences* makes the portrait still more vivid:

In the morning of autumn (he writes) I would run into the garden the moment I got up from sleep. A scent of leaves and grass, wet with dew, seemed to embrace me, and the dawn, all tender and fresh with the newly awakened rays of the sun, held out its face to me to greet me beneath the trembling vesture of palm-leaves. Nature shut her hands and laughingly asked every day: "What have I got inside?" and nothing seemed impossible.

II

Rabindranath Tagore went on to tell me that his first literary awakening came from reading the old Bengali poets, Chandidas and Vidyapati. He studied them in a recently published edition, when he was twelve or thirteen, and revelled in their beauty. He went still further, and, with the precocity of youth, imitated their style and published some poems under the name of Bhanu Sinha. Literary Bengal wondered for a time who this Bhanu Sinha could be. He laughed as he told me of this exploit of his boyhood, and went on to say that these and many other juvenile poems were merely conventional and imitative. They followed the old classical style.

When he wrote, however, the poems published later under the name of *Sandhya Sangit* (Evening Songs), he broke away from the classical style altogether and became purely romantic. At first, he was derided by the older generation for his new metres; but the younger generation was with him. He chose no English model; the early Vaishnava religious literature was the source of his inspiration. These religious poems ever afterwards remained intimately endeared to him. Their influence is marked in his own lyrics, and especially in the *Gitanjali* series.

III

The time of his real birth as a poet, he dates from a morning in Free School Lane, Calcutta, when with dramatic suddenness the veil seemed to be withdrawn from his eyes and he saw the inner soul of reality.

It was morning (he said to me). I was watching the sunrise from Free School Lane. A veil was suddenly withdrawn and everything became luminous. The whole scene was one perfect music—one marvellous rhythm. The houses in the street, the men moving below, the little children playing, all seemed parts of one luminous whole—inexpressibly glorious. The vision went on for seven or eight days. Everyone, even those who bored me, seemed to lose their outer barrier of personality; and I was full of gladness, full of love, for every person and every tiniest thing. Then I went to the Himalayas, and looked for it there, and I lost it. ... That morning in Free School Lane was one of the first things which gave me the inner vision, and I have tried to explain it in my poems. I have felt, ever since, that this was my goal: to express the fullness of life, in its beauty, as perfection—if only the veil were withdrawn.

I copied this account down as the Poet told it on that dark, misty London morning; and I can remember distinctly even now the quiet laugh he gave as he said, "And I lost it," and also the emphasis he laid upon the words "fullness of life." In Rabindranath's own prose writings the same incident is also recorded. It may be well to compare this other record with the picture he gave me in London. They corroborate and explain one another.

Where the Sadar Street ends, trees in the garden of Free School Street are visible. One morning, I was standing in the verandah, looking at them. The sun was slowly rising above the screen of their leaves; and as I was watching it, suddenly, in a moment, a veil seemed to be lifted from my eyes. I found the world wrapt in an inexpressible glory with its waves of joy and beauty bursting and breaking on all sides. The thick shroud of sorrow that lay on my heart in many folds was pierced through and through by the light of the world, which was everywhere radiant.

That very day the poem known as *The Fountain Awakened from its Dream* flowed on like a fountain itself. When it was finished, still the curtain did not fall on that strange vision of beauty and joy. There was nothing and no one whom I did not love at that moment....I stood on the verandah and watched the coolies as they tramped down the road. Their movements, their forms, their countenances seemed to be strangely wonderful to me, as if they were all moving like waves in the great ocean of the world. When one young man placed his hand upon the shoulder of another and passed laughingly by, it was a remarkable event too....I seemed to witness, in the wholeness of my vision, the movements of the body of all humanity, and to feel the beat of the music and the rhythm of a mystic dance.

For some days I was in this ecstatic mood. My brothers had made up their minds to go to Darjeeling, and I accompanied them. I thought I might have a fuller vision of what I had witnessed in the crowded parts of the Sadar Street, if once I reached the heights of the Himalayas.

But when I reached the Himalayas the vision all departed. That was my mistake. I thought I could get at truth from the outside. But however lofty and imposing the Himalayas might be, they could not put anything real into my hands. But God, the Great Giver, Himself can open the whole Universe to our gaze in the narrow space of a single lane.

IV

The volume of lyrics called *Morning Songs* was the direct outcome of this time of ecstatic early vision. There is a romantic longing to know intimately the secret of the beauty of the world. But as yet he had not the deep-laid basis of practical experience whereon to build. His first lyrics, therefore, are mainly in the realm of imagination, and not closely related to common human experience.

But outer circumstances, as well as his own inner spirit, prevented the young writer from remaining too long in that enchanted garden of the soul. His father, seeing his son's remarkable genius, very wisely insisted that he should leave Calcutta and go down to the banks of the Ganges in order to supervise there the family estate. This work brought him into closest touch with the village life of Bengal. He had to deal each day with the practical affairs of men, and to understand and appreciate the elemental hopes and fears of mankind, stripped of all convention. To his own good fortune, also, as a poet, his joy in communing with Nature found at the same time its fullest and freest expression. During pauses in his active business life he would live all alone on the sand-flats of the Ganges, moving up and down from village to village in his boat.

> Sometimes (he told me) I would pass many months absolutely alone without speaking, till my own voice grew thin and weak through lack of use. I used to write from my boat the stories of the village life which I had witnessed in the course of my work, and put into written words the incidents and conversations which I had heard. This was my "short-story" period; and some think these stories better than the lyrics which I had written before.

It was during this long residence at Shileida that the deepest love for Bengal, his motherland, developed. The national movement had not yet come into actual outward shape and form; but the forces which were to break forth later were already acting powerfully in the hearts of leading Bengali thinkers; and Rabindranath's soul caught the flame of patriotism, not in Calcutta itself, but among the villagers. His unshaken faith in the destiny of his country received its strongest confirmation from what he saw in the village life of his own people. He was not unaware of the dangers which threatened that life through its contact with the new social forces from the West. Indeed, this forms the theme of many of his short stories. But he believed, with all his heart, from what he had witnessed, that the stock from which the new national life was to spring forth was sound at the core. He spoke to me, that morning, with the greatest possible warmth and affection of the Bengali villagers, and of the many lessons he owed to them of patience and simplicity, of human kindliness and sympathy.

V

Rabindranath Tagore dated the next stage in his literary life from the time when he went to Santiniketan Asram from Shileida.

He left his father's estate; and there seemed to come to him the strongest impression that a new period of adventure was about to arrive in his life. He anticipated some change, for which these quiet unbroken years in the country had been a preparation.

Slowly, there came to him the clear call to give up his life more wholly for his country. He first went to Calcutta in order to found a school, and afterwards to Santiniketan with the same object. On his arrival at Santiniketan, to take up this new work, he was handicapped for want of funds. "I sold my books," he said to me pathetically.

> I sold all my books, my copyrights, everything I had, in order to carry on with the school. I cannot possibly tell you what a struggle it was, and what difficulties I had to go through. At first, the object in view was purely patriotic, but later on it grew more spiritual. Then, in the very midst of all these outer difficulties and trials, there came the greatest change of all, the true *Varsha Sesha*, the change in my own inner life.

He went on to tell me how, when he was forty years old, his wife had died, and almost immediately after his daughter showed signs of consumption. He left the school and went away with his daughter to nurse her and tend her, but after six months of mingled hope and fear she passed away from his arms and left his heart still more desolate. Then came the third overwhelming wave of sorrow. His youngest son, to whom he had learnt to be father and mother in one, was taken suddenly ill with cholera and died in his presence—the child of his love.

As he spoke of these things that morning, the darkness of the London mists rolled away and the light shone through the clouds with a majestic radiance. This outward scene was but a faint symbol of the story that was being told to me quietly in that upper room.

The Poet spoke of the days and hours wherein Death itself became a loved companion—no longer the king of terrors, but altogether transformed into a cherished friend.

> You know (he said to me), this death was a great *blessing* to me. I had through it all, day after day, a sense of fulfilment, of completion, as if nothing were lost. I felt that if even an atom in the universe seemed lost, it could never actually perish. It was not mere resignation that came to me, but the sense of a fuller life. I knew then, at last, what Death was. It was perfection.

Through what depth of suffering that peace and joy came out at last triumphant, the lines in his face told me as he spoke these words.

VI

It was during this period that *Gitanjali* was written in his own mother-tongue, Bengali. "I wrote," he said, "those poems for myself. I did not think of publishing them when I was writing."

They mark the great transition in his life, when the Poet's social and national longings became wholly merged in the universal. He has attempted—to use his own words—"to express the fullness of human life, in its beauty, as perfection."

Since that period of sorrow he has fared forth as a voyager, a pilgrim. This is the last phase of all. It was his own health which first compelled him to set out to the West. But here again, as in the former period mentioned, the outward circumstance has brought with it a new spiritual development.

> As I crossed the Atlantic (he wrote to me), and spent on board the ship the beginning of a new year, I realized that a new stage in my life had come, the stage of a voyager. To the open road! To the emancipation of self! To the realization in love!

In another letter, which he wrote earlier to me, dealing with the meeting of the conflicting races of the world and the removal of colour prejudice, he uses these words:

> This meeting of the races affords the greatest of all problems that men have ever been asked to solve. It is, I believe, the one question of the present age, and we must be prepared to go through the martyrdom of suffering and humiliation till the victory of God in man is achieved.

Since *Gitanjali* was written, Rabindranath Tagore has been facing, day by day, these larger international questions and casting aside altogether that narrower nationalism which for one period in his life had affected his own songs. He has attempted, also, to comprehend the inner harmony of his own life's work and to read its deeper meaning. The stage of philosophy has been reached by the Poet. Yet, his lyrical powers seem in no way to be diminished. The fountain of song is still sending forth new streams.

VII

When Rabindranath Tagore first landed in London, in 1912, he had placed before his English friends some translations of his Bengali poems. He had offered them with singular diffidence, without at all realizing the value of his great achievement. "I found," he said, "that I had to strip my Bengali verses of all their gaudy ornaments and to clothe them in the simplest English dress."

That English setting has since been acknowledged, by those who are best able to judge, to represent a beautiful and musical prose—a comparatively new form of English, which has enriched the literature of Great Britain. The triumph has been won—a triumph hardly ever before achieved in literary history—of an author translating his own poems into a wholly new language, thus giving his message to two peoples at once in a noble literary form.

This crowning success of Rabindranath Tagore has already brought East and West closer together in a common fellowship and understanding. Where the forces of racial rivalry and religious division are so strong, it is indeed no small blessing to humanity when a generous voice can be clearly heard, above the discordant tumult of the times, which the whole world welcomes as a messenger and revealer of peace and goodwill to mankind.

Chapter I

The letters contained in this opening chapter were written to me by the poet Rabindranath Tagore in the early years when my work as teacher at Santiniketan had only just begun. He came back from Europe in September 1913, but I was not able to join him then on account of an attack of malarial fever. Later on, it was necessary for me to go out to South Africa along with my friend W.W. Pearson in order to take part in the Passive Resistance struggle which was being carried on against the evils of the indenture system of Indian labour. We both returned to India in April 1914, and were with the Poet until we went out to Fiji together in September 1915.

Some explanation must be given concerning the special series of letters which the Poet sent to me each day from Ramgarh, near Naini Tal, in the latter part of May 1914.

He had gone in good health to the Hills in order to spend there his summer holidays; but he told me afterwards that the mental pain he experienced soon after his arrival was almost equivalent to a death-agony. He had hardly expected to survive it. This was all the more strange because it came upon him quite suddenly at a moment when he was feeling a sense of physical exhilaration in the supreme beauty of the Himalayas and also the delight of the change from the intense heat of the plains. I remember him saying to me that the shock of agony overtook him like a thunderstorm out of a clear, unclouded sky.

This suffering, which is referred to in the letters written in May, entirely passed away. The Poet was in the best of health and spirits all through the month of June, renewing his own full, active work in his schools among his boys after the holidays were over. Indeed, I can remember June 1914 as a singularly happy month.

But early in July the darkness again came down upon his life and seemed once more to overwhelm him. It appeared to have no external source, either in bad health or bad climate; and the school work was progressing wonderfully. But he spoke to me constantly of the mysterious and unbearable weight of mental oppression which drove him into solitude. He went away from the school and lived alone at Surul. For nearly three months this depression continued. There are hardly any letters written during this period; but I have the most vivid and painful recollections of his suffering.

Long before any news reached us about the World War that was impending, and before any hint of it had come to us in the midst of our comparative retirement from the world at Santiniketan, his mind was entirely preoccupied with the foreboding of some disaster which was about to overwhelm humanity. He wrote at this time, and published some weeks before the war began, a very remarkable Bengali poem called *The Destroyer*, in which he spoke of the sudden destruction that was coming upon the earth. It contained the following lines:

Is it the Destroyer who comes?
For the boisterous sea of tears heaves in the flood-tide of
pain.
The crimson clouds run wild in the wind, lashed by lightning,
and the thundering laughter of the Mad is over the sky.
Life sits in the chariot crowned by Death.
Bring out your tribute to him of all that you have.

Looking back now on that period, when humanity was suddenly torn in pieces by internecine war, it seems certain to me that the Poet's highly sensitive nature had made him feel dimly beforehand the tragedy which was about to happen. In no other way can I account for his intense mental suffering.

London, *August 16ᵗʰ, 1913*

I am so glad to know that you are now in Santiniketan. It is impossible to describe to you my longing to join you there.

The time has come at last when I must leave England; for I find that my work here in the West is getting the better of me. It is taking up too much of my attention and assuming more importance than it actually possesses. Therefore, I must, without delay, go back to that obscurity where all living seeds find their true soil for germination.

This morning, I am going to take a motor-ride to Rothenstein's country house, and if I delay any longer I may not have time to write to my other correspondents by this mail, so I must close this letter.

Calcutta, *October 11ᵗʰ, 1913*

I have gone through a period of difficulty. My life had appeared to me lonely and burdened with responsibilities too heavy for a single man to bear. Evidently, my mind has got into a habit of leaning too much upon my friends whom I had acquired in England, and letting most of its current flow outward. Therefore, coming to my own country, where the contact of humanity is not so close as in the West, I felt suddenly stranded and in a desolation, wherein every individual has to struggle through his own problem unaided. For some length of time, solitariness weighed upon my heart like a heavy load, till I gained my former mental adjustment and felt again the current turn inward from the world outside.

Now I feel the flood-tide of life and companionship. It sweeps the burden from off my shoulders and carries me along with it on its joyous course.

In India the range of our lives is narrow and discontinuous. This is the reason why our minds are often beset with provincialism. In our Asram at Santiniketan we must have the widest possible outlook for our boys, and universal human interests. This must come spontaneously—not merely through the reading of books, but through dealings with the wider world.

Santiniketan, *October 11th, 1913*

You must certainly rid your system of this malarial poison before you take up your regular work at Santiniketan.

Is it wholly impossible for you to come down here at once, and stay with us quietly and indulge in absolute rest for some time? Jagadananda had a very bad type of malaria before he joined his work here. His coming to Bolpur has been the saving of his life. Do give our Asram a trial. She will nurse you back to health. Your room shall be fitted with a desk and writing materials and other necessaries. You can start a little gardening in our school grounds and take occasional excursions into our *Sal* grove. Possibly, giving me a Greek lesson now and then will not fatigue you too much, if you feel so inclined.

Just now the singing mood is upon me, and I am turning out fresh songs everyday.

Santiniketan, *February 1914*

[*Written to meet me in England after
my return from South Africa*]

I send you my love and the translation of a song of mine written about two months ago. We are waiting for you, knowing that you are coming to us with your heart filled with the wisdom of death and the tender strength of sorrow. You know our best love was with you, while you were fighting our cause in South Africa along with Mr Gandhi and others.

My days of turmoil are not yet over. Indeed, I have not yet been able to settle down to my work and to my rest. Interruptions come almost daily to me in various forms. At last I have made up my mind to be rude, and to leave all invitations ignored and letters unanswered.

The mango blossoms have appeared in our Asram. The air is full of music, heard and unheard, and I do not know why we should be callous to the call of the seasons and foolishly behave as if the Spring and the Winter are the same to human beings, with the same round of works to follow, without having the option to be occasionally useless and absurd. However, I am in that mood when one forgets that he has any other obligations to meet than to be good for nothing and glad.

Santiniketan, *March 5th, 1914*

Lately I have been spending some days alone in the solitude of Shileida; for I needed it very greatly, and it has done me good. I feel that I must protect myself from all distractions for some time, so as to be able to add to my inner resources, never considering it a duty to force myself to work merely with the vain intention of doing good, but rather making the work I do living and real.

To try to benefit others, and yet not to have enough of oneself to give others, is a poor affair.

Santiniketan, *May 10th, 1914*

When are you coming to stay with me in the Hills? I am afraid, you are passing through a great deal of worry, and you are in need of a good rest. I won't let you work during this vacation. We must have no particular plans for our holidays. Let us agree to waste them utterly, until laziness proves to be a burden to us. Just for a month or so we can afford to be no longer useful members of society. The cultivation of usefulness produces an enormous amount of failure, simply because in our avidity we sow seeds too closely.

Ramgarh, *May 14th, 1914*

Here I feel that I have come to the place that I needed most in all the world. I hated to be disloyal to the plains of Bengal, where the earth lies so meek and unobtrusive, leaving the sky to the undisputed dominion of all the horizons. But happily the poet's heart is inconstant; it is easily won; and to-day I am already bending my knees to Father Himalaya asking pardon for keeping aloof for so long in blind distrust.

The hills all round seem to me like an emerald vessel brimming over with peace and sunshine. The solitude is like a flower spreading its petals of beauty and keeping its honey of wisdom at the core of its heart. My life is full. It is no longer broken and fragmentary.

Ramgarh, *May 15ᵗʰ, 1914*

At last I am supremely happy, not simply because the quiet of this place affords me the needful change from the worries of a crowded life, but because it supplies my mind with its natural food. Directly I come to a place like this, I can realize at once that I had been living before on half-rations.

I have found myself since I came here, and I am filled with the wonder that the infinite Power and Joy has become what I am and what this blade of grass is. When we are restless we raise dust all about us and we forget the supreme truth that "we are". I cannot tell you the great joy of seeing everything through the sight which comes from within.

Ramgarh, *May 17th, 1914*

To-day is my father's birthday anniversary. We have just had our morning prayer, and my mind is full. It is a stormy morning, dark and threatening, with an occasional burst of pallid light. It seems like the symbol of a spiritual new birth. I have been experiencing the feeling of a great expectation, although it has also its elements of very great suffering. To be born naked in the heart of the eternal Truth; to be able to feel with my entire being the life-throb of the universal heart—that is the cry of my soul. I tell you all this, so that you may understand what I am passing through and may help me when the occasion arrives.

Do take care of yourself and get well, so as to be fit to fight your own battle with renewed strength and hope.

Ramgarh, *May 21st, 1914*

I am struggling on my way through the wilderness. The light from across the summit is clear; but the shadows are slanting and deep on the slope of the dark valley. My feet are bleeding, and I am toiling with panting breath. Wearied, I lie down upon the dust and cry and call upon His name.

I know that I must pass through death. God knows, it is the death-pang that is tearing open my heart. It is hard to part with the old self. One does not know, until the time comes, how far it had spread its roots, and into what unexpected, unconscious depths it had sent its thirsty fibres draining out the precious juice of life.

But the Mother is relentless. She will tear out all the tangled untruths. We must not nourish in our being what is dead. For the dead is death-dealing. "Through death lead us to deathlessness." The toll of suffering has to be paid in full.

For we can never enter the realm of white light and pure love until all our debts are cleared and nothing binds us to the dead past. But I know my Mother is with me and before me.

Ramgarh, *May 22ⁿᵈ, 1914*

The spiritual bath is not that of water, but of fire. For the water merely takes away the dirt that is superficial, not the dead matter that clings to life, abusing its hospitality. So we must take our plunge into fire, time after time.

We shrink and tremble at the prospect; but the Mother assures us that it will never touch anything that is true and living.

The fire consumes the sin, but not the soul. Our soul is the last thing that we come to know; for it is dark where the Mother feeds the soul in secret. And we can see that sacred sight in the intense glow of the fire of suffering. Sometimes Death brings the torch to light it, and sometimes a messenger whose face is hidden from us.

The latter is at my door. I ask him questions. He answers not. But the fire is burning fiercely, exposing the hidden corners of my being with all their unsuspected accumulations of untruth and self-deception. Let the fire burn until it has nothing to feed upon. Let nothing be spared that awaits destruction.

Ramgarh, *May 23ʳᵈ, 1914*

Now I feel that I am emerging once again into the air and light and am breathing freely. It is an unspeakable relief to come out into the open and the normal, to regain the balance of life once more, to be able to take again my natural part in the open fair of the world.

Strenuousness is the open foe of attainment. The strength that wins is calm and has an exhaustless resource in its passive depth. Greed is sure to frustrate itself, even the greed after God.

I had been struggling, during these last few days, in a world where shadows held sway and right proportions were lost. The enemies with whom I was fighting were mostly phantoms. But this experience of the dark has had a great lesson for me. Untruth when spread thinly over a large area of life is hardly felt and seen. We live in truce with it. Now that I have had its vision, in all its concentrated ugliness, I am called upon to fight it every day of my life.

Ramgarh, *May 24th, 1914*

To-day I feel as sound as these mountain oaks, ready to store my share of light from the sky and joyfully try my strength with the storm when it comes. Again I feel that I must have all my interests alive, grow on all sides, and enter into various relations with the world, keeping my body and mind fully awake.

Harmony is difficult when one's own nature is complicated; when the strings in the *vina* are numerous and each one claims its right to be tuned.

But I know life is simple, however complex the organism may be; and everything goes to pieces when the living truth of the central simplicity is lost.

Ramgarh, *May 25th, 1914*

Morning is simple, though infinitely more varied than night; for it is open and luminous. Night tries to hide and suppress all problems of reality, making the tyranny of dreams absolute. Light bares the heart of truth; and whatever is unformed or struggling, dying or dead is revealed, not merely at the side but at the root of all that is growing in strength and grace.

We see all the contradictions, yet we feel the inner harmony; strife and struggle are everywhere, yet beauty is supreme. This makes Night, with its phantoms of false mystery of exaggeration, slink away in shame when Morning appears in her simple robe of white. Hope and joy come in her wake all the more triumphant, because not a single blade of grass or thorn is hidden. Morning has dawned upon me at last. My wrestlings with the shadows are over. My heart looks out upon the undulating field of life, chequered with the fruitful green and the pallor of the sandy waste, and feels that all is good. It is vast; it is free to all the horizons; and over it from end to end reigns the light of the sky.

Chapter II

The Period of the next few months was one of increased tension, followed later by a gradual recovery from the mental strain that had been oppressing the Poet for so long.

At the beginning of the European War this strain had become almost unbearable, owing both to the world tragedy of the war itself and the suffering of Belgium, which the Poet felt most acutely. He wrote and published simultaneously in India and England three poems which expressed the inner conflict going on in his own mind. The first of these was called *The Boatman,* and he told me, when he had written it, that the woman in the silent courtyard, "who sits in the dust and waits," represented Belgium. The most famous of the three poems was *The Trumpet*. The third poem was named *The Oarsmen*. Its outlook is beyond the war; for it reveals the daring venture of faith that would be needed by humanity if the old world with its dead things were to be left behind and the vast uncharted and tempestuous seas were to be essayed leading to a world that was new.

A fourth poem, which was not published then, but later, was given to me by the Poet towards the end of the year 1914. On Christmas Day that year he delivered in the Asram a very remarkable address to the students and teachers, speaking of

Christ, who was called the Prince of Peace, and how the name of Christ was being denied in Europe.

Santiniketan, *October* 4th, 1914

It seems as though I am coming out of the mist once more, and I am trying to throw off my shoulders the burden that has been oppressing me all these days. As my mind feels lighter, I hope I have rightly earned my freedom.

We have all come to Santiniketan from Surul; and this change has done me good. Dr Maitra has sent me a long letter about you. He thinks you will have to be very careful in future about your health, if you are not to get ill again.

Santiniketan, *October* 7*th*, 1914

My period of darkness is over once again. It has been a time of very great trial to me, and I believe it was absolutely necessary for my emancipation. I know that I am being lifted from the sphere where I was before; and it is the loneliness of the new situation and the cry of the old life that is still troubling me. But I have glimpses of the ineffable light of joy which I am sure will not fail me. Preaching I must give up, and also trying to take up the role of a beneficent angel to others. I am praying to be lighted from within, and not simply to hold a light in my hand.

Darjeeling, *June* 12*th*, 1914

Real love is always a wonder. We can never take it for granted. Your love for me I accept with joy and thankfulness, and wonder to which account to put it. Perhaps every man has some worth unknown to himself, inspiring love through the cover of his self. It gives one a hope that truth is more than appearance, and that we deserve more than we can claim with apparent reason. Love is for the unlimited in us, not for the one who is loudly evident.

Some say that we idealize him we love; but the fact is that we realize through love the ideal in him—and the ideal is the real, if we know it. We have the eternal contradiction in us, that our worth unfolds itself through our unworthiness, and love can go beyond the process, overtaking the ultimate truth. We could never be certain that we are more in truth than we are in fact, if we were not loved.

Give my love to Mr Rudra. Tell him I am hopelessly lost in the wilderness of correspondence, distributing thanks to all quarters of the globe, till not an atom of gratitude is left in my nature.

Calcutta, November 12th, 1914

I know these school financial difficulties are good for us, but I must have strength enough to extract the good. We must have faith in the Truth. But this faith must be active and self-respecting. The whole Asram must rouse itself from its passive inanity and be ready to meet the danger, never expecting help from outside, but using all its wisdom, self-restraint and resourcefulness.

Our school is a living body. The smallest of us must feel that all its problems are his own; that we must give, in order to gain. Even the little boys should not be kept entirely ignorant of our difficulties. They should be made proud of the fact that they also bear their own share of the responsibility.

Calcutta, November 15th, 1914

Critics and detectives are naturally suspicious. They scent allegories and bombs where there are no such abominations. It is difficult to convince them of our innocence.

With regard to the criticism of my play, *The King of the Dark Chamber*, that you mention in your letter, the human soul has its inner drama, which is just the same as anything else that concerns Man, and Sudarshana is not more an abstraction than Lady Macbeth, who might be described as an allegory representing the criminal ambition in man's nature. However, it does not matter what things are, according to the rules of the critics. They are what they are, and therefore difficult of classification.

Ramgarh is said to be not unfavourable for wintering; and this it is that has induced me to try to go there for quiet during the next few months till it becomes decently warm and comfortable. But it is a secret of mine, and you must not let it out. Whatever may happen, I must remain beyond the reach of correspondence. I need to be entirely alone. By going to an inaccessible region, I shall escape anniversary meetings, addresses and conferences, and other evils that the flesh is *not* heir to, but which, all the same, fasten upon it without ceremony. It is wicked of me to be away when you are returning to the Asram after your illness; but I feel that you will have a better opportunity of coming closer to the boys and teachers if I am not there, and that will compensate you for my absence.

Agra, *December 5th, 1914*

I was surprised to read in the *Modern Review* that our Bolpur boys are going without their sugar and ghee in order to open a relief fund. Do you think this is right? In the first place, it is an imitation of your English schoolboys and not their own original idea. In the second place, so long as the boys live in our institution they are not free to give up any portion of their diet which is absolutely necessary for their health. For any English boy, who takes meat and an amount of fat with it, giving up sugar is not injurious. But for our boys in Santiniketan, who can get milk only in small quantities, and whose vegetable meals contain very little fat ingredients, it is mischievous.

Our boys have no right to choose this form of self-sacrifice—just as they are not free to give up buying books for their studies. The best form of self-sacrifice for them would be to do some hard work in order to earn money; let them take up menial work in our school—wash dishes, draw water, dig wells, fill up the tank which is a menace to their health, do the building work. This would be good in both ways. What is more, it would be a real test of their sincerity. Let the boys think out for themselves what particular works they are willing to take up without trying to imitate others.

Allahabad, *December 18th, 1914*

I feel happy to imagine you lost in the sunny blue and the silent green of our Asram, and I am glad that we have had our talk together before you left. I know from my own experience that our Asram will give you the peaceful detachment of mind needed so much for bringing oneself face to face with one's own inner being and the deeper reality of the world.

You must have recognized by this time that I have something elusive in me, which eludes myself no less than others. Because of this element in my nature, I have to keep my environments free and open, fully to make room in my life for the Undreamt-of who is expected every moment. Believe me, I have a strong human sympathy, yet I can never enter into such relations with others as may impede the current of my life, which flows through the darkness of solitude beyond my ken. I can love, but I have not that which is termed by phrenologists "adhesiveness"; or to be more accurate, I have a force acting in me, jealous of all attachments, a force that ever tries to win me for itself, for its own hidden purpose.

If this purpose were only moral, it could be more easily tolerated—nay, welcomed; but it is life-purpose—the purpose of growth—and for this very reason it meets with a certain amount of opposition when it crosses with other life-currents. It may seem to be egoistic. But this life-impulse I speak of belongs to a personality which is beyond my ego. I must own this Master in me, who is not a mere abstract moral ideal, but a Person. I must be true to it, even at the cost of what men call happiness, at the risk of being misunderstood, forsaken and hated. I am sociable by nature, and would intensely like to enjoy the company of friends, the pleasures and advantages of friendship. But I am not free to give myself away, even when it seems necessary and good; and the somewhat wide expanse of time and space that I always try to keep in reserve about me is not mine to use as I wish. This loneliness often becomes hard for me to bear, but I have my ample compensation; and I dare say it will bear fruit for those who know what to expect from it.

The human soul is God's flower. It gives its best bloom and scent, not when shut up in eager palms to be squeezed, but when left alone in the immense freedom of light and air. But, very unfortunately,

> The World is too much with us; late and soon
> Getting and spending, we lay waste our powers;
> Little we see in Nature that is ours;
> We have given our hearts away, a sordid boon!

My love is bare and reticent. It was gaudily covered in its youthful flowering season; bulging with gifts in its fruitful maturity; but now that its seed-time has come, it has burst its shell and is abroad in the air; it has thrown away all the extra burden of allurements, carrying in its minute covering the density of its life. So when you come and shake the bough for it, it will not answer; for it is not there. But if you can believe in its silence, and accept it in silence, you will not be disappointed.

The following is the translation of the Bengali poem given to me by the Poet at Christmas, 1914:

Judgement

When, mad in their mirth, they raised dust to soil thy robe, O Beautiful, it made my heart sick.

I cried to thee and said: "Take thy rod of punishment and judge them."

The morning light struck upon those eyes, red with the revel of the night; the place of the white lily greeted their burning breath; the stars through the depth of the sacred dark stared at their carousing—at those that raised dust to soil thy robe, O Beautiful!

Thy judgement-seat was in the flower garden; in the birds' notes in springtime; in the shady river banks, where the trees muttered in answer to the muttering of the wave.

O my Lover, they were pitiless in their passion.

They prowled in the dark to snatch thy ornaments to deck their own desires.

When they had struck thee and thou wert pained, it pierced me to the quick, and I cried to thee and said:

"Take thy sword, O my Lover, and judge them!"

Ah, but thy justice was vigilant.

A mother's tears were shed on their insolence; the imperishable faith of a lover hid their spears of rebellion in its own wounds.

Thy judgement was in the mute pain of sleepless love; in the blush of the chaste; in the tears of the night of the desolate; in the pale morning light of forgiveness.

O Terrible, they in their reckless greed climbed thy gate at night, breaking into thy storehouse to rob thee.

But the weight of their plunder grew immense, too heavy to carry or to remove.

Thereupon I cried to thee and said: "Forgive them, O Terrible!"

Thy forgiveness burst in storms, throwing them down, scattering their thefts in the dust.

Thy forgiveness was in the thunderstone, in the shower of blood; in the angry red of the sunset.

Calcutta, January 20ᵗʰ, 1915

I could feel from your last letters, hastily written, that you were depressed. Your mind is still in that region of phantoms where shadows are exaggerated and the least thing makes one unhappy. I find that your very happiness is a strain to you— it is so jerky and violent—because very often it comes to you in the shape of reaction. It makes me feel far more anxious about you than your bad health.

Calcutta, January 29ᵗʰ, 1915

I don't like to frighten you with news of my ill-health, but it must be given to justify my absence from the Asram. I feel that I am on the brink of a breakdown. Therefore I must take flight to the solitude of the Padma. I need rest and the nursing of Nature.

If you ever have a relapse of your illness, do not despair. Try not to fret, or to strain, but to give yourself up to sleep. We must not force ourselves to be too conscious, even of God—our spirit cannot bear it. Depression comes very often from repletion. Our subconscious nature must have sufficient time to store up what our conscious nature requires.

Calcutta, *January 31ˢᵗ, 1915*

I hear that you are really ill. This won't do. Come to Calcutta. Consult some doctor; and if he recommends, come to Shileida, where I am going tomorrow morning. I dare not go to Bolpur. I have reached such a sublime depth of tiredness, that it has conferred a dignity on my selfish isolation; and I don't feel the least ashamed of my flight from all responsibilities. I must be alone, with all my heart and soul.

But you must not delay. We are very anxious about you, and we cannot let you breakdown completely.

Shileida, *February 1ˢᵗ, 1915*

You are right. I had been suffering from a time of deep depression and weariness. But I am sane and sound again, and willing to live another hundred years, if critics would spare me. At that time I was physically tired; therefore the least hurt assumed a proportion that was perfectly absurd. However, I am glad that there is still the child in me, who has its weakness for the sweets of human approbation. I must not feel myself too far above my critics. I don't want my seat on the dais; let me sit on the same bench with my own audience and try to listen as they do. I am quite willing to know the healthy feeling of disappointment when they don't approve of my things; and when I say 'I don't care!' let nobody believe me.

A great proportion of our humankind is inarticulate. I find I have quite a number of friends among them, and that I need not put any bounds to my estimation of their partiality towards my writings; so that though they do not confirm, neither do they contradict.

I am living in a boat here in a lovely spot. Mukul, Nandalal and another artist are my companions. Their enthusiasm of enjoyment adds to my joy. Every little thing brings to them a sense of surprise, and thus their fresh minds come to my service, bringing to my notice things that I have been getting into the habit of ignoring.

Shileida, February 3rd, 1915

Directly I reached here I came to myself, and am now healed. The cure for all the illness of life is stored in the inner depth of life itself, the access to which becomes possible when we are alone. This solitude is a world in itself full of wonders and resources unthought of. It is so absurdly near, yet so unapproachably distant. But I do not want to talk, please forgive my absence and my silence. I cannot afford to scatter my mind just now.

I do so earnestly hope that you are better.

Calcutta, February 18th, 1915

Calcutta will keep me till Sunday. I do not expect to free myself from its clutches before then, though I shall try. Anyhow, Monday will see me in Bolpur, somewhat feeble and worn-out, unfit to be trusted with any responsibility.

I hope that Mahatma and Mrs Gandhi have arrived in Bolpur, and Santiniketan has accorded them such a welcome as befits her and them. I shall convey my love personally to them when we meet.

I am glad that our Asram has given shelter to the persecuted Rajput boy. Let him feel that he has won a home in Santiniketan by being driven from his own place and by his own people.

Chapter III

In the middle of the month of May 1915, after repeated illnesses from which I had hardly recovered, an attack of Asiatic cholera came suddenly upon me, which proved very nearly fatal. The Poet himself helped to nurse me, and his care and affection were full of the most sensitive tenderness and sympathy. On my account, he did not go away for a holiday during the worst of the hot weather. He waited near at hand, while I was slowly recovering in a nursing home in Calcutta. At last, when I was able to be moved to Simla, as a convalescent, his letters began again.

During this year 1915 we were so completely outside the range and area of the war, in our isolation in India itself, that its horrors gradually tended to recede into the background of our minds; but the greater thoughts which had been awakened so painfully during the previous year, owing to the war itself—such as the problem of human suffering; the possibility of complete human brotherhood; the meeting of East and West in common fellowship—these were more present than ever before. Our talks together, while I was in the nursing-home in Calcutta, were continually about these problems. They remained deep in the subconscious mind of the Poet all through this year. At the same time, the whole burden of the school work at Santiniketan fell upon his shoulders and he threw himself into every detail of it with his own characteristic energy and determination.

Through the summer of 1915 the Poet's plans were maturing for a visit to the Far East. His father, Maharshi Debendranath Tagore, had made his Far Eastern journey more than half a century before, and it had formed one of the means by which he had realized so deeply in his own life the universal brotherhood of man. To the Poet, whose thoughts were always in the terms of Humanity rather than in those of any lesser unit, the fratricidal war in the West revealed the dangerously unbalanced condition of the human race. Out of the agony from which he had suffered in the previous year, both before and after the war had begun, the determination had been ever growing in his own mind to enlarge the bounds of this Asram at Santiniketan, which his father, the Maharshi, had founded as a home of religion. He looked more and more to the time when his Asram would pass beyond the school stage and become a centre of world fellowship, wherein students and teachers from the East and West should be equally honoured and welcomed.

These thoughts were brooding in his mind during the year 1915; therefore it became clear to him that a visit to the Far East, in order to win the friendship and co-operation of the leading thinkers of China and Japan, would be necessary if the cycle of his work at Santiniketan was to be completed. He had very nearly made up his mind to start in August, and had actually taken his passage on a Japanese steamer, when a series of circumstances intervened which made the journey impossible.

After these plans for a voyage to the Far East had been entirely abandoned, a sudden crisis arose in India itself with regard to a humanitarian struggle against the indentured system of Indian labour in the colonies. My friend W.W. Pearson and I had fully investigated and condemned this system in Natal, and we were, therefore, more immediately in touch with the direct problem than other people. The immoral and servile conditions of indentured Indian labour had to be thoroughly exposed. For this reason, after the tour to the Far East had been abandoned, we received the Poet's cordial consent, when we proposed to go out together to Fiji and carry through an independent inquiry into the indenture system of Indian labour in that colony. He felt very keenly, indeed, that this new journey of ours would be in keeping with his own ideals of universal brotherhood and fellowship, and he gave us his blessing on our departure. Two texts from the Upanishad were his own gift to me when we bade him farewell.

They may be translated as follows:

From Joy all things have their origin: in Joy they subsist, and unto Joy they return.
    I meditate upon His glory, who creates the earth, the sky and the stars, and sends into our minds the power of comprehension.

The inspiration which Rabindranath Tagore thus gave to us, by his encouragement and sympathy, carried us through what proved to be the most difficult journey we had ever undertaken. In the end, the inquiry we made very nearly effected its object; and the pledge was given that the whole indenture system of Indian labour would be abolished at the earliest possible moment.

Santiniketan, *June 30ᵗʰ, 1915*

Just now I am in Santiniketan. It still has the holiday atmosphere; for only a few boys have come back, and it is not unlikely that some of them have left for good. So our Finance Minister will have a hard time before him with arrears to clear off and the buildings to complete. Do not try to come now, however strong you may feel—for financial difficulties are just as bad as disease germs in their insidious attacks on our health. However, be assured that this bad time will not be thrown away on us altogether, and we shall come out of it with more freedom than ever, if considerably thinner.

As for myself, I have the call of the open road, though most of the roads are closed. I am in a nomadic mood, but it is becoming painful to me for want of freedom. I am carrying, as it were, my tents on my back, instead of living in them.

Possibly, my life is on the eve of another bursting of its pods and scattering of its seeds; there is that continual urgency in my blood, the purpose of which is hidden. The conclusion is being forced upon me that poets should never bind themselves to any particular work; for they are the instruments of the world's moods. And after the years of building up all kinds of benevolent schemes, my life is emerging once again upon the open health of irresponsibility, where the sun rises and sets, where there are wild flowers, but no committee meetings.

Calcutta, *July 7ᵗʰ, 1915*

Haven't I confessed elsewhere that renunciation is not for me, and that my freedom is to be moving from bondage to bondage? My mind must realize itself anew. Once I give form to my thought, I must free myself from it. For the time being, it seems to me that I want absolute freedom to create new forms for new ideas. I am sure physical death has the same meaning for us—the creative impulse of our soul must have new forms for its realization. Death can continue to dwell in the same sepulchre, but life must unceasingly outgrow its dwelling-place; otherwise the form gets the upper hand and becomes a prison. Man is immortal; therefore he must die endlessly. For life is a creative idea; it can only find itself in changing forms.

Forms are stupid dumb things, that struggle to stand still, until at last they break into pieces.

You will have heard about all my plans from Pearson. I am seeking my freedom by surrendering my ideas into the hands of a new bondage. In Santiniketan, some of my thoughts have become clogged by accumulations of dead matter. I do not believe in lecturing, or in compelling fellow-workers by coercion; for all true ideas must work themselves out through freedom. Only a moral tyrant can think that he has the dreadful power to make his thoughts prevail by means of subjection. It is absurd to imagine that you must create slaves in order to make your ideas free. I would rather see them perish than leave them in the charge of slaves to be nourished. There are men who make idols of their ideas, and sacrifice humanity before their altars. But in my worship of the idea I am not a worshipper of Kali.

So the only course left open to me, when my fellow-workers fall in love with the form and cease to have complete faith in the idea, is to go away and give my idea a new birth and create new possibilities for it. This may not be a practical method, but possibly it is the right one.

Calcutta, *July 11th, 1915*

Conscientious men are comfortable men; they live within the bounds of their duties, and consequently enjoy their fixed proportion of leisure. But I shirk my duties in order to create works that eat up all my time; and then I suddenly leave my work and try to elope with unmitigated indolence.

I shall be floating on the Padma before the next week is out, and shall forget to imagine that my presence in the Council of Creation is imperatively necessary for the betterment of Humanity. I am a born nomad—as I am sure you are—and my work has to be fluid, if it is to be my work. But absolute fluidity in work can only be had at its commencement.

Therefore, my duty is to start things and then leave them. Unless I leave them and keep at a distance, I cannot help them in maintaining their ideal character. But, this time, it is the fatigue of my body and mind that is driving me into solitude. The kind of work that I can do in a particular scheme requires freshness of mind more than perseverance. Therefore, there must be a break before I resume my duties.

It is easy for me to understand the stress of pain that you are feeling now about the wrongs of the world, and especially among the weaker races of mankind, who are oppressed by the strong. Human wrongs are not pitiable, they are terrible. Those who are in power forget every day that it is for their very power's sake that they have to be just. When God's appeal comes from the weak and the poor, then it is full of danger for those who are in power; for then they are apt to think that they can disregard it with impunity, especially if it upsets their office arrangements in the very least degree. They have more faith in their pitiful system and their prestige than in moral providence.

In India, when the upper classes ruled over the lower, they forged their own chains. Europe is closely following Brahmin India, when she looks upon Asia and Africa as her legitimate fields for exploitation. The problem would be simpler if she could altogether denude other continents of their population; but so long as there are alien races, it will be difficult for Europe to realize her moral responsibility with regard to them. The gravest danger is when Europe deceives herself into thinking that she is helping the cause of humanity by helping herself; that men are essentially different, and what is good for her people is not good for others who are inferior. Thus Europe, gradually and imperceptibly, is losing faith in her own ideals and weakening her own moral supports.

But I must not go on weaving truisms; and on our own side I must equally acknowledge this truth, that weakness is heinous because it is a menace to the strong and the surest cause of downfall for others than those who own it. It is a moral duty for every race to cultivate strength, so as to be able to help the world's balance of power to remain even. We are doing England the greatest disservice possible by making it easy for her to despise us and yet to rule; to feel very little sympathy for us and yet to judge us.

Will Europe never understand the genesis of the present war, and realize that the true cause lies in her own growing scepticism towards her own ideals—those ideals that have helped her to be great? She seems to have exhausted the oil that once lighted her lamp. Now she is feeling a distrust against the oil itself, as if it were not at all necessary for her light.

Shileida, July 16th, 1915

I wonder whether you got my last letter, which I wrote to you in a railway train, informing you of my proposed visit to Japan.

I am busy floating my dreams, as the children do their paper boats, on this wide expanse of green, gold and blue. This world is wonderfully beautiful, but you cannot help feeling that there is a lurking pain in its heart, which has its own immortal beauty. It is a pearl shell of wonderful tints and design, hiding in its bosom a teardrop, which gives it priceless value. All our payments have to be made in pain; otherwise life and this world would become cheap as dirt.

Shileida, July 23rd, 1915

After long years I have come among my tenants; and I feel, and they also, that my presence was needed. It was a great event of my life when I first dwelt among my own people here, for thus I came into contact with the reality of life. For in them you feel the barest touch of humanity. Your attention is not diverted, and then you truly know that Man is very much to man. One is apt to forget them, just as one does not think of the earth on which one walks. But these men compose the great mass of life, which sustains all civilizations and bears their burdens. They are content barely to live, so that others may prove that man's life is a great deal more than mere existence. They keep steady the level of the minimum, which is enormous quantitatively, so that the maximum may be unhampered by its own development. Thousands of acres of land are tilled, so that a University can be maintained upon one acre. Yet these men are insulted merely because while they are so absolutely necessary, it is their necessity to live that drives them to this position. They are in their place because they cannot help it.

We all hope that here, at this very point, Science in the end will help man. She will make the necessities of life easily accessible to every man, so that humanity will be freed from the tyranny of matter which now humiliates her. This struggling mass of men is great in its pathos, in its latency of infinite power. It is beautiful where it is simple and spontaneous; sublime where it is large, deep and enduring. I must confess that I have been neglecting these people, while I was away from them in Santiniketan; and I am glad that I am now with them once more, so that I may be more actively mindful of them. I am afraid my life at the Asram was at last making me into a teacher, which was unsatisfactory for me, because unnatural. But one has to be a helper to be a real man; for then you share your life with your fellow-beings and not merely your ideas.

Calcutta, *July* 29*th*, *1915*

The Infinite Being is not complete if He remains absolutely infinite. He must realize Himself through the finite; that is, through creation. The impulse to realize comes from the fullness of joy; but the process must be through pain. You cannot ask why it should be—why the Infinite should attain truth by passing through the finitude; why the joy should be the cause of suffering, in order to come back to itself—for it is so. And when our minds are illumined, we feel glad that it is so.

When we fix all our attention to that side of the Infinite where it is pain and death, where it is the process of fulfilment, we are overwhelmed. But we must know that there is the positive side; that always there is a completeness along with the incomplete. Otherwise, there would be no pity in us for the suffering; no love in us for the imperfect.

What I am trying to express is this: you saw the monkey dead entangled in the telegraph-wires, while round it was beauty in all its superbness. The incongruity struck you as cruel. That is something. The cruelty would not have been apparent to you if ugliness were absolute. You felt the pity of it, because there is the ideal of perfection. Here, in this ideal, lies our hope and the ultimate solution of our doubts. In creation, joy is always getting the better of pain, otherwise our sympathy for pain would be unmeaning.

Then why should we despair? We cannot fathom the mystery of existence. But this much we have known, that there is a love which is greater in truth than pain and death. Is not that sufficient for us?

Santiniketan, *August 7th, 1915*

Your letter was of great interest to me. I have one principle to guide my thoughts in most things of vital importance. It is this, that the figure which represents creation is not "one," but "two." In the harmony of two contradictory forces everything rests. Whenever our logic tries to simplify things, by reducing the troublesome "two" into "one," it goes wrong. Some philosophies say that motion is all *maya* and truth is static; others are of the opinion that truth is fluid and it is only *maya* that represents truth to us as static.

But truth is beyond logic; it is the everlasting miracle; it is static and dynamic at the same time; it is ideal and real; it is finite and infinite.

The principle of war and that of peace both make truth. They are contradictory; they seem to hurt each other, like the finger and the strings; but this very contradiction produces music. When only one predominates, there is the sterility of silence. Our problem is not only whether we should have war or peace, but how to harmonize them perfectly.

So long as there is such a thing as force, we cannot say that we must not use force, but rather that we must not abuse it, as we are prone to do when we make it the sole standard and ignore love. When love and force do not go together, then love is mere weakness and force is brutal. Peace becomes death when it is alone. War becomes a demon when it destroys its mate.

Of course, we must not think for a moment that killing one another is a necessary form of war. Man is pre-eminently on a moral plane, and his weapons should be moral weapons.

Santiniketan, *September 23rd, 1915*

[*Written on the eve of our departure to Fiji*]

The golden bell of the autumn sun tolls silently and the period for migration has come. You and Pearson are the first of our brood who have left their nest for the passage across the seas; and I can hardly control my wings. Things round us have their weight, and they gradually sink into our soul without our knowing it, till one day we are oppressed with a burden whose nature we hardly know. Movement is the only cure when life becomes heavy with *débris*.

My heart at this moment is like a leaky boat, full of water, that can just keep itself afloat, but the least burden of responsibility becomes too much for it. I must go to the wilderness and take upon myself the severe discipline of freedom. I want to say "No" emphatically to all the importunities of the world; to all the moral and social obligations. But in spite of my protestations, I am afraid that I shall have to end my days as an ascetic—with certain modifications.

I am going on with the rehearsal, and rather like it. For it gives me opportunity to come close to the little boys, who are a perpetual source of pleasure to me.

Chapter IV

After our return from Fiji, at the end of January 1916, the longings of the Poet to go out to the Far East became insistent. He took W.W. Pearson, Mukul Dey the artist and myself with him on this voyage. We sailed from Calcutta on the *Tosa Maru*. In the Bay of Bengal our vessel passed through a terrible cyclone and had great difficulty in weathering the storm. Our stay in China was very short, because the people of Japan were impatiently waiting for the Poet's arrival in their own country. They received him with enthusiasm at first, as one who had brought honour to Asia.

But when he spoke out strongly against the militant imperialism which he saw on every side in Japan and set forward in contrast to his own ideal picture of the true meeting of East and West, with its vista of world brotherhood, the hint went abroad that such "pacifist" teaching was a danger in war-time, and that the Indian Poet represented a defeated nation. Therefore, almost as rapidly as the enthusiasm had arisen, it subsided. In the end, he was almost isolated, and the object for which he had come to the Far East remained unfulfilled. It was at this time that he wrote his poem called *The Song of the Defeated*, which begins:

> My Master bids me, while I stand at the wayside, to sing
> the song of defeat.
> For that is the bride whom He woos in secret.

These summer months in Japan, at a time when the fever of militarism was at its height, were filled with disappointment. The mental suffering which had appeared at the beginning of the war returned. The Poet's whole inner nature was in revolt against the violently aggressive spirit of the age. All this is brought out in his book called *Nationalism*, the first chapters of which were written in Japan at a white heat. These lectures, delivered in Japan, were reprinted in Europe. They were translated into French in Switzerland by Romain Rolland towards the end of the year 1916. It needs to be added that at a later visit to Japan, in 1924, these earlier impressions, formed in war-time, were considerably modified. He found then in Japan, as also in China, those who were eager to appreciate his universal message.

The Poet went from Japan to America, accompanied by W.W. Pearson and Mukul Dey, while I returned to the Asram. His stay in America was crowded with engagements. He made new friends and received great kindness at their hands. In many ways he was satisfied with his visit, and felt that it had been a success. But he fell ill there, and after a short time came back home by way of the Pacific, only staying between steamers in Japan and China.

Shortly after his arrival at the Asram it became necessary for me to go out again to Fiji, in order to obtain the final and complete abolition of the indenture system of Indian labour. The years 1917 and 1918 were fully taken up by the Poet with quiet fruitful work at Santiniketan. All the while, his plans for widening the scope and aim of his educational enterprise, after the war was over, were slowly shaping themselves in his mind. These will come forward as the main subject in the succeeding chapters in this book; for they began to absorb his whole attention.

After returning from Fiji, early in the year 1918, I was free to remain at the Asram. Since I was constantly with the Poet from that time onwards, I received no letters from him, but some which he sent to W.W. Pearson in England may serve to keep in touch with his thoughts up to the close of this period.

Srinagar, Kashmir, October 12th, 1915

I am technically in Kashmir, but still have not entered its gate. I am passing through the purgatory of public receptions and friendly solicitations; but Paradise is in sight. Now I feel I am coming nearer myself; the intruder in me, who always fusses about arranging and dusting his absurd store of knicknacks, is, I hope, shut out at least for a few weeks. It is becoming easier for me to feel that it is I who bloom in flowers, spread in the grass, flow in the water, scintillate in the stars, live in the lives of men of all ages.

When I sit in the morning outside on the deck of my boat, before the majestic purple of the mountains, crowned with the morning light, I know that I am eternal, that I am *ananda-rupam*.[1] My true form is not that of flesh or blood, but of joy. In the world where we habitually live, the self is so predominant that everything in it is of our own making and we starve because we have to feed upon ourselves. To know truth is to become true; there is no other way. When we live the life of self, it is not possible for us to realize truth.

"Come out, come away." This is the urgent cry we have in our soul—the cry in the blood of the chick, living in its shell. It is not merely truth that frees us, but freedom that gives us truth. That is why Buddha dwelt on the importance of freeing our lives from trammels of self; for then Truth comes of itself.

---

1. Literally, "Joy-Form". This is a part of a famous Sanskrit text.

Now I understand at last that the restlessness that has been so persistent with me is of this nature—I must come out from the life of habit, the life of compromise, the life of self. I think the first step towards it is going to the solitude.

My coming to Kashmir has helped me to know clearly what I want. It is likely that it will become obscured again when I go back to my usual routine; but these occasional detachments of life from the usual round of customary thoughts and occupations lead to the final freedom—the Santam, Sivam, Advaitam. The first stage towards freedom is the Santam, the true peace, which can be attained by subduing self; the next stage is the Sivam, the true goodness, which is the activity of the soul when self is subdued; and then the Advaitam, the love, the oneness with all and with God.

Of course this division is merely logical; these stages, like rays of light, may be simultaneous or divided according to the circumstances, and their order may be altered, such as the Sivam leading the Santam. But all we must know is that the Santam, Sivam, Advaitam, is the only goal for which we live and struggle.

Shileida, *February 3rd, 1916*

Coming away from Calcutta, I have come to myself. Every time it is a new discovery to me. In the town, life is so crowded that one loses the true perspective. After a while it makes me feel weary of everything, simply because the truth of our own self is lost sight of. We have our Lover waiting in the depth of our being. Unless we come to him, time after time, the tyranny of things grows intolerable. We must know that our greatest resource of all is lying hidden in our heart. We have to be assured of it in order to be cured of our miserliness.

Shileida, *February 5ᵗʰ, 1916*

You know the English translation of my poem about "taking truth simply." Last night, while reading it in *The Gardener* along with others, it seemed to me strangely incongruous in its semi-metrical form. It was like meeting a woman dressed in tights in the midst of others dressed in simple *saris*. So I tried to divest it of its metrical disguise, though it is difficult to exorcise altogether the ghost of the old metre.

Whatever may come, my heart, take truth simply,

Though there be some who can love you, there must be others who never can, and if you must know the cause, it is as much in you as in them, and in all things around.

Some doors are closed against your knocks, while your doors are not open always and to all comers.

Such has been and shall be for evermore; and yet if you must have peace, my heart, take truth simply.

There is no need to be abusive if your boat founders by the shore, though it sailed through the storm.

Keep yourself afloat by all means; but if it is impossible to do so, then be good enough to sink without noise.

It is a commonplace fact that things may or may not fit you and events happen without asking for your leave.

Yet if you must have peace, my heart, take truth simply.

You press and are pressed hard in the crowd, but space there is enough and to spare in this world.

When you have counted your losses to the last farthing, your sky remains as blue as ever.

You find, when suddenly tested, that to live is sweeter than to die.

You may miss this and that and the other thing, but if you must have peace, my heart, take truth simply.

Must you stand with your back to the rising sun and watch your shadow lengthened before you?

Must you take pleasure in finding fault with your destiny and thus tease your soul to death?

Then for mercy's sake be quick and have done with it; for if, with the evening stars, you must light your lamp, my heart, take truth simply.

Shileida, *February 24th, 1916*

Where are you? Seven fathoms deep in your report-writing? When are you going to float up into the sun and sail on, dancing with all surface-drifts of existence?

I have my work here, but it is play as well. It does not savour of office and officials; it has its humour and some amount of pathos. It is almost like painting a picture.

Pearson has succeeded in getting ill and joining me on my trip.

Santiniketan, *July 9th, 1917*

This is the first time that you have given me your address in your letter since your departure for Fiji. We have been feeling very anxious since we learnt about your accident and injury to your back and leg.

The boys have begun their agriculture in right earnest under the leadership of Santosh Mitra and, I believe it is not going to be like the road—the brilliant work of Nepal Babu—which suddenly stops, with a sublime futility, at the brink of Nowhere. The artist Surendranath Kar has joined our school, and his presence is very much appreciated by the boys and the teachers. Our former student and a veteran of Calcutta football fields, Gora, has taken up the work of a mathematical teacher, and I am sure he will prove to be a valuable acquisition to us.

The rainy season this year, like a great many of our boys, did not wait until the vacation was over, but made its appearance before the time and has been very seriously attending to its business ever since. I have taken my seat of indolence at the window of my second storey—in the middle region between the extravagant pageantry of the clouds and the immense spread of the exuberant green of the earth. There was a time when my life seemed to be an overflow of spendthriftness in a reckless Universe, before Purposefulness crept into the Eden Garden of my youth and changed the naked felicity of existence into the draped decency of a fashionable cut. I am waiting to regain that Lost Paradise of mind, to forget that I must be of any use of anybody, and to know that the true purpose of my life is the great purpose in me of All-time and All-world, urging me to be fully what I am.

And am I not a poet? What business have I to be anything else? But unfortunately I am like an inn, where the poet lodger has to accommodate strange bedfellows by his side. Yet is it not high time for me to retire from this none-too-lucrative business of the innkeeper? Anyway, I am feeling tired, and my duty to my numerous lodgers is in imminent danger of being shamefully neglected.

Shileida, *July 20th, 1917*

The accompanying letter is from Pearson. I am glad that he has come out of his seclusion feeling better in mind and body.

After a separation of nearly a year and a half, I have come once more to my Padma and have renewed my courtship. She is unchanged in her changeableness. She is shifting her course and leaving the side of Shileida. She is showing a decided preference for Pabna. My only consolation is that she cannot remain constant for long.

It is a beautiful day to-day. The sunshine is coming out after the fitful showers of rain, like a boy emerging from his

dive in the sea with his naked limbs glowing and glistening.
[*The letters that follow were written to W.W. Pearson.*]

Calcutta, *March 6ᵗʰ, 1918*

Each one of us in this unfortunate country is looked upon
with suspicion, and our British rulers cannot see us clearly
through the dust which they themselves raise. Humiliation
follows us at every step and in each good work we try to do.
All blind methods are easy methods at the beginning. But
such cheap methods as these do not pay in the end. For, after
all, mere bullying is stupidity; it assumes frightfulness only
because it does not know its way. What is radically wrong
with our rulers is this: they are fully aware that they do not
know us, and yet: they do not *care* to know us. And, in
consequence, thorny hedges are springing up of unscrupulous
intermediaries between the rulers and the ruled, giving rise
to conditions which are not only miserable, but unspeakably
vulgar.

I have just received a letter from Thadani, complaining
of the insults and harassment which only Indian British subjects
have to go through in British ports. These have the effect of
making them feel ashamed of the Government under which
they live. Such invidious treatment is sinking deeply into the
memory of my people, and the moral providence of history
cannot altogether ignore such an accumulated burden of
indignities loaded upon humanity.

Santiniketan, *March 10ᵗʰ, 1918*

I can guess from your letter that some questions are
troubling your mind about the best way of self-realization.
There can be no single path for all individuals; for we vastly
differ in our natures and habits. But all great masters agree
in their teaching on one cardinal point, saying that we must
forget our personal self in order to attain our spiritual freedom.

Buddha and Christ have both of them said that this self-abnegation is not something which is negative—its positive aspect is love.

We can only love that which is profoundly real to us. The larger number of men have the most intense feeling of reality only for themselves; and they can never get out of the limits of their self-love. The rest of mankind can be divided into two classes—those who have their love for persons and those who have their love for ideas.

Generally speaking, women fall into the first category and men into the second. In India this fact has been recognized. Therefore, our teachers have pointed out two different paths for the two different sexes.

It has been said that women can attain their emancipation by sublimating their personal relationships into the realm of the ideal. If, in spite of all obvious contradictions, a woman can realize in her husband something which transcends his personal limitations, then through her devotion to him she touches the Infinite and thus is freed from the bondage of self. Through the luminous intensity of her love, her husband and her child reveal to her the ultimate Truth which is divine. For biological reasons, men's natures have had comparative freedom from the attachment to persons, and therefore it has become easier for them to find direct access to those ideas, lying behind the screen of things, which they have ever been pursuing in all their knowledge and creative activities. Once you become conscious of the idea, as the inner spirit of reality, the joy becomes so unbounded that your self becomes obliterated, and you can easily lay aside all that you have for its sake.

But we must keep in mind that love of persons and love of ideas can both be terribly egoistic, and therefore may lead to bondage instead of setting us free.

It is only constant sacrifice in service which can loosen the shackles. We must not merely enjoy our love (whether personal or ideal) by contemplating its beauty and truth, but rather make it fruitful giving expression to it in our life's work. Our life is the material whereby we have to build the image of the ideal of Truth that we have in our mind. But life, like all other materials, contains an obstinate antagonism to the idea to which it must give shape. Only through the active process of creation can such antagonism be discovered at every step and chiselled away at every stroke.

Look at the aboriginal Santal women around our Asram. In them the ideal of physical life finds perfect development only because they are ever active in giving it expression in work. Their figures and their movements attain their beautiful harmony because they are always being tuned by life's activities. The one thing which I am never tired of admiring is the vigorous cleanliness of their limbs, which never get soiled even by the constant contact with dirt. Our ladies, with their soaps and scents, only give an artificial polish to the superficial body; but the cleanliness which is induced by the body's own current of movement, coming from the completeness of physical health, can never be theirs.

The same happens with regard to our spiritual body. It is not by meticulous care in avoiding all contaminations that we can keep our spirit clean and give it grace, but by urging it to give vigorous expression to its inner life in the very midst of all the dust and heat.

But I must stop to find out if I have given in what I have written any answer to the original question you have put to me. It may be that I have not; for it is difficult to know exactly what you want of me. You have spoken of impersonal love and impersonal work, and you ask me which I consider to be the greater. To me, they appear as one, like the sun and the light; for love's expression is in work. Where love has no work, there is a dead world.

Santiniketan, *October 6ᵗʰ, 1918*

All through this last session in the Asram, I have been taking school classes in the morning and spending the rest of the day in writing text-books. It is a kind of work apparently unsuitable for a man of my temperament. Yet I have found it not only interesting but restful. The mind has its own burden, which can be lightened when it is floated on a stream of work. Some engrossing ideas also help us in the same way. But ideas are unreliable; they run according to no time-table whatever; and the hours and days you spend in waiting for them grow heavy.

Lately I have come to that state of mind when I could not afford to wait for inspiration of ideas; so I surrendered myself to some work which was not capricious, but had its daily supply of coal to keep it running. However, this teaching was not a monotonous piece of drudgery for me; for I have been treating my students as living organisms; and any dealing with life can never be dull.

Unfortunately, poets cannot be expected to enjoy lucid intervals for long. Directly some new subject takes possession of their minds, they become useless for all decent purposes. They are intellectual gypsies; vagrancy is in their blood; and already I feel the call of the irresponsible vagabondage, a kind of passion for extravagant idleness. The schoolmaster in me is perilously near being lured away by the mischievous imps of truancy.

I am going to move away from this place in a day or two, with the ostensible reason of visiting South India, from where invitations have been pouring in upon me for a long time; but I tell you in confidence, it is the lapse of reason—my frequent visitor—the Spirit of Truancy, that is beckoning me, ready to escort me over all lines of proscribed works. I long to discover some fairy-land of holidays—not a lotus-land— not a world where all weekdays are Sundays—but where

Sundays are not at all needed, where all works carry their rest in themselves, where all duties look delightfully undutiful, like clouds bearing rain, appearing perfectly inconsequential.

Santiniketan, *December 11ᵗʰ, 1918*

Yesterday I had a letter from the University of Sydney asking me if it was true that I would not visit Australia, even if I was wanted there. I have written, in answer, that it would be wrong on my part if I refused to accept any invitation sent in the right spirit. Pride of patriotism is not for me. I earnestly hope that I shall find my home anywhere in the world, before I leave it. We have to fight against wrongs, and suffer for the cause of righteousness; but we should have no petty jealousies or quarrels with our neighbours merely because we have different names.

The barrier of Self is *maya*. When it is dispelled, then we in our suffering have tasted the draught of sorrow that wells up from the heart of creation, flowing out to be merged and transformed into the sea of endless joy.

When we do not see ourselves in the Infinite, when we imagine our sorrow to be our very own, then life becomes untrue and its burden becomes heavy. I understand more and more the truth of Buddha's teaching, that the root of all our miseries is this self-consciousness. We have to realize the consciousness of the All before we can solve the mystery of pain and be free.

Our emancipation lies through the path of suffering. We must unlock the gate of joy by the key of pain. Our heart is like a fountain. So long as it is driven through the narrow channel of self it is full of fear and doubt and sorrow; for then, it is dark and does not know its end. But when it comes out into the open, on the bosom of the All, then it glistens in the light and sings in the joy of freedom.

Chapter V

The letters that now remain to be quoted form an almost uninterrupted series, though I have continued to divide them into chapters. They were written by the Poet during a long tour, in Europe and America, in which he was accompanied by his friend W.W. Pearson.

Out of the misery and darkness of the Great War, Rabindranath Tagore had been led, step by step, to the one fixed purpose of gradually forming at Santiniketan Asram a home of brotherhood and peace, where East and West might meet in a common fellowship of study and work.

At first his design had been to gather together at his Asram the scattered religious cultures of Asia in order to present them in a united manner to the rest of the world. But his comprehensive vision could not stop at any horizon that was less wide than humanity. During the years 1918 and 1919, he took me with him on many tours, while he wandered up and down India, seeking to find a seed-ground in which his thoughts concerning human progress might take root in the soil and afterwards bear fruit. I was able to watch in these tours this one central purpose that I have mentioned taking concrete shape. He pictured to himself Santiniketan opening its doors to the whole world, and inviting those who were lovers of peace and goodwill, in East and West alike, to come together there, on equal terms, without distinction of caste or race or creed.

He named the institution which should offer such world-hospitality, Visva-bharati. "Visva" in Sanskrit means "world,"—in its universal aspect. "Bharati" is more difficult to translate, but implies knowledge, wisdom, culture. Visva-bharati was to be a House of Learning for all peoples and all religions.

The Poet traced back his whole conception to the Upanishads and had in his mind those forest Asrams, or religious retreats, of ancient India, which were freely open to all who came to them, and made their guests welcome with the fullness of fellowship and love. One of the most celebrated of his lectures was called "The Religion of the Forest." In a noble passage from another lecture he concludes with the following words:

> Our forefathers spread a single pure white carpet, whereon all the world was cordially invited to take its seat in amity and good-fellowship. No quarrel could have arisen there; for He in whose name the invitation went forth, for all time to come, was Santam, Sivam, Advaitam—the Peaceful, in the heart of all conflicts; the Good, who is revealed through all losses and sufferings; the One, in all diversities of creation. And in His name was this eternal truth declared in Ancient India:
>
> He alone sees truly who sees all beings as himself.

For the fulfilment of his central purpose it was necessary for him to go once more to Europe and America in order to gain the support of the West and invite the West to his Asram. But at the very time when he was beginning to prepare for his journey, certain disturbances occurred in the Punjab which for a time threw everything else into the background. Riots had occurred and reprisals had been taken. At the critical moment when the news came about Amritsar I happened to be with him in Calcutta, and it will be impossible for me ever to forget the torture of his mind. Night after night was passed sleeplessly. At last, some relief came to him by renunciation of his knighthood as a protest against what had been done. For a time it seemed as though "Amritsar" had shattered all his hopes and aims.

But while he felt such intense sensitiveness, as a poet, at the wrong which had been done to humanity in Jallianwalla Bagh, he took his stand at once against any memorial being erected upon the spot as a permanent record of the deed of blood. In the same way, on an earlier occasion, when asked in Japan to celebrate, by means of a short poem, to be engraved on a rock, a tragic story concerning a blood-feud, he wrote:

They hated and killed, and men praised them,

But God in shame hastened to hide its memory under the green grass.

I have mentioned these facts because they belong essentially to the period covered by the letters which follow. They reveal the inner spirit of the Poet as at last, after long absence, he approached Europe in the year 1920. With a great effort he had recovered his serenity of mind. His faith in the generous spirit of the West had passed through its ordeal of fire. Deep down in his subconscious nature he had been wounded at heart by the events of the previous year in the Punjab. Therefore, it was with great anxiety that I watched his vessel depart from Bombay, and went back to the Asram.

Red Sea, *May 24ᵗʰ, 1920*

We shall reach Suez this evening. It is already beginning to grow cold, and now I feel that we have reached a truly foreign part of the world under the rule of different gods than ours. Our hearts are strangers in this region and even the atmosphere of this place looks askance at us. The people here want us to fight their battle and supply them with our raw materials, but they keep us standing outside their doors, over which is written on the notice-board: "Trespassers from Asia will be prosecuted." When I think of all this, my thoughts shiver with cold and I feel home-sick for the sunny corner in my Santiniketan bungalow.

To-day is Monday, and next Sunday morning our steamer will reach Marseilles. But I am already counting the days for my return journey; and I know the sight of the bare rocks of Aden will give a thrill of delight to my heart while pointing with lifted fingers the way to India.

London, *June 17th*, 1920

Time is scarce, and sugar, and butter, and a quiet place where I can gather thoughts and recognize myself. Do not expect long letters from me, or indeed anything else. The fury of social engagements is on me. It is a thing on which one might compose an Ode like that on the West Wind. I am willing to try, if only it would allow me some time to do it. The poet Hafiz was willing to exchange the wealth of Samarkand and Bokhara for a mole on the cheek of his beloved. I am willing to give the whole of London away for my corner in Santiniketan. But London is not mine to dispose of; neither was the wealth of Samarkand and Bokhara the Persian poet's. So, our extravagance does not cost us anything, nor does it bring us any help.

I am going to Oxford to-morrow. Then I shall be knocking about in different places. Just at this moment I am starting for a tea-party given in my honour, from which I cannot absent myself on any pretext, unless I can manage to be run over by a motor-car in the London streets. It is a matter of eternal wonder to me that this does not happen to me four times a day. You won't believe in my scarcity of time if I go on to the end of the note-paper. So, I hastily bid you farewell.

London, *July 8th, 1920*

Every day I have been wishing to write you a letter—but the flesh is weak. My days have become solid like cannon-balls, heavy with engagements. It is not true that I have no leisure at all, but unfortunately I cannot utilize interrupted leisure for any work whatever. Therefore, those intervals are lost doing nothing.

I am sure you know it, better than anybody else, that doing nothing is a burden hard to bear. But if you look at my exterior, you will find no trace of damage there—for my health is absurdly good.

I hope Pearson is regularly furnishing you with all the news. He has been of very great help to me, as you can well imagine, and I find that the arduous responsibility of looking after a poet suits him wonderfully well. He is looking the very picture of health, and on the whole his dreams are felicitous. For instance, last night he dreamt that he had been buying strawberries as large as gourds. It proves the magnificent vitality of his dreams.

I know our school vacation is over. The boys are back at school and the Asram is resounding with laughter and song. The advent of the rains is also contributing its portion to the general rejoicing. How I wish I had wings! Give my love to all the children, and my blessings.

London, *July 12th, 1920*

It gave me great joy, and a feeling of relief, when your sister came to see me yesterday and gave me reassuring news about your other sister. She repeatedly asked me to tell you that there was not the least cause for anxiety on account of them, and that they were comfortably settled in their new home. I gave her all the news about you, but unfortunately could not assure her that you were careful of your own health.

Invitations are pouring in from the continental countries, and I feel sure that a hearty welcome is awaiting me in these places. When I am weary and feel a longing to go back, it gives me strength to think that the migratory flock of my thoughts have found their nest on these shores, and with genuine love and wonder these enormously busy people have listened to a voice from the distant East.

This is a constant surprise to me. However, there is no question that one only truly and fully lives where one's thoughts and works find their medium of responsive life. When I am in the West, I feel more strongly than ever that I am received in a living world of mind. I miss here my sky and light and leisure, but I am in touch with those who feel and express their need of me and to whom I can offer myself.

It is not unlikely that some time hence my thoughts will no longer be necessary to them and my personality will lose its flavour; but does it matter? The tree sheds its leaves, but the fact is that so long as these were living they brought sunshine into the heart of the tree and their voice was the voice of the forest; and my communication with Western humanity has been a communication of life. Even when it ceases, the fact remains that it brought some rays of light there, which have been transformed into the living stuff of their minds. Our span of life is short and opportunities are rare, so let us sow our seeds of thought where the soul claims them and where the harvest will ripen.

London, July 22nd, 1920

The result of the Dyer debates in both Houses of Parliament makes painfully evident the attitude of mind of the ruling classes of this country towards India. It shows that no outrage, however monstrous, committed against us by agents of their Government, can arouse feelings of indignation in the hearts of those from whom our governors are chosen.

The unashamed condonation of brutality expressed in their speeches and echoed in their newspapers is ugly in its frightfulness. The feeling of humiliation about our position under the Anglo-Indian domination had been growing stronger everyday for the last fifty years or more; but the one consolation we had was our faith in the love of justice in the English people, whose soul had not been poisoned by that fatal dose of power which could only be available in a Dependency where the manhood of the entire population had been crushed down into helplessness.

Yet the poison has gone further than we expected, and it has attacked the vital organs of the British nation. I feel that our appeal to their higher nature will meet with less and less response every day. I only hope that our countrymen will not lose heart at this, but employ all their energies in the service of their country with a spirit of indomitable courage and determination.

The late events have conclusively proved that our true salvation lies in our own hands; that a nation's greatness can never find its foundation in half-hearted concessions of contemptuous niggardliness.

It is the sign of a feeble character to seek for a short-cut to fulfilment through the favour of those whose interest lies in keeping it barred—the one path to fulfilment is the difficult path of suffering and self-sacrifice. All great boons come to us through the power of the immortal spirit we have within us, and that spirit only proves itself by its defiance of danger and loss.

London, *August 1ˢᵗ, 1920*

We live on the top-most floor of this house far away from the surging life of the town. Only the crest of the swell of the London street-noise reaches me, gently undulating like those clustering tree-tops of Kensington Gardens that I watch from my window. The long and persistent spell of bad weather seems to have exhausted its spite, and the mellow light of the morning sun from behind the fleecy clouds is greeting me like the smile of a child whose eyes are still heavy with sleep. It is nearly seven o'clock, and everyone of our party, including Pearson, is fast asleep within shut doors and behind drawn blinds. To-day is our last day in London, and I am not sorry to leave it. I wish it were the day for sailing home, but that day looks hazily distant and my heart aches.

London, *August 4ᵗʰ, 1920*

Owing to a change of plans, we are still detained in London. We hope to leave it the day after to-morrow. Now that people believe that we are away, and since your London weather has ceased to persecute me, these last two days have been very restful for me. I wonder if you know that at the last moment we decided not to start on our tour to Norway, though our tickets were bought. I am sure you are ready to ascribe this to the inconstancy of mind!

P.S.—I have just written this about Dr Geddes:

What so strongly attracted me in Dr Patrick Geddes when I came to know him in India was not his scientific achievement but, on the contrary, the rare fact of the fullness of his personality rising far above his science. Whatever he has studied and mastered has become vitally one with his humanity. He has the precision of the scientist, and at the same time the vision of the prophet. He has also the power of an artist to make his ideas visible through the language of symbol. His love of man has given him the insight to see the truth of man and imagination to realize in the world not merely the mechanical aspect but also the infinite mystery of life.

Paris, *August 13th*, *1920*

I have come to Paris, not to stay here, but to decide where to go. The sun is shining bright and the spirit of exhilaration is in the atmosphere. Sudhir Rudra received me at the station and made all arrangements for us. Pearson has gone to stay with his mother for some weeks before we start for America. Therefore, I am in the hands of Sudhir just at present and he is taking proper care of me. Paris is empty, and there is no chance of our meeting the people whom I should like to meet. Our stay in England has been wasted. Your Parliament debates about Dyerism in the Punjab and other symptoms of an arrogant spirit of contempt and callousness about India have deeply grieved me, and it was with a feeling of relief that I left England.

Near Paris, *August 20th*, *1920*

We are in a delightful country, in a delightful place in France, meeting with people who are so human.

I feel clearly that the ultimate reality for man's life is his life in the world of ideas, where he is emancipated from the gravitational pull of the dust and he realizes that he is spirit. We, in India, live in a narrow cage of petty interests; we do not believe that we have wings, for we have lost our sky; we chatter and hop and peck at one another within the small range of our obstructed opportunities. It is difficult to achieve greatness of mind and character where our responsibility is diminutive and fragmentary, where our whole life occupies and affects extremely limited area.

And yet through the cracks and chinks of our walls we must send out our starved branches to the sunlight and air, and the roots of our life must pierce the upper strata of our soil of desert sands till they reach down to the spring of water which is exhaustless. Our most difficult problem is how to gain our freedom of soul in spite of the cramped condition of our outward circumstances; how to ignore the perpetual insult of our destiny, so as to be able to uphold the dignity of man.

Santiniketan is for this *tapasya* of India. We who have come there often forget the greatness of our mission, mostly because of the obscurity and insignificance with which the humanity of India seems to be obliterated. We have not the proper light and perspective in our surroundings to be able to realize that our soul is great; and therefore we behave as if we were doomed to be small for all time.

Ardennes, August 21st, 1920

Here we are in a most beautiful part of France. But of what avail is the beauty of Nature when you have lost your trunks which contained all your clothes? I could have been in perfect sympathy with the trees surrounding me if, like them, I were not dependent upon tailors for maintaining self-respect. The most important event for me in this world at present is not what is happening in Poland, or Ireland, or Mesopotamia, but the fact that all the trunks belonging to our party have disappeared from the goods-van in their transit from Paris to this place!

And therefore, though the sea is singing its hymns to the rising and setting sun and to the starlit silence of the night, and though the forest round me is standing tiptoe on the rock, like an ancient Druid, raising its arms to the sky, chanting its incantation of primeval life, we have to hasten back to Paris to be restored to respectability at the hands of tailors and washermen!

I have just received your letter, and for some time I have felt myself held tight in the bosom of our Asram. I cannot tell you how I feel about the prolonged separation from it which is before me; but at the same time I know that unless my relationship with the wide world of humanity grows in truth and love, my relationship with the Asram will not be perfect.

Paris, September 7th, 1920

Your letters always bring the atmosphere of Santiniketan round my mind, with all its colour and sounds and movements; and my love for my boys, like a migratory bird, crosses back over the sea, seeking its own dear nest in the Asram. Your letters are great gifts to me—I have not the power to repay them in kind. For now my mind faces the West, and all that it has to give naturally flows towards it. Therefore, for the time being, my direct communication with you has become thin, like the stream of the Kopai River in the summer. But I know Santiniketan will not bring forth its fullness of flower and fruit if, through me, it does not send its roots into the Western soil. Stung by the insult of cruel injustice, we try to repudiate Europe, but by doing so we insult ourselves. Let us have the dignity not to quarrel or retaliate; not to pay back smallness by being small ourselves. This is the time when we should dedicate all our resources of emotion, thought and character to the service of our country in a positive direction of duty. We are suffering because of our offences against Shivam, against Advaitam. We spend all our energy in quarrelling with the punishment and nothing of it is left for the reparation of wrongs we have done and are doing. When we have performed our part of the duties, we shall have the fullest right and power and time to bring others to book for their transgressions.

Let us forget the Punjab affairs—but never forget that we shall go on deserving such humiliation over and over again until we set our house in order. Do not mind the waves of the sea, but mind the leaks in your vessel. Politics in our country is extremely petty. It has a pair of legs, one of which has shrunk and shrivelled and become paralytic and therefore, feebly waits for the other one to drag it on. There is no harmony between the two, and our politics, in its hoppings and totterings and falls, is comic and undignified. The entreaty and anger, which alternately are struggling to find expression in the ludicrously lame member of this tragic partnership, both belong to our abject feebleness. When Non-cooperation comes naturally as our final moral protest against the unnaturalness of our political situation, then it will be glorious, because true; but when it is only another form of begging, then let us reject it.

The establishment of perfect co-operation of life and mind among ourselves must come first through sacrifice and self-dedication, and then will come in its natural course the non-cooperation. When the fruit completely ripens, it finds its freedom through its own fulfilment of truth.

Our country is crying to her own children for their co-operation in the removal of obstacles in our social life which for centuries have been hampering us in our self-realization. We need co-operation in the sacrifice of love, more than anything else, to prove to our country that she is ours; and then, we shall have the moral right to say to others: "we have nothing to do with you in our affairs." And for this, all the moral fervour which the life of Mahatma Gandhi represents, and which he, of all men in the world, can call up, is needed.

That such a precious treasure of power should be put into the mean and frail vessel of our politics, allowing it to sail across endless waves of angry recrimination, is terribly unfortunate for our country, when our mission is to revive the dead with the fire of the soul. The external waste of our resources of life is great owing to external circumstances; but that the waste of our spiritual resources should also be allowed to happen on adventures that are wrong from the point of view of moral truth is heartbreaking. It is criminal to turn moral force into a blind force.

Our time to go to Holland is drawing near. I have numerous invitations from over there to lecture, but I am not yet fully ready. Just now I am busy writing. My subject is the Meeting of the East and West. I hope it will be finished before I leave Paris.

Paris, *September 12th, 1920*

I had invitations from Germany and decided to go. But travelling from one country to another has become so difficult nowadays that I had to give it up. Specially, going from France to Germany is beset with obstacles. On my way back from Holland, I shall try my best at least to visit Hamburg. Germany needs sympathy, and I hope I shall have the opportunity to go there and offer it to her.

A short time ago I was taken to Rheims and other devastated regions of France in a motor-car. It was a most saddening sight. It will take a tremendous effort and also an immense lapse of time to make this a thing of the past. When the spiritual ideal is lost, when the human relationship is completely broken up, then individuals freed from the creative bond of wholeness find a fearful joy in destruction.

In such catastrophes, one can realize what a stupendous force of annihilation is not only kept in check in our society, but made into multitudinous manifestations of beauty and fruitfulness. Then we know that evils are like meteors, stray fragments, wreckage of a broken-up wholeness, which need the attraction of a great planet of life's ideal to be assimilated into the peace of creation.

Only spiritual ideals have that great power of attraction that can transmute these rebellious fractions into a perfect roundness. The evil forces are literally outlaws. They only need the control and cadence of creative laws to change them into good. Our Shiva[1] is the Lord of terrible spirits, who are spirits of death; and he is also Shivam, the Good. True goodness lies not in the negation of badness, but in the mastery of it. It is the miracle that turns the tumult of chaos into the dance of beauty. True education is that power of miracle, that ideal of creation. Punishments and disciplines imposed from outside are negative. The Teacher is Shiva. He has the divine power of destroying the destructiveness; of sucking out the poison. If France had the Shiva in her heart, she could transform evil into good, she could forgive. And that forgiveness could prove her own immortality, and truly save her from the hurt which was inflicted upon her.

This is difficult, but is the one way of salvation. Only the creative ideal can completely get over the acts of destruction. It is the spiritual ideal, it is love, it is forgiveness. God is perpetually exercising it, and thus the creation is ever kept sweet.

In the heart of death, life has its ceaseless play of joy.

Do we not know this is our individual life? Have we our own right to exist in this wonderful world? Would we not burn it, destroy it? Has not God's creative power given us our place in His universe? Must we forget that, when we judge and deal with our own fellow-beings?

Paris, *September 18th, 1920*

I find our countrymen are furiously excited about Non-cooperation. It will grow into something like our Swadeshi movement in Bengal. Such an emotional outbreak should

---

1. The God Shiva in Indian mythology is regarded as the Lord of Terrors. But the name "Shivam" indicates beneficence; and thus Shiva is also the God of Goodness. He swallows the deadly poison without harm.

have been taken advantage of in starting independent organizations all over India for serving our country.

Let Mahatma Gandhi be the true leader in this; let him send his call for positive service, ask for homage in sacrifice, which has its end in love and creation. I shall be willing to sit at his feet and do his bidding if he commands me to co-operate with my countrymen in service and love. I refuse to waste my manhood in lighting fires of anger and spreading it from house to house.

It is not that I do not feel anger in my heart for injustice and insult heaped upon my motherland. But this anger of mine should be turned into the fire of love for lighting the lamp of worship to be dedicated through my country to my God.

It would be an insult to humanity if I use the sacred energy of my moral indignation for the purpose of spreading a blind passion all over my country. It would be like using the fire from the altar of sacrifice for the purpose of incendiarism.

Antwerp, October 3rd, 1920

I have spent about a fortnight in Holland. This fortnight has been most generous in its gifts to me. Of one thing you may be sure, that a communication of heart has been opened up between this little country and Santiniketan; and it remains with us to widen it and make use of it for the interchange of spiritual wealth. Altogether, Europe has come closer to us by this visit of ours. I only wish that all my friends in Santiniketan could realize how true this is and what a wealth it represents. Now I know more clearly than ever before that Santiniketan belongs to the world and we have to be worthy of this great fact. It is extremely difficult for us Indians to forget all the irritations that ever keep our consciousness concentrated on our own daily annoyances. But emancipation of consciousness is both the means and end of spiritual life.

Therefore Santiniketan must be saved from the whirlwind of our dusty politics.

I am writing this letter from Antwerp, where I came yesterday morning; and I am getting ready to go to Brussels, where I have an invitation. And then I go to Paris.

London, *October 18th, 1920*

Our vision of truth varies according to its perspective. I feel certain that this perspective has become narrow in India owing to the density of mental atmosphere caused by political unrest. There are politicians who must make hasty decisions and act without delay. It is their function to take short-cuts to immediate success and dash through blunders with their lumbering 'tanks' of political organizations. But there are needs that belong to all mankind and to all time. Those have to be satisfied through the rise and fall of empires. We all know that there is a vast difference between journalism and literature. Journalism is necessary and there are multitudes of men eager to carry it out. But if it suppresses the light of literature, then it will produce the London fog of November, which substitutes gaslight for the sunlight.

Santiniketan is there for giving expression to the Eternal Man—*asato ma sad gamaya,*[2] the prayer that will ring clearer as the ages roll on, even when the geographical names of all countries are changed and lose their meaning. If I give way to the passion of the moment and the claims of the crowd, then it will be like speculating with my Master's money for a purpose which is not His own.

I know that my countrymen will clamour to borrow from this capital entrusted to me and exploit it for the needs that they believe to be more urgent than anything else. But all the same, you must know that I have to be true to my trust.

_____

2. Literally, "Lead me from Untruth to Truth."

Santiniketan must treasure in all circumstances the *santi* which is in the bosom of the Infinite. With begging and scrambling we find very little, but with being true to ourselves we find a great deal more than we desire. The best reward that I have gained in my life is through the spontaneous and disinterested expression of truth in me, and never through straining for a result, whatever high-sounding name it may have carried.

Chapter VI

The journey undertaken to America, described in the letters contained in this chapter, was directly for the purpose of obtaining sympathy and support for the Poet's Visva-bharati ideal. His earlier visits to America in 1913 and 1916 had given him the hope that the young heart of the New World would respond to him more definitely than the peoples of Europe, who were still involved in their national prejudices and their narrow provincial boundaries.

Since the Poet's conception of Visva-bharati lies in the background in all the letters which he wrote to me from America, it may be well as an introduction to this chapter to give his own explanation of his purpose, as he presented it during his lecture tours in India before he started for the West. The following passages from these lectures appear to me to explain the Poet best:

> The age has come when all artificial fences are breaking down. Only that will survive which is basically consistent with the universal; while that which seeks safety in the out-of-the-way hole of the special will perish. The nursery of the infant should be secluded, its cradle safe. But the same seclusion, if continued after the infant has grown up, makes it weak in mind and body.
>
> There was a time when China, Egypt, Greece and Rome had, each of them, to nurture its civilization in comparative

seclusion. The greatness of the universal, however, which was more or less in each, grew strong within its protecting sheath of individuality. Now has come the age for co-ordination and co-operation. The seedlings that were reared within their enclosures must now be transplanted into the open fields. They must pass the test of the world-market if their maximum value is to be obtained.

So we must prepare the grand field for the co-ordination of all the cultures of the world, where each will give to and take from the other; where each will have to be studied through the growth of its stages in history. This adjustment of knowledge through comparative study, this progress in intellectual co-operation, is to be the key-note of the coming age. We may hug our holy aloofness from some imagined security of a corner, but the world will prove stronger than our corner, and it is our corner that will have to give way, receding and pressing against its walls till they burst on all sides.

But before we in India are in a position to stand a comparison with the other cultures of the world, or truly to co-operate with them, we must base our structure on a synthesis of all the different cultures we have. When taking our stand at such a centre we turn towards the West, our gaze shall no longer be timid and dazed; our heads shall remain erect, safe from insult. For then, we shall be able to take our own views of truth from the standpoint of our own vantage-ground, thus opening out a new vista of thought before a grateful world.

All great countries have their vital centres for intellectual life, where a high standard of learning is maintained, where the minds of the people are naturally attracted to find their genial atmosphere, to prove their worth, to contribute their share to the country's culture, and thus to kindle on some common altar of the land a great sacrificial fire of intellect which may radiate the sacred light in all directions.

Athens was such a centre in Greece, Rome in Italy, and Paris is such to-day in France. Benares has been, and still continues to be, the centre of our Sanskrit culture. But Sanskrit learning does not exhaust all the elements of culture that exist in the present-day India....That is why the inner spirit of India is calling to us to establish in this land great centres, where all her intellectual forces will gather for the purpose of creation, and all her resources of knowledge and thought, Eastern and Western, will unite in perfect harmony. She is seeking for the glorious opportunity to know her own mind and give her mind to the world, to help it in its progress; when she will be released from the chaos of scattered powers and the inertness of borrowed acquisitions.

Let me state clearly that I have no distrust of any culture because of its foreign character. On the contrary, I believe that the shock of such forces is necessary for the vitality of our intellectual nature. It is admitted that much of the spirit of Christianity runs counter, not only to the Classical culture of Europe, but to the European temperament altogether. And, yet this alien movement of idea, constantly running against the natural mental current of Europe, has been the most important factor in strengthening and enriching her civilization on account of the very antagonism of its direction. In fact, the European vernaculars first woke up to life and fruitful vigour owing to the impact of this foreign thought-power with all its Oriental forms and feelings. The same thing is happening in India. European culture has come to us, not only with its knowledge, but with its velocity. Though our assimilation of it is imperfect and the consequent aberrations numerous, still it is rousing our intellectual life from its inertia of former habits into growing consciousness by the very contradiction it offers to our mental traditions.

What I object to is the artificial arrangement by which this foreign education tends to occupy all the space of our national mind and thus kills, or hampers, the great opportunity for the creation of a new thought-power by a new combination of truths. It is this which makes me urge that all the elements in our own culture have to be strengthened, not to resist Western culture, but truly to accept and assimilate it; to use it for our food and not as our burden; to get mastery over this culture, and not to live at its outskirts as the hewers of texts and the drawers of book-learning.

Rabindranath Tagore suffered from illness during his visit to America, and this brought with it depression of mind. The response to his appeal for co-operation in his work of international fellowship was not at first as direct and full as he had expected. His longing to go back became at last intense. The letters which he wrote to me during these months were often full of gloom. Those that follow are some of the most important of them dealing with his ideal of a centre of international fellowship at Santiniketan.

New York, *October 28th, 1920*

Our steamer has arrived in port—too late for us to land to-night. Between one shore and the other there are tossings on the angry waves and menaces of the shrieking winds, but peace comes at the end and shelter when the desolation that divides the world appears unreal and is forgotten. This crossing of the sea has not yet been completed by those who are voyagers from one age to another. Storms have raged and the moaning of the salt sea has haunted their days and nights. But the haven is not very far distant and the new continent of time is ready with its greeting of light and life and its invitation to the unexplored. Already I feel the breath of that future and see birds from the shore bringing songs of hope.

You must know that our Santiniketan belongs to that future. We have not yet reached it. We need stronger faith and clearer vision to direct our course towards its hill of sunlight. There are chains which still keep our boat clinging to the sheltered cove of the past. We must leave it behind. Our loyalty must not be for any land of a limited geography. It should be for the nationality of the common idea, to which are born individuals belonging to various nations, who are carrying their gifts of sacrifice to the one great shrine of Humanity.

New York, *November 4th, 1920*

There is one thing about which I wish to speak to you. Keep Santiniketan away from the turmoils of politics. I know that the political problem is growing in intensity in India and its encroachment is difficult to resist. But all the same, we must never forget that our mission is not political. Where I have my politics, I do not belong to Santiniketan.

I do not mean to say that there is anything wrong in politics, but only that it is out of harmony with our Asram.

We must clearly realize this fact, that the name of Santiniketan has a meaning for us, and this name will have to be made true. I am anxious and afraid lest the surrounding forces may become too strong for us and we succumb to the onslaught of the present time. Because the time is troubled and the minds of men distracted, all the more must we, through our Asram, maintain our faith in Shantam, Shivam, Advaitam.

New York, *November 25th, 1920*

A friend of mine, who is actively interested in my cause, is a Quaker, and he takes me every Sunday morning to the Quakers' meetings. There, in the silence of meditation, I am able to find the eternal perspective of truth, where the vision of outward success dwindles away to its infinitesimal minuteness. What is needed of me is sacrifice. Our payment is for success, but our sacrifice is for truth. If the spirit of sacrifice is pure in quality, then its reward will be more than can be counted and proved, and let my gift to my country and to the world be a life of sacrifice.

But my earnest request to you is to keep your mind high above politics. The problem of this new age is to help to build the world anew. Let us accept this great task. Santiniketan is to make accommodation for the workers from all parts of the world. All other things can wait. We must make room for Man, the guest of this age, and let not the nation obstruct his path. I am afraid lest the cry of our own sufferings and humiliations should drown the announcement of His coming. For His sake we shall set aside our grievances and shall say: 'Whatever may happen to us, let His cause triumph; for the future is His.'

New York, *November 30ᵗʰ, 1920*

I am often reminded of my *Gitanjali* poem in which the woman tells how she found God's sword when she had been seeking for a petal from God's flower-garden. All through my life I have been seeking for such a petal, and I stand puzzled at the sight of the gift waiting for me. This gift has not been my choice, but my God has chosen for me this gift. And now I say to myself that we prove our worthiness for God's gift of responsibility by acceptance of it and not by success or anything else.

The past has been for men, the future is for Man. These *men* are still fighting for the possession of the world: the din and the clash are deafening; the air is obscured with the dust rising from the trampled earth. Standing in the heart of this struggle, we have to build a seat for the one God revealed to all human races. We may be mocked and pushed away by the crowd, but the fact will remain and invisibly grow into truth that we have believed.

I was born a poet, and it is difficult for me to suffer myself to be rudely hustled in my path by busy men who have no leisure for ideas. I am not an athlete. I do not belong to the arena. The stare of the curious crowd scorches my soul. And yet I, of all persons, am called upon to force my way into the thick of the Western public with a mission for which I have never been trained. Truth fashions its own arrows out of reeds that are light and frail.

New York, *December 13th, 1920*

Our Seventh Paus Festival at the Asram is near at hand. I cannot tell you how my heart is thirsting to join you in your festival. I am trying to console myself with the thought that something very big and great is going to be the outcome of the effort I am making. But deep in my heart I know that simplicity of life and endeavour makes for real happiness. When we realize in some measure our ideal of perfection in our work, it matters very little what its dimensions are. Our trust in bigness very often betrays our want of faith in truth. The kingdom of the earth boasts of the magnitude of its possessions, but the Kingdom of Heaven is content with the depth of its self-realization. There are certain institutions which have for their object some external success. But Santiniketan is there for giving us opportunity to realize ourselves in truth. This can never be done through big funds, but through dedication of our life in love.

In this country I live in the dungeon of the Castle of Bigness. My heart is starved. Day and night I dream of Santiniketan, which blossoms like a flower in the atmosphere of the unbounded freedom of simplicity. I know how truly great Santiniketan is, when I view it from this land. Here I feel every day what a terrible nightmare it is for the human soul to bear this burden of the monster Arithmetic. It incessantly drives its victims and yet leads them nowhere. It raises storms of battle which are for sowing broadcast the seeds of future conflict.

The giant reptiles of the primitive earth were proud of their hypertrophied tails, which did not save them from the doom of destruction. I long to leave all this, totally reject this unreality, take the next steamer I can get, and run back to my Santiniketan and serve it with my life and love.

That life which I dedicate to it, if it is true, will make it live. The true wisdom is there, which can spurn the greed for result and is only concerned with the expression of truth. This wisdom found its utterance in India. But there is imminent danger of its being drowned in the flood of noise which the votaries of success are bellowing forth in the prosperous West. My prayer is growing everyday more and more intense, to get away from the dark tower of unreality, from this dance of death trampling sweet flowers of life under its tread.

New York, *December 17ᵗʰ, 1920*

When all my thoughts were furiously revolving, like dead leaves, in a whirlwind of desire for raising funds, a picture came to my hand; it was that of Sujata offering a cup of milk to Buddha. Its message went deep into my heart. It said to me: "The cup of milk comes to you unasked when you have gone through your *tapasya*. It is offered to you with love, and only love can bring its homage to truth."

Then your figure at once came to my mind. The milk has been sent to me through you. It is infinitely more than anything that can come from the cheque-book of the rich. I had become famished in the wilderness of solitude for lack of sympathy and comradeship, when you brought your cup of love to me, which is the true life-giving food freely offered by life. And as the poet Morris says, "Love is enough." That voice of love calls me away from the lure of dollars— the voice that comes to nestle in my heart from across the sea, from the shady avenue of *sal* trees resonant with laughter and songs of simple joy.

The mischief is that ambition does not fully believe in love. It believes in power. It leaves the limpid and singing water of everlasting life for the wine of success. Every day I seem to be growing afraid of the very vision of this success. It had been said in the Upanishad, "Happiness is in greatness." Ambition points out bigness and calls it greatness, and our track is hopelessly lost. When I look at the picture of Buddha, I cry for the great peace of inner fulfilment. My longing grows painfully intense as my mind becomes distracted at the stupendous unmeaningness of monstrosity in things around me. Every morning I sit by my window and say to myself: "I must not bow my head to this ugly idol worshipped by the West with daily human sacrifice." I remember that morning at Shileida when the Vaishnava woman came to me and said: "When are you coming down from your three-storeyed building to meet your love under the shade of the trees?"

Just now, I am on the top storey of the skyscraper to which the tallest of trees dare not send its whisper; but love silently comes to me saying: "When are you coming down to meet me on the green grass under the rustling leaves, where you have the freedom of the sky and of sunlight and the tender touch of life's simplicity?" I try to say something about money, but it sounds so ludicrous and yet so tragic, that my words grow ashamed of themselves and they stop.

New York, *December 19th, 1920*

When Life began her first experiments, she was mightily proud of the hugeness of her animal specimens. The bigger the bodies were, the more extravagantly large the armour had to be made for their protection. The ludicrous creatures, in order to maintain their balance, had to carry a tail which was absurdly disproportionate to the rest of their bodies. It went on like this till life became a burden to itself and to the exchequer of creation. It was uneconomical, and therefore not only harmful but ungainly. True economy is the principle of beauty in practical arithmetic. Driven to bewilderment, life began to seek for a pause in her insanity of endless multiplication.

All forms of ambitious powers are obsessed by this delirium of multiplication. All its steps are steps towards augmentation and not completeness. But ambitions, that rely solely upon the suggestion of their tails and armour, are condemned to carry their own obstruction till they have to stop.

In its early history, Life, after its orgies of megalomania, had at last to think of disarmament. But how did she effect it? By boldly relinquishing the ambition to produce bigness— and man was born helplessly naked and small. All of a sudden he was disinherited of the enormity of flesh, when apparently he was most in need of it. But this prodigious loss gained for him his freedom and victory.

Then began the reign of Mind. It brought its predecessor of gigantic bulk under subjection. But, as often happens, the master became the parasite of the slave, and mind also tried to achieve greatness by the bigness of materials. The dynasty of mind followed the dynasty of flesh, but employed this flesh as its prime minister.

Our history is waiting for the dynasty of Spirit. The human succeeded the brutal; and now comes the turn of the Divine.

In our mythology we have often heard of a man taking the side of the Gods and saving Paradise from the dominion of Giants. But in our history we often notice man holding alliance with Giants and trying to defeat the Gods. His guns and ships of huge power and proportion are turned out from the arsenal of the Giant. In the fight of bigness against goodness, man has joined the former, counting the coins of his reward in number and not in quality—in lead and not in gold.

Those whose are in possession of material resources have become slaves of their own instruments. Fortunately for us, in India, these resources are beyond all immediate possibility of realization. We are disarmed, and therefore we have no option but to seek for other and higher sources of power. The men who believe in the reality of brute force have made enormous sacrifices in order to maintain it. Let us, in India, have faith in the moral power in man and be ready to sacrifice for it all we have. Let us do our best to prove that Man has not been the greatest mistake in Creation. Let it not be said that, for the sake of peace and happiness in the world, the physical brutes were preferable to the intellectual brutes who boast of their factory-made teeth and nails and poison fangs.

New York, *December 20ᵗʰ, 1920*

In every age and in every country facts are given to us in order that we may provide with them some special expression of Truth. Facts are like atoms in gases: they fight with, or else fly away from, one another. But when they are united into a drop of dew they attain beauty and reality. Man must have that creative magic to bring the facts of his time into some unity of creation. In Christ and in Buddha this creative ideal tried to unite men who were divided because of their formalism in religious faith.

Formalism in religion is like nationalism in politics: it breeds sectarian arrogance, mutual misunderstanding and a spirit of persecution. Our Indian mediaeval saints, through their light of love and inner perception of truth, could realize the spiritual unity of man. For them, the innumerable barriers of formalism had no existence. Therefore the mutually antagonistic creeds of Hindus and Muhammadans, irreconcilable as they seemed, did not baffle them. Our faith in truth has its trial in the apparent difficulty of its realization.

The most important of all facts in the present age is that the East and West have met. So long as it remains a mere fact, it will give rise to interminable conflicts; it will even hurt man's soul. It is the mission of all men of faith to raise this fact into truth. The worldly-rise will shake their heads and say it is not possible—that there is a radical difference between the East and the West and that only physical power will have its sway in their relationship.

But physical power is not creative. Whatever laws and organizations it may produce, it will never satisfy spiritual humanity. Ram Mohun Roy was the first great man in our age who had the profound faith and large vision to feel in his heart the unity of soul between the East and West. I follow him, though he is practically rejected by my countrymen.

I only wish you had been with me in Europe! You would know at once what was the purpose of the modern age; what is the cry of man, which the politicians never hear. There were politicians in the courts of the Moghul Emperors. They have left nothing behind them but ruins. But Kabir and Nanak! They have bequeathed to us their imperishable faith in the unity of man through God's love.

New York, *December 21ˢᵗ, 1920*

All about me is a desert of crowds, a monotony of multitude. Man is drowned in his own deluge of desultoriness. It is an unceasing struggle in me to have to pass through this— especially when I carry in myself such a heavy load of helplessness. Every moment I am made conscious of it, and I am tired. When we have the banner of an idea to carry against obstacles of indifference, the burden of our personal self should be extremely light. But I am so awkwardly cumbersome with my ineptitude.

I remember, when I was young, how a blind old beggar used to come to our door every morning led by a boy. It was a tragic sight; the blindness of the old man robbed the boy of his freedom. The boy looked so wistful and eager for release. Our incapacity is a fetter with which we tie others to our limitations. Consciousness of this, every day adds to my feeling of weariness. But this depression of spirit is likely to do me a service. It has led me to the brink of a discovery that a great measure of one's impotence is *maya*.

Latterly I have been constantly giving myself a shaking, trying to arouse myself from this stupor of self-delusion. During the greater part of my life my mind has been made accustomed to travel the inner paths of dreams, till it has lost all confidence in its power to thread its way through the zigzags of the outer world. In fact, its attention has never been trained to accept the miscellaneous responsibilities of the clamorous surface life of society. Therefore, the West is not my world.

And yet I have received the gift of love from the West, and my heart acknowledges her claims to my service and I must unreservedly offer myself to her before I die. I do not belong to the present age, the age of conflicting politics. Nevertheless I cannot repudiate the age which has given me birth. I suffer and struggle. I crave for freedom and yet am held back. I must share the life of the present world, though I do not believe in its cry. I sit at its table, and while it fills its cup with wine to slake its unnatural thirst, I try to listen, through the noisy carousal, to the murmur of the stream carrying its limpid waters to the sea.

New York, *December 22nd, 1920*

To-day is the seventh of Paus. I wish it were allowed to me to stand among you and mingle my voice with yours in uttering our prayer. It is real starvation of my heart to be deprived of this great privilege. To-day I realize more than ever before that nothing can be truer for me than to be with my dear children and friends, this beautiful sunny morning of December, and bow my head to my Father and dedicate my service to Him. By that dedication our works become great, and not by extension of external resources.

Oh, how simple is truth and how full of light and happiness! Not to be distracted by the curiosity of crowds, only to be rewarded by the approval of Him who knows our heart, in the fulfilment of our endeavour. I only hope that what I am doing here is in response to the call of the Shantam, that my lonely celebration of seventh Paus in this hotel room finds its harmony with your festival. Let our faith in the real be not overcome by the lure of the unreal. Let come to us what is good and not what we desire. Let us bow our heads to the Good, to the supreme Good.[1]

I have often felt the desire that you were with me in my adventure. And yet I am deeply thankful that you could remain at the Asram while I was away. For you understand me with the understanding of love, and therefore through you I seem to dwell in Santiniketan. I know that I am in your mind today and you know that my heart is with you. Is it not a great good fortune that there is a spot in this world where all that is best in us can meet in truth and love? Can anything be greater than that? Please give my blessings to all my boys and girls, and my greetings of love to my friends.

Near New York, *December 25th, 1920*

To-day is Christmas Day. We are about forty-five guests gathered in this inn from different parts of the United States. It is a beautiful house, nestling in the heart of a wooded hill, with an invitation floating in the air of a brook broadening into a lake in the valley. It is a glorious morning, full of peace

---

1. These sentences are a free translation of the prayer repeated together in the *mandir* (or chapel) at Santiniketan.

and sunlight, of the silence of the leafless forest untouched by bird songs or humming of bees.

But where is the spirit of Christmas in human hearts? The men and women are feeding themselves with extra dishes and laughing extra loud. But there is not the least touch of the eternal in the heart of their merriment, no luminous serenity of joy, no depth of devotion. How immensely different from the religious festivals of our country! These Western people have made their money but killed their poetry of life. Here life is like a river, that has heaped up gravel and sand and choked the perennial current of water that flows from an eternal source on the snowy height of an ancient hill. I have learnt since I came here to prize more than ever the infinite worth of the frugal life and simple faith. These Western people believe in their wealth, which can only multiply itself and attain nothing.

How to convince them of the utter vanity of their pursuits! They do not have the time to realize that they are not happy. They try to smother their leisure with rubbish of dissipation, lest they discover that they are the unhappiest of mortals. They deceive their souls with counterfeits, and then, in order to hide that fact from themselves, they artificially keep up the value of those false coins by an unceasing series of self-deceptions.

My heart feels like a wild-duck from the Himalayan lake lost in the endless desert of Sahara, where sands glitter with a fatal brilliance but the soul withers for want of the life-giving spring of water.

New York, *January 8ᵗʰ, 1921*

There are a large number of ideas about which we do not even know that they are inaccessible to us, only because we have grown too familiar with their names.

Such is our idea of God. We do not have to realize it in order to be made aware of it. This is why it requires a great deal of spiritual sensitiveness to be able to feel the life-throb of God's reality behind the vulgar callosity of words. Things that are small naturally come to their limits for us, when they are familiar. But the truth which is great should reveal its infinity all the more vastly when it is near to us. Unfortunately, words that represent truth have not the same immensity of life as truth itself. Therefore, the words (and with them our attention and interest) become inert by constant handling, obscuring our faith underneath them without our being conscious of that tragic fact.

This is the reason why men who are obviously religious are frequently more irreligious, in reality, than those who openly ignore religion. Preachers and ministers of religion have made it their business to deal with God at every moment. They cannot afford to wait until they come in touch with Him. They dare not acknowledge the fact that they have not done so. Therefore they have to strain their minds into a constant attitude of God-Knowingness. They have to delude themselves, in order to fulfil the expectations of others, or what they consider to be their duty.

And yet the consciousness of God, like that of all other ideas, comes to us only with intense moments of illumination, of inspiration. If we do not have the patience to wait for it, we only choke the path of inspiration with the *débris* of our conscious efforts. Those who make it their business to preach God, preach creeds. They lose their sense of distinction between these two. Therefore their religion does not bring peace into this world, but conflict. They do not hesitate to make use even of their religion for the propaganda of national self-seeking and boastfulness.

You may wonder, in your mind, as to the reason of my bringing up this topic in my present letter. It is in connection with the same endless conflict within me between the poet and the preacher, one of whom depends for his mission upon inspiration and the other upon conscious endeavour. Straining of consciousness leads to insensitiveness, of which I am more afraid than anything else. The preacher is the professional dealer in particular ideas. His customers come at all hours of the day and put questions to him. The answers, which he gets into the habit of producing, gradually lose their living quality, and his faith in his ideas runs the risk of being smothered under the deadness of his words. I believe that such a tragedy is more common than people suspect, especially with those who are good and therefore, are ever ready to sign their cheque of benefit for others without waiting to see if the cash has had time to accumulate in the bank.

This makes me think that it is safe to be nothing better than a mere poet. For poets have to be true to their best moments and not to other peoples' requirements.

New York, *January 14ᵗʰ, 1921*

Even when I was very young my mind ever sought for all experiences in an environment of completeness. That is to say, fact indicated some truth to me, even though I did not clearly understand it. That is why my mind was constantly struck with things that in themselves were commonplace.

When I watched, from over the wall of the terrace of the inner apartments of our Jorashanko house, the coconut-trees and the tank surrounded by the huts of the milk vendors, they came before me with a more-than-themness that could not be exhausted. That faculty—though subsequently mingled with reasoning and self-analysis—has still continued in my life. It is the sense and craving for wholeness. Constantly, it has been the cause of my separation from others and also their misunderstanding of my motives.

Swadeshi, Swarajism, ordinarily produce intense excitement in the minds of my countrymen, because they carry in them some fervour of passion generated by the exclusiveness of their range. It cannot be said that I am untouched by this heat and movement. But somehow, by my temperament as a poet, I am incapable of accepting these objects as final. They claim from us a great deal more than is their due. After a certain point is reached, I find myself obliged to separate myself from my own people, with whom I have been working, and my soul cries out: "The complete man must never be sacrificed to the patriotic man, or even to the merely moral man."

To me humanity is rich and large and many-sided. Therefore I feel deeply hurt when I find that, for some material gain, man's personality is mutilated in the Western world and he is reduced to a machine.

The same process of repression and curtailment of humanity is often advocated in our country under the name of patriotism. Such deliberate impoverishment of our nature seems to me a crime. It is a cultivation of callousness, which is a form of sacrilege. For God's purpose is to lead man into perfection of growth, which is the attainment of a unity comprehending an immense manifoldness. But when I find man, for some purpose of his own, imposing upon his society a mutilation of mind, a niggardliness of culture, a Puritanism which is spiritual penury, it makes me inexpressibly sad.

I have been reading a book by a Frenchman on Japan. The sensitiveness to the ideal of beauty, which has been made universal in Japan, is not only the source of her strength, but of her heroic spirit of renunciation. For true renunciation blossoms on the vigorous soil of beauty and joy—the soil which supplies positive food to our souls.

But the negative process of making the soil poor produces a ghastly form of renunciation which belongs to the nihilism of life. An emancipation of human nature has already been going on for a long time in India. Let us not add to it by creating a mania for self-immolation. Our life to-day needs more colour, more expansion, more nourishment, for all the variety of its famished functions. Whatever may be the case in other countries, we need in India more fullness of life, and not asceticism.

Deadness of life, in all forms, gives rise to impurities, by enfeebling our reason, narrowing our vision, creating fanaticism, owing to our will-power being forced into abnormal channels. Life carries its own purification when its sap finds the passage unbarred through all ramifications.

New York, *January 23rd, 1921*

I have just come back from Greenwich, a suburban part of New York, where last night I had a reception and a speech and a dinner and a discussion, till I felt empty, like a burst balloon with no gas left in it!

At the far-distant end of the wilderness of such trials as this what do I see? But what matters it? Results of our efforts delude us by appearing as final. They raise expectation of fulfilment and draw us on. But they are not final. They are roadside inns where we change our horses for a farther journey. An ideal is different. It carries its own progress within itself. Each stage is not a mere approach to the goal, but carries with it its own meaning and purpose.

Trees proceed on their upward career, not along a railway track constructed by engineers. We, who have been dreamers, should never employ coolies to build railway lines of social service. We must solely deal with living ideas, and have faith in life. Otherwise we are punished, not necessarily with bankruptcy, but with success—behind which sits the Mephistopheles of worldliness, chuckling at the sight of an idealist dragged through the dust by the chariot of the prosperous.

What has made us love Santiniketan so deeply is the ideal of perfection, which we have tasted all through its growth. It has not been made by money, but by our love, our life. With it we need not strain for any result; it is fulfilment itself— the life which forms round it, the service which we daily render it. Now I realize, more than ever before, how precious and how beautiful is the simplicity of our Asram, which can reveal itself all the more luminously because of its background of material poverty and want.

New York, February 2nd, 1921

After a break of three weeks and a sultriness of weary waiting, your letters have come in a downpour; and I cannot possibly tell you how refreshing they are! I seem to be travelling across a desert, and your letters are like weekly provisions dropped by some air-service from cloud-land. They are expected; and yet they have the element of surprise. I hungrily attack them and fall upon extra portions supplied from your letters written to others.

Your letters are delightful, because you have your interest in details that are generally overlooked. The world is made beautiful by the unimportant things. They furnish this great world-picture with all its modulations of shades and tints. The important things are like the sunshine. They come from a great source. But the unimportant compose the atmosphere of our life. They scatter the sun's rays, break the atmosphere into colours, and coax it into tenderness.

You have asked for my permission to abolish the matriculation class from our school. Let it go. I have no tenderness for it. In our classical literature it was the strict rule to give all dramas a happy ending. Our matriculation class has ever been the fifth act in our Asram, ending in a tragedy. Let us drop the scene, before that disaster gathers its forest!

I am enclosing with this a translation, which runs thus:

Woman

The fight is ended.
Shrill cries of loss trouble the air,
The gains, soiled and shattered, are a burden too heavy to
carry home.
Come, woman, bring thy breath of life.
Close all cracks with kisses of tender green,
Nurse the trampled dust into fruitfulness.

The morning wears on;
The stranger sits homeless by the roadside, playing on
his reed.
Come, woman, bring thy magic of love!
Make infinite the corner between walls,
There to build a world for him,—
Thine eyes its stars, thy voice its music.

The gate-door creaks in the wind.
The time is for leave-taking at the day's end.
Come woman, bring thy tears!
Let thy tremulous touch call out its last lyric
From the moment of parting.
Let the shadow of thy sad gaze
Haunt the road across the hills.

The night deepens;
The house is empty; its loneliness aches with silence.
Come, woman, bring thy lamp of vigil!
Enter thy secret chamber of sorrow.
Make the dark hours quiver with the agony of thy prayer.
Till the day dawns in the East.

New York, *February 5th, 1921*

Civilization in the West is a magnifying glass. It makes the most ordinary things hugely big. Its buildings, business, amusements, are exaggerations. The spirit of the West loves its high-heeled boots, whose heels are much bigger than itself.

Since I came to this continent my arithmetic has become absurdly bloated. It refused to be compressed within decent limits. But I can assure you that to carry such a burden even in my imagination is wearisome.

Yesterday, some Santiniketan photographs came by chance into my hands. I felt as if I was suddenly wakened up from a Brobdingnagian nightmare. I say to myself, This is our Santiniketan. It is ours, because it is not manufactured by a machine. Truth is beautiful—like woman in our own country. She never strains to add to her inches by carrying extravagances under her feet. Happiness is not in success, not in bigness, but in truth.

What makes me feel so sad, in this country, is the fact that people here do not know that they are not happy. They are proud, like the sandy desert, which is proud of its glitter. This Sahara is mightily big; but my mind turns its back upon it, and sings:

I will arise and go now, and go to Innisfree,
And a small cabin build there, of clay and wattles made;
Nine bean rows will I have there, a hive for the honey-bee,
And live alone in the bee-loud glade.

In the modern age, with all its facilities of communication, the access to Innisfree has become most difficult. Central Africa opens its secret to the inquisitive man, and also the North and South Pole—but the road to Innisfree lies in an eternal mystery.

Yet I belong to that "Isle of Innisfree": its true name is Santiniketan. But when I leave it, and cross over to the western shore, I feel occasionally frightened, lest I should lose my path back to it.

Oh! But how sweet is our *Sal* avenue, the breath of autumn in our *Shiuli* groves, the rainy evening resonant with music in Dinu's absurd little room!

And I shall have some peace there, for peace comes dropping slow,
Dropping from the veils of the morning to where the cricket sings;
There midnight's all a glimmer and noon a purple glow,
And, evening full of the linnet's wings.

Chapter VII

During the months of February and March 1921 the Non-co-operation movement reached its height in India. The appeal made to boycott the Government Schools and Colleges stirred the hearts of the students of Calcutta and some thousands of them came out. The atmosphere was electrical and the spirit of sacrifice was in the very air we breathed. My letters to the Poet were full of these things, and I myself was carried away in the enthusiasm of the moment. It is necessary to understand that the letters which the Poet wrote to me at this time were, in part at least, his own reaction to this news which reached him, week by week, from me. Gradually, as his health improved, his stay in America became brighter, and he wrote more cheerfully. He was specially delighted with his first visit to the Southern States, and deeply appreciated the warmth of heart he found among every class of people in those regions. With this very brief note of explanation, the letters that follow tell their own story and are easily intelligible.

On the voyage to Europe the Poet wrote, day after day, a separate letter to me. He did the same on his later journey from Europe to India and with some amusement gave me the whole series from his own letter-case on arrival at Santiniketan. This will account for the different letters written on board the ship which are reproduced in this volume.

New York, *February 8th, 1921*

I have just read a letter published in *Prabasi* by one who is at the Asram, and it has deeply hurt me. This is the ugliest side of patriotism. For in small minds, patriotism dissociates itself from the higher ideal of humanity. It becomes the magnification of self, on a stupendous scale—magnifying our vulgarity, cruelty, greed; dethroning God, to put up this bloated self in its place.

The whole world is suffering from this cult of Devil-worship in the present age, and I cannot tell you how deeply I am suffering, being surrounded in this country by endless ceremonials of this hideously profane cult. Everywhere there is an antipathy against Asia vented by a widespread campaign of calumny. Negroes are burnt alive, sometimes merely because they tried to exercise their right to vote, given to them by law. Germans are reviled. Conditions in Russia are deliberately misrepresented. They are furiously busy building their towers of political civilization upon the quagmire of mob psychology, spreading over it a crust of deliberate lies. They have to subsist upon a continual supply of hatred, contempt, jealousy, and lies and lies!

I am afraid I shall be rejected by my own people when I go back to India. My solitary cell is awaiting me in my motherland. In their present state of mind, my countrymen will have no patience with me, who believe God to be higher than my country.

I know such spiritual faith may not lead us to political success, but I say to myself, as Indian has ever said: "Even then—what?"

The more I live in this country the more I understand the true meaning of emancipation.

It is for India to keep her breast supplied with the *Amrita*[1] of wisdom, with which to feed the new-born age and nourish it into a mighty future.

---

1. *Amrita* is the divine nectar which gives immortal life.

The ideas to which politicians still cling belong to a past that is doomed. It is a wreck rushing towards annihilation. The West is beginning to have doubts about its shelter, but its habit of mind is preventing it from leaving the old shelter for a new one. But we unfortunate creatures are getting ready to jump into the stream and swim across to the sinking ship and fight for our place in its corner. Yet I know that our huts are safer than that doomed and drifting monster.

I long to live in the heart of Peace. I have done my work, and I hope that my Master will grant me leave to sit by Him, not to talk, but to listen to His own great silence.

Houston, Texas, February 23rd, 1921

Tied to the chariot-wheel of Karma we flit from one birth to another. What that means to the individual soul I have been made to realize in these last few days. It is my tyrant Karma which is dragging me from one hotel to another. Between my two hotel incarnations I usually have my sleep in a Pullman car, the very name of which suggests the agency of death. I am ever dreaming of the day when I shall attain my Nirvana, freed from this chain of hotel lives, and reach utter peace in Uttarayana.[2]

I have not written to you for some time. For I am tired to the profound depth of my being.

Yet, since coming to Texas, I have felt as it were a sudden coming of Spring into my life through a breach in the ice castle of Winter. It has come to me like a revelation that all these days my soul had been thirsting for the draught of sunshine poured from the beaker of infinite space. The sky has embraced me, and the warmth of its caress thrills me with joy.

---

2. The Poet's cottage at Santiniketan.

Chicago, *February 24th, 1921*

We have engaged our passage in a Dutch steamer, which will sail from New York on the 19th of March. My days in this country have not given me much pleasure—the simple course would have been for me to go straight back home.

Why did I not do so? No fool can say why he has been foolish. I have often dreamed of the time when my wayward youth took me to the loneliness of the sandbanks of the Padma, wandering in the neighbourhood of the wild-ducks under the gaze of the evening star. Certainly, that was not the life of the sane, but it fitted me like a fool's cap lined with dreams.

The fool who is content to do nothing whatever is at any rate free from care; but the one who tries in vain to change the face of the world knows no peace. I long to go back to my ducks, and yet I madly whirl round these manufacturing towns like a breath of the wild south breeze stirring the leaves of the documents of an attorney's office. Does it not know that these leaves do not shelter the flowers that wait for its whisper of love? Why should I be anything else but a poet? Was I not born a music-maker?

Chicago, *February 26th, 1921*

I have often wondered in my mind whether my path is the path of the good. When I came to this world I had nothing but a reed given to me, which was to find its only value in producing music. I left my school, I neglected my work, but I had my reed and I played on it "in mere idle sport." All along I had my one playmate, who also in His play produced music, among leaves, in rushing water, in silence of stars, in tears and laughter rippling into lights and shadows in the stream of human life. While my companion was this eternal Piper, this Spirit of play, I was nearest to the heart of the world. I knew its mother-tongue, and what

I sang was caught up by the chorus of the wind and water and the dance-master of life.

But now came the schoolmaster in the midst of my dream-world, and I was foolish enough to accept his guidance. I laid aside my reed, I left my playground, where the Infinite Child is spending his eternity "in mere idle sport." In a moment I became old and carried the burden of wisdom on my back, hawking truths from door to door.

Why have I been made to carry this burden, I ask myself over and over again, shouting myself hoarse in this noisy world where everybody is crying up his own wares? Pushing the wheelbarrows of propaganda from continent to continent—is this going to be the climax of a poet's life? It seems to me like an evil dream, from which I occasionally wake up in the dead of night and grope about in the bed asking myself in consternation: "Where is my music?"

It is lost, but I had no right to lose it, for I did not earn it with the sweat of my brow; it was a gift to me, which I could deserve if I knew how to love it. You know I have said somewhere that "God praises me when I do good; but God loves me when I sing." Praise is reward; it can be measured against the work you render; but love is above all rewards; it is measureless.

The poet who is true to his mission reaps his harvest of love; but the poet who strays into the path of the good is dismissed with applause. So I founded my International University—a great work! But I lose my little song—which loss can never be made up to me. How I wish I could find my reed again and be contemptuously ignored by the busy and the wise as a hopeless ne'er-do-well!

When I know for certain that I shall never be able to go back to that sweet obscurity which is the birthplace of flowers and songs, I feel home-sick. It is a world which is so near and yet so far away; so easy of access and yet so immensely difficult. Happiness we go on missing in our life, because it is so simple.

Chicago, *March 2nd, 1921*

Your last letter gives wonderful news about our students in Calcutta.[3] I hope that this spirit of sacrifice and willingness to suffer will grow in strength; for to achieve this is an end in itself. This is the true freedom! Nothing is of higher value—be it national wealth or independence—than disinterested faith in ideals, in the moral greatness of man.

The West has its unshakable faith in material strength and prosperity; and therefore, however loud grows the cry for peace and disarmament, its ferocity growls louder, gnashing its teeth and lashing its tail in impatience. It is like a fish, hurt by the pressure of the flood, planning to fly in the air. Certainly the idea is brilliant, but it is not possible for a fish to realize. We, in India, have to show the world what is that truth which not only makes disarmament possible but turns it into strength.

The truth that moral force is a higher power than brute force will be proved by the people who are unarmed. Life, in its higher development, has thrown off its tremendous burden of armour and a prodigious quantity of flesh, till man has become the conqueror of the brute world. The day is sure to come when the frail man of spirit, completely unhampered by air-fleets and dread-noughts, will prove that the meek are to inherit the earth.

It is in the fitness of things that Mahatma Gandhi, frail in body and devoid of all material resources, should call up the immense power of the meek that has been waiting in the heart of the destitute and insulted humanity of India. The

---

3. Referring to the boycott of schools and colleges by thousands of students.

destiny of India has chosen for its ally the power of soul, and not that of muscle. And she is to raise the history of man from the muddy level of physical conflict to the higher moral altitude.

What is Swaraj! It is *maya;* it is like a mist that will vanish, leaving no stain on the radiance of the Eternal. However we may delude ourselves with the phrases learnt from the West, Swaraj is not our objective. Our fight is a spiritual fight—it is for Man. We are to emancipate Man from the meshes that he himself has woven round him—these organizations of national egoism. The butterfly will have to be persuaded that the freedom of the sky is of higher value than the shelter of the cocoon. If we can defy the strong, the armed, the wealthy— revealing to the world the power of the immortal spirit—the whole castle of the Giant Flesh will vanish in the void. And then Man will find his Swaraj.

We, the famished ragged ragamuffins of the East, are to win freedom for all humanity. We have no word for "Nation" in our language. When we borrow this word from other people, it never fits us. For we are to make our league with *Narayan,*[4] and our triumph will not give us anything but victory itself: victory for God's world. I have seen the West; I covet not the unholy feast in which she revels every moment, growing more and more bloated and red and dangerously delirious. Not for us is this mad orgy of midnight, with lighted torches, but awakenment in the serene light of the morning.

Chicago, March 5th, 1921

Lately I have been receiving more and more news and newspaper cuttings from India, giving rise in my mind to a painful struggle that presages a period of suffering which is waiting for me. I am striving with all my power to tune my

---

4. The godlike element in man.

mood of mind to be in accord with the great feeling of excitement sweeping across my country. But, deep in my being, why is there this spirit of resistance maintaining its place in spite of my strong desire to remove it? I fail to find a clear answer; and through my gloom of dejection breaks out a smile and a voice saying: "Your place is on 'the sea-shore of worlds,' with children; there is your peace, and I am with you there."

This is why lately I have been playing with inventing new metres. These are merest nothings that are content to be borne away by the current of time, dancing in the sun and laughing as they disappear. But while I play, the whole creation is amused, for are not flowers and leaves never-ending experiments in metres? Is not my God an eternal waster of time? He flings stars and planets in the whirlwind of changes, he floats paper-boats of ages, filled with his fancies, on the rushing stream of appearance. When I tease him and beg him to allow me to remain his little follower and accept a few trifles of mine as the cargo of his play-boat, he smiles and I trot behind him catching the hem of his robe.

But where am I among the crowd, pushed from behind, pressed from all sides? And what is this noise about me? If it is a song, then my own *sitar* can catch the tune and I can join in the chorus; for I am a singer. But if it is a shout, then my voice is wrecked, and I am lost in bewilderment. I have been trying all these days to find in it a melody, straining my ear, but the idea of non-co-operation, with its mighty volume of sound, does not sing to me; its congregated menace of negation shouts. And I say to myself: "If you cannot keep step with your countrymen at this great crisis of their history, never say that you are right and the rest of them wrong; only, give up your rôle as a soldier, go back to your corner as a poet, be ready to accept popular derision and disgrace."

R—, in support of the present movement, has often said to me that passion for rejection is a stronger power in the beginning than the acceptance of an ideal. Though I know this to be a fact, I cannot take it as a truth. We must choose our allies once for all; for they stick to us even when we might be glad to be rid of them. If we once claim strength from intoxication, then in the time of reaction our normal strength is bankrupt, and we go back again and again to the demon that lends us resources in a vessel whose bottom it takes away.

Brahma-vidya, the cult of Brahma, the Infinite Being, has for its object *mukti,* emancipation; while Buddhism has *nirvana,* extinction. It may be argued that both have the same ideas in different names. But names represent attitudes of mind and emphasize particular aspects of truth. *Mukti* draws our attention to the positive, and *nirvana* to the negative side of truth. Buddha kept silence through his teachings about the truth of the *Om,* the Everlasting Yes, his implication being that by the negative path, destroying the self, we naturally reach that truth. Therefore he emphasized the fact of *dukkha,* misery, which had to be avoided. But *Brahma-vidya* emphasized the fact of *ananda,* joy, which had to be attained. The latter cult also needs for its fulfilment the discipline of self-abnegation; yet it holds before its view the idea of Brahma, not only at the end, but all through the process of realization.

Therefore the idea of life's training was different in the Vedic period from that of the Buddhistic. In the former it was the purification of life's joy; in the latter it was the eradication of it. The abnormal type of asceticism, to which Buddhism gave rise in India, revelled in celibacy and mutilation of life in all different forms. The forest life of the Brahman was not antagonistic to the social life of man, but harmonious with it. It was like our musical instrument, the *támbura,* whose duty is to supply the fundamental notes to the music to save it from straying into discordance. It believed in the music of the soul, and its own simplicity was not to kill it, but to guide it.

The idea of non-co-operation is political asceticism. Our students are bringing their offering of sacrifices to what? Not to a fuller education, but to non-education. It has at its back a fierce joy of annihilation, which at its best is asceticism, and at its worst that orgy of frightfulness in which human nature, losing faith in the basic reality of normal life, finds a disinterested delight in an unmeaning devastation, as has been shown in the late war and on other occasions which came nearer to us. "No," in its passive moral form, is asceticism, and in its active moral form violence. The desert is as much a form of *himsa*, violence, as is the raging sea in storm; they are both against life.

I remember the day, during the Swadeshi movement in Bengal, when a crowd of young students came to see me in the first floor of our Vichitra[5] house. They said to me that if I would order them to leave their schools and colleges they would instantly obey. I was emphatic in my refusal to do so, and they went away angry, doubting the sincerity of my love for my motherland. And yet long before this popular ebullition of excitement, I myself had given a thousand rupees, when I had not five rupees to call my own, to open a Swadeshi store and courted banter and bankruptcy.

The reason of my refusal to advise those students to leave their schools was because the anarchy of mere emptiness never tempts me, even when it is resorted to as a temporary measure. I am frightened at an abstraction which is ready to ignore living reality. These students were no mere plantoms to me. Their life was a great face to them and to the All, I could not lightly take upon myself the tremendous responsibility of a mere negative programme for them which

---

5. The Poet's hall of music in Calcutta.

would uproot their life from its soil, however thin and poor that soil might be. The great injury and injustice which had been done to those boys, who were tempted away from their career before any real provision was made, could never be made good to them. Of course, that is nothing from the point of view of an abstraction, which can ignore the infinite value even of the smallest fraction of reality. I wish I were the little creature Jack, whose one mission is to kill the Giant Abstraction, which is claiming the sacrifice of individuals all over the world under highly painted masks of delusion.

I say again and again that I am a poet; that I am not a fighter by nature. I would give everything to be one with my surroundings.

I love my fellow-beings and prize their love. Yet I have been chosen by destiny to ply my boat at that spot where the current is against me. What irony of fate is this, that I should be preaching co-operation of cultures between East and West on this side of the sea just at the moment when the doctrine of non-co-operation is preached on the other side!

You know that I do not believe in the material civilization of the West, just as I do not believe the physical body to be the highest truth in man. But I believe still less in the destruction of the physical body, and the ignoring of the material necessities of life. What is needed is the establishment of harmony between the physical and spiritual nature of man, the maintaining of balance between the foundation and superstructure. I believe in the true meeting of East and West. Love is the ultimate truth of soul. We should do all we can not to outrage that truth, but to carry its banner against all opposition. The idea of non-co-operation unnecessarily hurts that truth. It is not our hearth-fire, but the fire that burns out our hearth and home.

New York, *March 13ᵗʰ, 1921*

Things that are stationary have no responsibility and need no law. For death, even the tombstone is a useless luxury. But for a world, which is in ever-moving multitude advancing towards an idea, all its laws must have one principle of harmony. This is the law of creation.

Man became great when he found out this law for himself, the law of co-operation. It helped him to move together, to utilize the rhythm and impetus of the world march. He at once felt that this moving together was not mechanical, not an external regulation for the sake of some convenience. It was what the metre is in poetry—not a mere system of enclosure for keeping ideas from running away in disorder, but for vitalizing them, making them indivisible in a unity of creation.

So far this idea of co-operation has developed itself into individual communities, within the boundaries of which peace has been maintained and varied wealth of life produced. But outside these boundaries the law of co-operation has not been realized. Consequently, the great world of man is suffering from ceaseless discordance. We are beginning to discover that our problem is world-wide, and no one people of the earth can work out its salvation by detaching itself from others. Either we shall be saved together or drawn together into destruction.

This truth has ever been recognized by all the great personalities of the world. They had in themselves the perfect consciousness of the undivided spirit of man. Their teachings were against tribal exclusiveness, and thus we find that Buddha's India transcended geographical India and Christ's religion broke through the bonds of Judaism.

To-day, at this critical moment of the world's history, cannot India rise above her limitations and offer the great ideal to the world that will work towards harmony and co-operation between the different peoples of the earth? Men of feeble faith will say that India requires to be strong and rich before she can raise her voice for the sake of the whole world. But I refuse to believe it. That the measure of man's greatness is in his material resources is a gigantic illusion casting its shadow over the present-day world—it is an insult to man. It lies in the power of the materially weak to save the world from this illusion; and India, in spite of her penury and humiliation, can afford to come to the rescue of humanity.

The freedom of unrestrained egoism in the individual is licence and not true freedom. For his truth is in that which is universal in him. Individual human races also attain true freedom when they have the freedom of perfect revelation of Man and not that of their aggressive racial egoism. The idea of freedom which prevails in modern civilization is superficial and materialistic. Our revolution in India will be a true one when its forces are directed against this crude idea of liberty.

The sunlight of love has the freedom that ripens the wisdom of immortal life; but passion's fire can only forge fetters for ourselves. The Spiritual Man has been struggling for its emergence into perfection, and every true cry of freedom is for this emancipation. Erecting barricades of fierce separateness, in the name of national necessity, is offering hindrance to it. Therefore in the long run it is building a prison for the nation itself. For the only path of deliverance for nations is in the ideal humanity.

Creation is an endless activity of God's freedom; it is an end in itself. Freedom is true when it is a revelation of truth. Man's freedom is for the revelation of the truth of Man, which is struggling to express itself. We have not yet fully realized it. But those people who have faith in its greatness, who acknowledge its sovereignty, and have the instinctive urging in the heart to break down obstructions, are paving the way for its coming.

India has ever nourished faith in the truth of the Spiritual Man, for whose realization she has made in the past innumerable experiments, sacrifices and penances, some verging on the grotesque and the abnormal. But the fact is she has never ceased in her attempt to find it, even though at the tremendous cost of losing material success. Therefore I feel that the true India is an idea, and not a mere geographical fact. I have come into touch with this idea in far-away places of Europe, and my loyalty was drawn to it in persons who belonged to countries different from mine. India will be victorious when this idea wins the victory—the idea of "Purusham mahantam adityavarnam tamasah parastat"—"The Infinite Personality, whose Light reveals itself through the obstruction of Darkness." Our fight is against this Darkness. Our object is the revealment of the Light of this Infinite Personality of Man. This is not to be achieved in single individuals, but in one grand harmony of all human races. The darkness of egoism which will have to be destroyed is the egoism of the Nation. The idea of India is against the intense consciousness of the separateness of one's own people from others, which inevitably leads to ceaseless conflicts. Therefore my own prayer is, let India stand for the co-operation of all peoples of the world.

The spirit of rejection finds its support in the consciousness of separateness; the spirit of acceptance finds its base in the consciousness of unity. India has ever declared that Unity is Truth, and separateness is *maya*. This unity is not a zero; it is that which comprehends all, and therefore can never be reached through the path of negation.

Our present struggle to alienate our heart and mind from the West is an attempt at spiritual suicide. If, in the spirit of national vainglory, we shout from our house-tops that the West has produced nothing that has an infinite value for man, then we only create a serious cause of doubt about the worth of any product of the Eastern mind. For it is the mind of Man, in the East and West, which is ever approaching Truth in her different aspects from different angles of vision. If it can be true that the standpoint of the West has betrayed it into an utter misdirection then we can never be sure of the standpoint of the East. Let us be rid of all false pride and rejoice at any lamp being lit in any corner of the world, knowing that it is a part of the common illumination of our house.

The other day I was invited to the house of a distinguished art-critic of America who is a great admirer of old Italian Art. I questioned him if he knew anything of our Indian pictures, and he brusquely said that most probably he would hate them. I suspected he had seen some of them and hated them already. In retaliation, I could have said something in the same language about Western Art. But I am proud to say it was not possible for me to do so. For I always try to understand Western Art and never to hate it.

Whatever we understand and enjoy in human products instantly becomes ours, wherever they might have their origin. I am proud of my humanity, when I can acknowledge the poets and artists of other countries as my own. Let me feel with unalloyed gladness that all the great glories of man are mine. Therefore it hurts me deeply when the cry of rejection rings loud against the West in my country with the clamour that Western education can only injure us.

It cannot be true. What has caused the mischief is the fact that for a long time we have been out of touch with our own culture and therefore Western culture has not found its true perspective in our life. Very often its perspective is wrong, giving our mental eye a squint. When we have intellectual capital of our own, the commerce of thought with the outer world becomes natural and fully profitable. But to say that such commerce is inherently wrong is to encourage the worst form of provincialism, productive of nothing but intellectual indigence.

The West has misunderstood the East. This is at the root of the disharmony that prevails between them. But will it mend matters if the East in her turn tries to misunderstand the West? The present age has been powerfully possessed by the West; it has only become possible because to her is given some great mission for man. We, from the East, have come to her to learn whatever she has to teach us; for by doing so we hasten the fulfilment of this age. We know that the East also has her lessons to give, and she has her own responsibility of not allowing her light to be extinguished. The time will come when the West will find leisure to realize that she has a home of hers in the East where her food is and her rest.

New York, March 18th, 1921

I wish that I could be released from this mission. For such missions are like a mist that envelops our soul—they seem to shut us off from the direct touch of God's world. And yet, I have such an immense hunger for this touch. The springtime has come—the sky is overflowing with sunshine. I long to be one with the birds and trees and the green earth. The call comes to me from the air to sing, but, wretched creature that I am, I lecture—and by doing it I ostracize myself from this great world of songs to which I was born. Manu, the Indian lawgiver, enjoins us not to cross the sea. But I have done so; I have sailed away from my native universe—from the birthplace of those morning jasmines, from the lotus lake of Saraswati, which greeted me when I was a child even as the finger-touch of my own mother. Now, when occasionally I come back to them, I am made to feel that I have lost my caste; and though they call me by my name and speak to me, they keep themselves apart.

I know that my own river Padma, who has so often answered to my music with an amused gleam of tender tolerance in her face, will separate herself from me behind an invisible veil when I come to her. She will say to me in a sad voice: "Thou hast crossed the sea!"

The losing of Paradise is enacted over and over again by the children of Adam and Eve. We clothe our souls with messages and doctrines and lose the touch of the great life in the naked breast of Nature. This letter of mine, carrying the cry of a banished soul, will sound utterly strange to you in the present-day India.

We hold our mathematical classes in Santiniketan under the *madhavi*[6] bower. Is it not good for the students and others that, even in the busiest time of lessons, the branches overhead do not break out into a shower of geometrical propositions? Is it not good for the world that poets should forget all about the resolutions carried at monster meetings? Is it not right that God's own regiment of the useless should never be conscripted for any military contingency of the useful?

When the touch of spring is in the air, I suddenly wake up from my nightmare of giving "messages" and remember that I belong to the eternal band of good-for-nothings; I hasten to join in their vagabond chorus. But I hear the whisper round me: "This man has crossed the sea," and my voice is choked.

We are leaving Europe to-morrow and my days of exile are coming to an end. Very likely my letters will be fewer in number from now, but I shall make up for this when I meet you in person under the shadow of the rain-clouds of July.

Pearson is busy seeking health and happiness, making himself ready for the time when he will join us in India in the cold season.

S.S. "Rhyndam"

The very fact that we have turned our face towards the East fills my heart with joy. For me my East is the poet's East,

6. White jasmine.

not that of a politician or scholar. It is the East of the magnanimous sky and exuberant sunlight, where once upon a time a boy found himself straying in the dim twilight of child-consciousness peopled with dreams. The child has grown, but never grown out of his childhood.

I realize it all the more strongly when some problem, political or otherwise, becomes clamorous and insistent, trying to exact its answer from me. I rouse myself, strain my mind, raise my voice for prophetic utterances, and try in every way to be worthy of the occasion, but in my heart of hearts I feel exceedingly small and, to my utter dismay, discover I am not a leader, not a teacher, and farthest of all away from being a prophet.

The fact becomes fully evident to me, that I had forgotten to grow. It comes of an incorrigible absentmindedness. My mind has ever wandered away from those things that mature one into wisdom and old age. I have neglected my lessons. And this utter want of training makes me such a wretchedly bad reader of journals dealing with the practical questions of the day! But I am afraid the present time is a tremendously difficult one in India for the child, the poet. It is no use protesting that he is lacking in understanding—that he is congenitally incapable of paying attention to anything urgent and serious. No, he must attend meetings or write editorials; cultivate cotton-fields, or accept some responsibility of grave and national importance, in order to make a fool of himself.

And yet my heart is aching and longing to meet, with proper ceremony, the first day of the rainy season, or fill every pore of my mind with the smell of mango blossoms. Is that allowable at the present moment? Does our south breeze still enjoy all the frivolities of spring days? Have our sunset hours taken the vow of discarding all traces of colours from their cloud turbans?

But what is the use of complaining? The poets are too primitive for this age. If they had not ignominiously been discarded by the law of evolution, they would long ago have grown into their career as politicians. But the mischief is— they have been left behind in a world which has stopped growing, where things are still important which have no use or market value. The more the call for action grows loud from across the sea, the more I feel conscious of something in me that cries: "I am of no use—leave me alone to my utter inutility."

But I know, when I reach India, the Poet will be defeated; and I shall piously study the newspapers—every paragraph of them. But for the present even poetry is at a disadvantage— for the sea is rough, my head is swimming, and the English language is extremely difficult to manage in a rolling ship.

S.S. "Rhyndam"

Sometimes, it amuses me to see the struggle for supremacy that is going on between the different persons within me. In the present condition of India, when the call is sure to come to me to take some part, in some manner or other, in some political affairs, the Poet at once feels nervous, thinking that his claims are likely to be ignored, simply because he is the most useless member in the confederacy of my personality. He fully anticipates that argument against him, and takes special pains to glorify his deficiency even before any complaint has been submitted by anybody on this point. He has proudly begun to assert: "I belong to the great brotherhood of the supremely useless. I am the cup-bearer of the Gods. I share the common privilege with all divinities to be misunderstood. My purpose is to reveal Purposelessness to the children of the Immortal. I have nothing to do with committee meetings or laying of foundation-stones for structures that stand against the passage of time and are sure to be trampled to dust. I am to ply the ferry-boat that keeps open the traffic between this shore and the shore of Paradise—this is our King's mail-boat for the communication of messages, and not for carrying cargo to the markets."

I say to him: "Yes, I fully agree with you; but, at the same time, take my warning, that your mail-boat may have to be commandeered for other urgent purposes, wholly unconnected with the Celestial Postal Department." His cheeks grow pale; his eyes become bemisted; his frail body shivers like a cypress at the first breath of winter, and he says to me: "Do I deserve to be treated like this? Have you lost all your love for me, that you can talk of putting me under martial law? Did you not drink your first cup of Amrita from my hand, and has not the Citizenship of the Sphere of Music been conferred upon you through my persuasion?"

I sit dumb, and muse and sigh, when sheaves of newspaper-cuttings are poured upon my table, and a leer is spread upon the face of the Practical man; he winks at the Patriotic man sitting solemnly by his side; and the man who is Good thinks it his painful duty to oppose the Poet, whom he is ready to treat with some indulgence within proper limits.

As for me who am the President of this *Panchayat*,[7] I have my deepest sentiment of tenderness for this Poet, possibly because he is so utterly good-for-nothing and always the first to be ignored in the time of emergency. The timid Poet avoiding the observation of the Practical and the Good comes to my side and whispers: "Sir, you are not a man made for the time of emergency—but for the time that transcends it on all sides."

The rascal knows well how to flatter, and generally wins his case with me—especially when others are too certain of the result of their appeal; and I jump up from my judgement-seat

---

7. Committee.

and, holding the Poet by the hand, dance a jig and sing: "I shall join you Comrade, and be drunk and gloriously useless." Ah, my evil luck! I know why the chairmen of meetings hate me, newspaper editors revile me, and the virile call me effeminate! So I try to take shelter among the children, who have the gift of being glad with things and men that have no value.

S.S. "Rhyndam"

My difficulty is that when, in my environment, some intense feeling of pride or resentment concentrates its red light within a certain limited area, I lose my true perspective of life and the world, and it hurts deeply my nature. It is not true that I do not have any special love for my own country, but when it is in its normal state it does not obstruct outside reality; on the contrary, it offers a standpoint and helps me in my natural relationship with others. But when that standpoint itself becomes a barricade, then something in me asserts that my place is somewhere else.

I have not yet attained that spiritual altitude from which I can say, with perfect assurance, that such barricading is wrong, or even unnecessary; but some instinct in me says that there is a great deal of unreality in it, as there is in all passions that are generated through contraction of consciousness, through rejection of a great part of truth.

I remember your wondering why Christ gave no expression to His patriotism, which was so intense in the Jewish people. It was because the great truth of man, which He realized, through His love of God, would only be cramped and crushed within that enclosure. I have a great deal of the patriot and politician in me, and therefore I am frightened of them; and I have an inner struggle against submitting myself to their sway.

But I must not be misunderstood. There is such a thing as a moral standard of judgement. When India suffers from injustice, it is right that we should stand against it; and the responsibility is ours to right the wrong, not as Indians, but as human beings. There your position is higher than most of our countrymen's. You have accepted the cause of India for the sake of humanity. But I know that most of our people will accept your help as a matter of course and yet reject your lesson. You are fighting against that patriotism whereby the West has humiliated the East—the patriotism which is national egoism. This is a comparatively later growth in European history and a far greater cause of misery and injustice in the human world than the blood-thirsty ferocity, the nomadic savagery, in the primitive history of man. The Pathans came to India, and the Moghuls, and they perpetrated misdeeds in their heedlessness; but because they had no taint of patriotism they did not attack India at the very root of her life, keeping themselves superciliously aloof. Gradually they were growing one with us; and just as the Normans and Saxons combined into one people, our Muhammadan invaders would ultimately have lost their line of separateness and contributed to the richness and strength of Indian civilization.

We must remember that Hinduism is not the original Aryanism; in fact, a great portion of it is non-Aryan. Another great mixture had been awaiting us, the mixture with the Muhammadans. I know that there were difficulties in its way. But the greatest of all difficulties was lacking—the idolatry of Geography. Just see what hideous cries are being committed by British patriotism in Ireland! It is a python which refuses to disgorge this living creature which struggles to live its separate life. For patriotism is proud of its bulk, and in order to hold in a bond of unity the units that have their own distinct individualities it is ever ready to use means that are inhuman. Our own patriots would do just the same thing, if the occasion arose. When a minority of our population claimed its right of inter-caste marriage, the majority cruelly refused to allow it that freedom. It would not acknowledge a difference which was natural and real, but was willing to perpetrate a moral torture far more reprehensible than a physical one. Why? Because power lies in number and in extension. Power, whether in the patriotic or in any other form, is no lover of freedom. It talks of unity, but forgets that true unity is that of freedom. Uniformity is unity of bondage.

Suppose, in our Swaraj, the anti-Brahmin community refuses to join hands with us; suppose, for the sake of its self-respect and self-expression, it tries to keep an absolute independence—patriotism will try to coerce it into an unholy union. For patriotism has its passion of power; and power builds its castle upon arithmetic. I love India, but my India is an Idea and not a geographical expression. Therefore, I am *not* a patriot—I shall ever seek my compatriots all over the world. You are one of them, and I am sure there are many others.

S.S. "Rhyndam"

Plato threatened to banish all poets from his Republic. Was it in pity or in anger, I wonder? Will our Indian Swaraj, when it comes to exist, pass a deportation order against all feckless creatures who are pursuers of phantoms and fashioners of dreams, who neither dig nor sow, bake nor boil, spin nor darn, neither move nor support resolutions?

I have often tried to imagine the banished hordes of poets establishing their own Republic in the near neighbourhood of that of Plato. Naturally, as an act of reprisal, His Excellency the Poet President is sure to banish from the Rhymers' Republic all philosophers and politicians. Just think of the endless possibilities arising from feuds and truces of these rival Republics—peace conferences, deputations of representatives, institutions with busy secretaries and permanent funds having for their object the bridging of the gulf between the two adversaries. Then think of a trivial accident, through which a hapless young man and a melancholy maiden, coming from the opposite territories, meet at the frontier, and owing to the influence of the conjunction of their respective planets fall in love with each other.

There is no harm in supposing that the young man is the son of the President of the Philosophers' Republic, while the maiden is the daughter of that of the Poets'. The immediate consequence is the secret smuggling of forbidden love-lyrics by the desperate youth into the very heart of the commentaries and controversies of the two contradictory schools of Philosophy—the one professed by the yellow-turbaned sages, proclaiming that *one* is truth and *two* is an illusion, and the other, which is the doctrine of the green-turbaned sages, asserting that *two* is truth and *one* is an illusion.

Then came the day of the great meeting, presided over by the Philosopher President, when the pandits of the two factions met to fight their dialectic duels finally to decide the truth. The din of debates grew into a tumultuous hubbub; the supporters of both parties threatened violence and the throne of truth was usurped by shouts. When these shouts were about to be transmuted into blows, there appeared in the arena the pair of lovers who, on the night of the full moon of April, were secretly wedded, though such inter-marriage was against the law. When they stood in the open partition between the two parties, a sudden hush fell upon the assembly.

How this unexpected and yet ever-to-be-expected event, mixed with texts liberally quoted from the proscribed love-lyrics, ultimately helped to reconcile the hopeless contradiction in logic is a long story. It is well known to those who have had the privilege to pursue the subsequent verdict of the judges that both doctrines are held to be undoubtedly true: that *one* is in *two*, and therefore *two* must find itself in *one*. The acknowledgment of this principle helped to make the inter-marriage valid, and since then the two Republics have successfully carried out their disarmament, having discovered for the first time that the gulf between them was imaginary.

Such a simple and happy ending of this drama has caused widespread unemployment and consequent feeling of disgust among the vast number of secretaries and missionaries belonging to the institutions maintained, with the help of permanent funds, for the preaching of Union—those organizations which were so enormously perfect in their machinery that they could well afford to ignore the insignificant fact of their barrenness of result. A large number of these individuals gifted with an ineradicable passion for doing good are joining the opposite organizations, which have their permanent funds, in order to help them to prove and to preach that two is two and never the twain shall meet.

That the above story is a true one will, I am sure, be borne out by the testimony of even the august shade of Plato himself. This episode of the game of hide-and-seek of one in two should be sung by some poet; and therefore, I request you to give it, with my blessing, to Satyendranath Datta,[8] that he may set it in those inimitable verse forms of which he is a master, and make it ring with the music of his happy laughter.

S.S. "Rhyndam"

The sea has been exceedingly rough. The wild east wind, playing its snake-charmer's bagpipe, has made a myriad of hissing waves raise their hoods to the sky. The rude handling by the sea does not affect me much, but the gloom and unrest and the tremendous rise and fall of the waves, like a giant's beating of the breast in despair, depress my mind.

---

8. A young poet of Bengal, greatly admired by Rabindranath Tagore. He has since, unfortunately, died.

The sad thought very often comes to me, with an imaginary supposition, that I may never reach the Indian shore; and my heart aches with longing to see the arms of my motherland extended into the sea with the palm-leaves rustling in the air. It is the land where I gazed into the eyes of my first great sweetheart—my muse—who made me love the sunlight, touching the top of the coconut row through a pale mist of the serene autumn morning, and the storm-laden rain-clouds rolling up from some abyss behind the horizon, carrying in their dark folds a thrilling expectation of a mad outburst of showers.

But where is this sweetheart of mine, who was almost the only companion of my boyhood, and with whom I spent my idle days of youth exploring the mysteries of dreamland? She, my Queen, has died; and my world has shut against me the door of that inner apartment of beauty which gives the real taste of freedom. I feel like Shah-Jehan when his beloved Mumtaz was dead. Now I have left to me my own progeny— a magnificent plan of an International University. But it will be like Aurangzeb, who will keep me imprisoned and become my lord and master to the end of my days. Every day my fear and distrust against it are growing in strength. For it has been acquiring power from outside my own resources, and it is material power.

Santiniketan has been the playground of my own spirit. What I created on its soil was made of my own dream-stuff. Its materials are few; its regulations are elastic; its freedom has the inner restraint of beauty. But the International University will be stupendous in weight and rigid in construction; and if we try to move it, it will crack. It will grow up into a bully of a brother, and browbeat its sweet elder sister into a cowering state of subjection. Beware of organization, my friend! They say, organization is necessary in order to give a thing its permanence, but it may be the permanence of a tombstone.

This letter of mine will seem to you pessimistic. The reason is I am unwell and utterly home-sick; and the vision of home which haunts my mind night and day is "Amader Santiniketan."⁹ But the big towers of the International University obstruct its view. I am tired, to the marrow of my bones, trying all these months for a purpose and working in a direction which is against the natural current of my inner being.

S.S. "Rhyndam"

You, who are given a stable and solid surface on which to work out your problems of daily life, cannot fully realize what a trial it has been for us, these two days, to be tossed upon a wild sea every moment of our existence. I do not feel sea-sick, but the great fact for us is, that we are the children of the land. This is an immovable fact—and yet, when this fact begins to move, it is not only misery, but also an affront to us. The whole sea seems to laugh loud at the conceited creatures who only have a pair of tottering legs and not even a fraction of a fin.

Every moment the dignity of man is outraged by making him helplessly tumble about in an infinite variety of awkwardness. He is compelled to take part in a very broad farce; and nothing can be more humiliating for him than to exhibit a comic appearance in his very sufferings. It is like making the audience roar with laughter by having the clown kicked into all manners of helpless absurdities. While sitting, walking, taking meals, we are constantly being hurled about into unexpected postures which are shamefully inconvenient.

When Gods try to become funny in their sublime manner of perpetrating jokes we mortal creatures find ourselves at a

---

9. Referring to a song which the boys sing at the Asram, whose refrain is "Amader Santiniketan," meaning "Our Santiniketan."

terrible disadvantage; for their huge laughter, carried by the millions of roaring waves in flashing foam, keeps its divine dignity unimpaired, while we, on our side, find our self-respect knocked to pieces. I am the only individual in this steamer who is vying with the Gods by fashioning my misery into laughing words and refusing to be the mere passive instrument of an elemental foolery. A laughter which is tyranny has to be answered by another laughter of rebellion. And this letter of mine carries the laughter of defiance. I had no other object in sitting down to write this morning; I had nothing particular to say to you, and to try to think when the ship is rolling in such an insane manner is like trying to carry a full vessel of water while one is drunk; the greater part of the contents is spilt. And yet I must write this letter, merely to show that, though at the present moment I cannot stand erect on my legs, I can write. This is to assert, in the face of the ironical clapping of hands of the mighty Atlantic, that my mind not only can stand up straight in its world of language, but can run, and even dance. This is my triumph.

To-day is Tuesday; on the morning of Thursday we are expected to reach Plymouth. Your letters have helped me more than anything else during these extremely trying months of my exile—they have been like food and water to a soldier who is dragging his wounded and weary limbs, counting every step, across a difficult and doubtful road back to his camp-fire. However, I am coming to my journey's end and intensely hoping to see you when I reach home. What I have suffered, God only knows.—I am longing for rest.

Chapter VIII

The few days spent in England on the Poet's return from America were on the whole happier and brighter than those of the previous year when the Dyer Debate in the House of Lords had poisoned the air. But he did not stay long enough to meet all those who were eagerly waiting his arrival. He had received invitations from every part of the Continent, and his time was short; for he had determined to get back to India at the earliest possible moment. In the letters from the Continent which follow in this chapter only a very slight portion of what actually happened is told. Many of his letters to me, at his own special request, have not been published; for in his self-diffidence he was almost ashamed, afterwards, to allow any record of the scenes of enthusiasm that greeted him everywhere to appear in print. Very rarely in history has a poet received such a welcome.

What touched him most deeply was the spiritual longing that was behind it all—the earnest hope, especially in the regions of Europe recently devastated by the war, that some light might come from the East to illumine the darkness. The ideal of Visva-bharati, which had become somewhat vague and nebulous before, now took on a more definite concrete shape. At the same time, he could not help but feel sadly that the cries of non-co-operation, which were so strident in India, would lead to his rejection by his own countrymen on his return.

Such a rejection did not take place, because in the heart of the national movement, under the leadership of Mahatma Gandhi, there was a common centre in the universal principle of Ahimsa, or Non-violence, which Mahatma Gandhi professed. No one admired more than the Poet Mahatma Gandhi's spiritual appeal against brute force and his passionate devotion to the service of the poor.

London, *April 10th, 1921*

I am glad to be in England again. One of the first men whom I happened to meet here was H.W. Nevinson; I felt that man's soul was alive in this country, which had produced such a man as that!

A land should be judged by its best products, and I have no hesitation in saying that the best Englishmen are the best specimens of humanity in the world.

With all our grievances against the English nation, I cannot help loving your country, which has given me some of my dearest friends. I am intensely glad of this fact, for it is hateful to hate. Just as a general tries, for his tactics, to attract a whole army of men into a *cul-de-sac*, in order to demolish them, our feeling of anger generalizes the whole people of a country, in order mentally to give them a crushing blow on a tremendously big scale.

Things that are happening in Ireland are ugly. The political lies that are accompanying them are stupendous and in retaliation our anger seeks a victim adequately big; and we readily incriminate the whole people of England, though we know that a great number of Englishmen feel shame and sorrow for these brutalities quite as keenly as any disinterested outsiders.

The fact that such a great proportion of people here— whose interest in keeping Ireland tied to the British Empire is so vital—can feel so keenly the tyranny inflicted on the Irish people, proves the inherent love of justice that thrives in the heart of this country in spite of all aberrations. The saving of a people depends upon the noble personalities holding up the moral tradition high above the floods of iniquity that occasionally deluge the land.

Edmund Burke proves the greatness of Great Britain in spite of Warren Hastings; and we are grateful to Mahatma Gandhi for giving India the opportunity to prove that her faith in the Divine Spirit in man is alive still—in spite of a great deal of materialism in our religions, as they are practised, and a spirit of exclusiveness in our social system.

The fact is that the best people in all countries find their affinity with one another. The fuel displays its differences, but the fire is one. When the fire comes before my vision in this country I recognize it as the same thing which lights our path in India and illuminates our house. Let us seek that fire and know that wherever the spirit of separation is supreme there reigns darkness. But with the realization of unity comes truth and light. When we ignite our lamps, we at once send response to the eternal lights of heaven. You yourself are a bearer of a lamp from your own land, and let me in response light my own lamp with love for the great humanity revealed in your country.

[*The following letter (a copy of which he enclosed) was in answer to a lady who had complained that the Poet had appeared to give vent to a feeling of anger against the British people in one of his lectures.*]

London, *April 12th, 1921*

Dear Madam,

I received your letter late that morning, and was sorry to learn that you had come to this hotel while I was engaged.

It is not unlikely that some unsuspected remnant of race-consciousness in your mind made you imagine that I gave vent to my feeling of anger against the British people in my lecture. I deeply feel for all the races who are being insulted and injured by the ruthless exploitation of the powerful nations belonging to the West or the East. I feel as much for the negroes, brutally lynched in America, often for economic reasons, and for the Koreans, who are the latest victims of Japanese imperialism, as for any wrongs done to the helpless multitude of my own country. I feel certain that Christ, were He living at the present day, would have been angry with the nations who attempt to thrive upon the life-blood of their victim races, just as He was angry with those who defiled God's temple with their unholy presence and profession. Surely He would have taken upon Himself the chastisement of these miscreants, especially when those who professed to be His disciples, whose ostensible vocation was to preach peace and brotherhood of man, either kept a discreet silence whenever man's history waited for a voice of judgement or showed signs of virulence against the weak and down-trodden greatly surpassing that of men whose profession it was blindly to kill human beings.

On the other hand, though I sometimes congratulate myself on my own freedom from race-consciousness, very likely a sufficient amount of it is lingering in my subconscious mind, making itself evident to outsiders in my writings through special emphasis of indignation at any unjust suffering or humiliation that my own country is made to undergo. I hope that I can claim forgiveness for this weakness, considering that I never try to condone any wrongs done by my own countrymen against others belonging to different countries from ours.

Autour Du Monde, Paris, *April 18th, 1921*

I have come back to the domain of dust from my short aeroplane career in mid-air, when my namesake from the high heaven, the Sun[1] shed upon me his smile of amused tenderness and some vagabond clouds of the April sky seemed to wonder in their minds if I were about to join their ranks.

Whenever I find time and sit alone before the window, I gravely nod my head and say to myself in a sad voice: "Those who have been born foolish can gladden the heart of God only when they have the freedom of solitariness and can spread their idle wings in the air and flit and hum for nothing at all. You, poet, are one such creature—you have to be alone to fulfil your nature. What is all this that you are planning? Must you guide the multitude and work with them for the building of an Institution?"

All through my life I have ever worked alone; for my life and my work have been one. I am like the tree, which builds up its timber by its own living process; and therefore it needs leisure and space, sunlight and air and not bricks and mortar, masons and the civil engineer.

All my poems have their roots in my dreams. But an International University needs a foundation, and not roots. It needs to be solidly built upon international boards and committees and funds contributed by men of prudence and foresight. Foresight is a gift which I wholly lack. I may have some insight, but no foresight at all. Foresight has the power of calculation: insight has the power of vision. He may have faith in insight to whom it belongs; and therefore he is not afraid of making mistakes or even of apparent failures. But foresight is impatient of all deficiencies. It constantly dwells on the possibilities of mistakes, only because it has not the vision of the whole. Therefore its plans are mostly solid and inflexible.

In the establishment of the International University the foresight of the experienced will never forsake me; it will go

---

1. Referring to his name Rabi, which means the Sun.

straight to the helm and take charge; and only then the prudent who give money and the wise who give advice will be satisfied. But where will remain the place for the foolish and the irresponsible?

The whole thing will have to be established on a permanent basis; but this so-called permanence is only bought at the cost of life and freedom. The cage is permanent, not the nest. And yet all that is truly permanent has to pass through an endless series of impermanences. The spring flowers are permanent, because they know how to die. The temple made of stone cannot make truce with death by accepting it. Proud of its bricks and mortar, it constantly opposes death, till it is defeated in the end.

Our Santiniketan depends for its permanence upon life. But an International University tries to build its permanence with the help of rules and regulations. But—

Never mind! Let me forget it for a moment. Possibly I am exaggerating. The reason is, the day is full of gloom. It has been snowing and raining; the road is muddy; and am home-sick.

I am requested by some association to read a paper at one of their meetings. They asked me for a summary, which they will circulate among the members. I enclose a copy of it which I have given to them for circulation.

THE SUMMARY OF A LECTURE

From the beginning of their history the Western races have had to deal with Nature as their antagonist. This fact has emphasized in their minds the dualistic aspect of truth, the eternal conflict between good and evil. Thus it has kept up the spirit of fight in the heart of their civilization. They seek victory and cultivate power.

The environment in which the Aryan immigrants found themselves in India was that of the forest. The forest, unlike the desert or sea, is living; it gives shelter and nourishment to life. In such surroundings, the ancient forest-dwellers of India realized the spirit of harmony with the universe and emphasized in their minds the monistic aspect of Truth. They sought the realization of their souls through union with all. The spirit of fight and the spirit of harmony both have their importance in the scheme of things. For making a musical instrument, the obduracy of materials has to be forced to yield to the purpose of the instrument-maker. But music itself is a revelation of beauty, it is not an outcome of fight; it springs from an inner realization of harmony. The musical instrument and the music both have their own importance for humanity.

The civilization that fights and conquers for Man, and the civilization that realizes for him the fundamental unity in the depth of existence, are complementary to each other. When they join hands, human nature finds its balance; and its pursuits, through rugged paths, attain their ultimate meaning in an ideal of perfection.

Autour Du Monde, Paris, *April 21ˢᵗ, 1921*

When I sent my appeal for an International Institution to the Western people, I made use of the word "University" for the sake of convenience. But that word has not only an inner meaning, but also an outer association in the minds of those who use it; and that fact tortures my idea into its own rigid shape. It is unfortunate.

I should not allow my idea to be pinned to a word for a foreign museum, like a dead butterfly. It must be known, not by a definition, but by its own life-growth.

In the past I saved our Santiniketan School from being trampled into smoothness by the steam-roller of the Education Department. Our school is poor in resources and equipment, but it has the wealth of truth in it which no money can ever buy; and I am proud of the fact that it is not a machine-made article perfectly modelled in a workshop—it is our very own.

If we must have a University, it should spring from our own life and be maintained by our own life. Someone may say that such freedom is dangerous and that a machine will help to lessen our personal responsibility and make things easy for us. Yes! Life has its risks, and freedom has its responsibility; and yet they are preferable on account of their own immense value, and not for any other ulterior results.

So long, I have been able to retain my perfect independence and self-respect, because I had faith in my own resources and proudly worked within their sovereign limits. My bird must still retain its freedom of wings and not be tamed into a sumptuous non-entity by any controlling agency outside its own living organism. I know that the idea of an International University is complex, but I must make it simple in my own way. I shall be content if it attracts round it men who have neither name nor fame nor worldly means, but who have the mind and faith; who are to create a great future with their dreams.

Very likely I shall never be able to work with a Board of Trustees, influential and highly respectable—for I am a vagabond at heart. But the powerful people of the world, the lords of the earth, make it difficult for me to carry out my work. I know it, and I have had experience of it in connection with Santiniketan. But I am not afraid of failure. I am only afraid of being tempted away from truth, in pursuit of success. The temptation assaults me occasionally; but it comes from the outside atmosphere. My own abiding faith is in life and light and freedom. And my prayer is:

"Lead me from the unreal to Truth."

This letter of mine is to let you know that I free myself from the bondage of help and go back to join with you the great "Brotherhood of the Tramps," who seem helpless, but are recruited by God for His own army.

Strasbourg, *April 29ᵗʰ, 1921*

I am writing this from Strasbourg, where I am going to read my lecture at the University this evening.

I miss you very much at this moment; for I feel certain it would overwhelm you with happiness could you be with me now, realizing the great outburst of love for me in the continental countries of Europe which I have visited. I have never asked for it, or striven for it, and I never can believe that I have deserved it. However, if it be more than is due to me, I am in no way responsible for this mistake. For I could have remained perfectly happy in my obscurity to the end of my days, on the banks of the Ganges, with the wild-ducks as my only neighbours on the desolate sand islands.

"I have only sown my dreams in the air," for the greater part of my life, and I never turned back to see if they bore any harvest. But the harvest now surprises me, almost obstructs my path, and I cannot make up my mind to claim it for my own. All the same, it is a great good fortune to be accepted by one's fellow-beings from across the distance of geography, history and language; and through this fact we realize how truly One is the mind of Man, and what aberrations are the conflicts of hatred and the competitions of self-interest.

We are going to Switzerland to-morrow, and our next destination will be Germany. I am to spend my birthday this year in Zurich. I have had my second birth in the West, and there is rejoicing at the event. But by nature all men are *dwija* or twice-born—first they are born to their home, and then, for their fulfilment, they have to be born to the larger world. Do you not feel yourself that you have had your second birth among us? And with this second birth you have found your true place in the heart of humanity.

It is a beautiful town, this Strasbourg, and to-day the morning light is beautiful. The sunshine has mingled with my blood and tinged my thoughts with its gold, and I feel ready to sing:

"Brothers, let us squander this morning with futile songs." This is a delightful room where I am sitting now, with its windows looking over the fringe of the Black Forest. Our hostess is a charming lady, with a fascinating little baby, whose plump fingers love to explore the mystery of my eye-glasses.

We have a number of Indian students in this place, among whom is Lala Harkishen Lal's son, who asks me to send you his respectful regards. He is a fine young man, frank and cheerful, loved by his teachers.

We have missed this weeks' letters, which are now evidently lost beyond recovery. It is difficult for me to forgive the Mediterranean for doing me this disservice! The present week's mail is due, and if Thos. Cook & Son are prompt about it we shall find our letters to-day!

Geneva, May 6ᵗʰ, 1921

To-day is my birthday. But I do not feel it; for in reality it is a day which is not for me, but for those who love me. And away from you, this day is merely a date in the calendar. I wish I had a little time to myself to-day, but this has not been possible. The day has been crowded with visitors and the talk has been incessant, some part of which has unfortunately lapsed into politics, giving rise to a temperature in my mental atmosphere of which I always repent.

Political controversies occasionally overtake me like a sudden fit of ague, without giving sufficient notice; and then they leave me as suddenly, leaving behind a feeling of *malaise*. Politics are so wholly against my nature; and yet, belonging to an unfortunate country, born to an abnormal situation, we find it so difficult to avoid their outbursts. Now when I am alone I am wishing that I could still my mind in the depth of that infinite peace where all the wrongs of the world are slowly-tuned up, out of their discordance, into the eternal rhythm of the flowers and stars.

But men are suffering all over the world, and my heart is sick. I wish I had the power to pierce this suffering with music and bring the message of abiding joy from the deeper regions of the world soul, and repeat to the people who are angry and to the people whose heads are bowed down in shame: "From joy all things are born, by joy they are maintained, and into joy they proceed and find their end."

Why should I be the one to air our grievances and give shrieking expression to the feeling of resentment? I pray for the great tranquillity of truth, from which have welled forth the immortal words that are to heal the wounds of the world and soothe the throbbing heat of hatred into forbearance.

The East and the West have met—this great fact of history has so far produced only our pitiful politics, because it has not yet been turned into truth. Such a truthless fact is a burden for both parties. For the burden of gain is no less than the burden of loss—it is the burden of the enormity of corpulence. The fact of the meeting of the East and the West still remains concentrated on the surface—it is external. The result is, all our attention is diverted to this surface where we are hurt, or where we can only think of material profits.

But deep in the heart of this meeting is surely maturing the seed of a great future of union. When we realize it, our mind regains its detachment from the painful tension of the immediate present and attains its faith in the eternal—it is relieved from the hysterical convulsions of exasperated despair. We have learnt from our ancestors that the Advaitam is the eternal significance of all passing events—which is the principle of unity in the heart of dualism. The dualism of

East and West contains that unity, and therefore, it is sure to be fulfilled in union.

You have expressed that great truth in your life. In your love for India you carry that message of Eternity. In you, the apparent conflict of the East and the West has unveiled the great beauty of its inner reconciliation. We, who are clamouring for vengeance, only conscious of the separateness, and therefore expecting absolute separation, have not read the great purpose of our history right.

For passion is darkness. It exaggerates isolated facts and makes our minds stumble against them at every step. Love is the light that reveals to us the perfection of unity and saves us from the constant oppression of the detached—of the immediate.

And therefore I embrace you, take my inspiration from your love and send you my birthday *namaskar*.[2]

Near Zürich, *May 10th, 1921*

I have just received a birthday greeting from Germany through a committee consisting of men like Eucken, Harnack, Hauptmann and others, and with it a most generous gift, consisting of at least four hundred copies of valuable German books. It has deeply touched my heart, and I feel certain that it will find response in the hearts of my countrymen.

To-morrow I have my invitation at Zürich, and on the 13th of this month I leave Switzerland for Germany. Haven't I said to you, in some letter of mine, that my life has followed the course of my celestial namesake, the Sun, and that the last part of my hours is claimed by the West? How genuine has been the claim I never realized before I had visited the continent of Europe. I feel deeply thankful for this privilege, not only because it is sweet to realize appreciation from one's fellow-

2. Greeting.

beings, but because it has helped me to feel how near we are to the people who in all appearances are so different from ourselves.

Such an opportunity has become rare to us in India because we have been segregated from the rest of the world. This has acted upon the minds of our people in two contrary ways. It has generated that provincialism of vision in us which either leads to an immoderate boastfulness, urging us to assert that India is unique in every way—absolutely different from other countries—or to a self-depreciation which has the sombre attitude of suicide. If we can come into real touch with the West through the disinterested medium of intellectual co-operation, we shall gain a true perspective of the human world, realize our own position in it, and have faith in the possibility of widening and deepening our connection with it. We ought to know that a perfect isolation of life and culture is not a thing of which any race can be proud of. The dark stars are isolated, but stars that are luminous belong to the eternal chorus of lights.

Greece was not shut up in the solitude of her culture, nor was India, when she was in the full radiance of her glory. We have a Sanskrit expression, "That which is not given is lost." India, in order to find herself, must give herself. But this power of giving can only be perfected when it is accompanied by the power of receiving. That which cannot give, but can only reject, is dead. The cry, which has been raised to-day, of rejecting Western culture only means the paralysing of our own power to give anything to the West. For, in the human world, as I have said, giving is exchanging. It is not one-sided. Our education will attain its perfection, not by refusing to accept all lessons from the West, but by realizing its own inheritance. This will give us the means to pay for such lessons. Our true wealth, intellectual as well as material, lies not in the acquisition itself, but in our own independent means of acquisition.

So long as our intellectual attainments were solely dependent on an alien giver, we have been accepting and not acquiring. Therefore these attainments have mostly been barren of production, as I have discussed in my pamphlet on Education. But it would be wrong to blame the Western culture itself for such futility. The blame lies in our not using our own receptacle for this culture. Intellectual parasitism causes degeneracy in the intellectual organs of the mind. It is not the food, but the parasitism, that has to be avoided.

At the same time, I strongly protest against Mahatma Gandhi's depreciation of such great personalities of modern India as Ram Mohun Roy in his zeal for declaiming against our modern education.[3] Every Indian ought to be proud of the fact that, in spite of immense disadvantages, India still has been able to produce greatness of personality in her children, such as we find in Ram Mohun Roy. Mahatmaji has quoted the instances of Nanak, Kabir and other saints of mediaeval India. They were great because in their life and teaching they made organic union of the Hindu and Muhammadan cultures— and such realization of the spiritual unity through all differences of appearance is truly Indian.

In the modern age, Ram Mohun Roy had that comprehensiveness of mind to be able to realize the fundamental unity of spirit in the Hindu, Muhammadan and Christian cultures. Therefore he represented India in the fullness of truth; and this truth is based, not upon rejection, but on perfect comprehension. Ram Mohun Roy could be perfectly natural in his acceptance of the West, only because his education had been perfectly Eastern—he had the full inheritance of the Indian wisdom. He was never a schoolboy

---

3. Mahatma Gandhi had been reported as saying that Ram Mohun Roy was a pigy as compared with Kabir and Nanak, who had never had any touch with the West.

of the West, and therefore he had the dignity to be a friend of the West. If he is not understood by modern India, this only shows that the pure light of her own truth has been obscured for the moment by the storm-clouds of passion.

Hamburg, *May 17th, 1921*

It has been a perpetual sunshine of kindness for me all through my travels in this country. While it delights me, it makes me feel embarrassed. What have I to give to these people? What have they received from me? But the fact is, they are waiting for the daybreak after the orgies of the night, and they have their expectation of light from the East.

Do we feel in the soul of India that stir of the morning which is for all the world? Is the one string of her *ektara*[4] being tuned, which is to give the key-note to the music of a great future of Man—the note which will send a thrill of response from shore to shore? Love of God in the hearts of the mediaeval saints of India—like Kabir and Nanak—came down in showers of human love, drowning the border-lines of separation between Hindus and Mussulmans.

They were giants, not dwarfs, because they had spiritual vision, whose full range was in the Eternal—crossing all the barriers of the moment. The human world in our day is much larger than in theirs; conflicts of national self-interest and race-traditions are stronger and more complex; the political dust-storms are blinding; the whirlwinds of race antipathy are fiercely persistent; the sufferings caused by them are world-wide and deep. The present age is waiting for a divine word, great and simple, which creates and heals. What has moved me profoundly is the fact that suffering Man in this continent has turned his face to the East.

---

4. A one-stringed instrument.

It is not the man of politics, or the man of letters, but the simple man whose faith is living. Let us believe in his instinct; let his expectation guide us to our wealth. In spite of the immense distractions of our latter-day degeneracy, India still cherishes in her heart the immortal *mantram* of Peace, of Goodness, of Unity—

"Santam, Sivam, Advaitam."

The message of the "One in the All," which had been proclaimed in the shade of India's forest solitude, is waiting to bring reconciliation of the men who are fighting in the dark and have lost the recognition of their brotherhood.

Of all men in modern India, Ram Mohun Roy was the first man and the greatest who realized this truth. He held up high the pure light of the Upanishads that shows the path whereby the conquerors of the self "enter into the heart of the all"—the light which is not for rejection, but for comprehension.

The Mussulmans came to India with a culture which was aggressively antagonistic to her own. But in her saints the spirit of the Upanishads worked in order to attain the fundamental harmony between things that were apparently irreconcilable. In the time of Ram Mohun Roy the West had come to the East with a shock that caused panic in the heart of India. The natural cry was for exclusion. But this was the cry of fear, the cry of weakness, the cry of the dwarf. Through the great mind of Ram Mohun Roy the true spirit of India asserted itself and accepted the West, not by the rejection of the soul of India, but by the comprehension of the soul of the West.

The mantram which gives our spiritual vision its right of entrance into the soul of all things is the mantram of India, the mantram of Peace, of Goodness, of Unity—Santam, Sivam, Advaitam. The distracted mind of the West is knocking at the gate of India for this. And is it to be met there with a hoarse shout of exclusion?

Hamburg, *May 20th, 1921*

I trust that my long voyage has now come nearly to its end. Every moment I hear the call of the beach and see the vision of the evening lamp watching behind the window for the return of the weary traveller. But there is one thought that never ceases to buzz in my mind. It is that the weather-beaten boat, after its voyage across the sea, may be utilized as the ferry for the miscellaneous errands of daily traffic.

Today, life is nowhere normal in the world. The atmosphere is swarming with problems. Singers are not allowed to sing; they have to shout messages. But, my dear friend, is my life to be one perpetual polar summer, an endless monotony of a day of lidless light, of ceaseless duties, with never a night of stars to open before my vision the gateway of the Infinite? Is the fact of death a mere fact of stoppage? Does it not speak to us of our right of entrance into a region beyond the bounds of patriotism? When am I going to make my final adjustment of life and be ready for the invitation to the world of Spirit?

We are taught by our Western schoolmaster that there is nothing of importance that is not shown in the national school map; that only *my* country is my earth and heaven; that only in *my* country are united my life and my immortality. And when we try to reject the West, in our pride of country, we, like a ragged scamp, pick the pocket of the same West and pilfer that same spirit of rejection.

But our fathers had a clearer consciousness of a truth of freedom, which was never clipped of its wings and shut up in a geographical cage. I feel that my time has come for the realization of that truth; and I pray that I may never die a patriot, or a politician, but as a free spirit; not as a journalist, but as a poet.

Stockholm, *May 27th, 1921*

I have been following the track of spring from Switzerland to Denmark, and from Denmark to Sweden, watching everywhere flowers breaking out in a frenzy of colours. And it seems to me like the earth's shouting of victory, and flinging up its coloured cap to the sky. My path in the West also has had the same exuberant outburst of welcome.

At first, I felt the impulse to describe it to you in detail; for I was sure it would give you great delight. But now I shrink from doing it. For somehow it does not cause exultation in my own mind, but makes me sad. It would be absurd for me to claim what has been offered to me as fully mine. The fact is, there is a rising tide of heart in the West rushing towards the shores of the East, following some mysterious law of attraction. The unbounded pride of the European peoples has suddenly found a check, and their mind appears to be receding from the channel it had cut for itself.

The giant, being weary, is seeking peace; and as the fountain of peace has ever flowed from the East, the face of troubled Europe is instinctively turned to-day towards the East. Europe is like a child who has been hurt in the midst of her game. She is shunning the crowd and looking out for her mother. And has not the East been the mother of spiritual humanity, giving it life from its own life?

How pitiful it is that we, in India, are unaware of this claim for succour from Europe which has come to our door; that we fail to realize the great honour of the call to serve humanity in her hour of need!

Bewildered at heart by the great demonstrations made in my honour in these countries, I have often tried to find out the real cause. I have been told that it was because I loved humanity. I hope that this is true; and all through my writings, my love of man has found its utterance and touched human hearts across all barriers. If it *be* true, then let that truest note in my writings guide my own life henceforth!

The other day, when I was resting alone in my room in the hotel at Hamburg, timidly there entered two shy and sweet German girls, with a bunch of roses for their offering to me. One of them, who spoke broken English, said to me: 'I love India.' I asked her: "Why do you love India?" She answered: "Because you love God."

The praise was too great for me to accept with any degree of complaisance. But I hope its meaning was in the expectation from me which it carried, and therefore was a blessing. Or possibly she meant that my country loved God, and therefore she loved India. That also was an expectation whose meaning we should try to appreciate and understand.

The nations love their own countries; and that national love has only given rise to hatred and suspicion of one another. The world is waiting for a country that loves God and not herself. Only that country will have the claim to be loved by men of all countries.

When we hear "Bande Mataram" from the house-tops, we shout to our neighbours: "You are not our brothers." But that is not true. Therefore, because it is untrue, it pollutes the air, and darkens the sky. Whatever may be its use for the present, it is like the house being set on fire simply for roasting the pig! Love of self, whether national or individual, can have no other destination except suicide. Love of God is our only fulfilment; it has in it the ultimate solution of all problems and difficulties.

On the day after to-morrow we shall be leaving Sweden for Berlin. The Czecho-Slovakian Government has promised us an air trip from Berlin to Prague, and from Prague to Munich. From Munich we are expected to visit Darmstadt, where a gathering of some notable persons of Germany will be held to meet us. It will be over on or about the 15th of

June, and then through France and Spain we shall be able to take our ship at the beginning of July—if not earlier.

Berlin, May 28th, 1921

I am leaving Germany to-night for Vienna. From there I go to Czecho-Slovakia, and then to Paris—and then, to the Mediterranean Sea! Our steamer sails on the 2nd of July, and so this letter is likely to be my last.

You can have no idea what an outbreak of love has followed me and enveloped me everywhere I have been in Scandinavia and Germany. All the same, my longing is to go back to my own people. I have lived my life there, done my work there, given my love there, and I must not mind if the harvest of my life has not had its full payment there. The ripening of the harvest itself brings its ample reward for me. And therefore the call comes to me from the field where the sunlight is waiting for me; where the seasons, each in turn, are making their inquiries about my home-coming. They know me, who all my life have sowed there the seeds of my dreams. But the shadows of evening are deepening on my path, and I am tired. I do not want praise or blame from my countrymen. I want to take my rest under the stars.

Berlin, June 4th, 1921

To-day my visit to Berlin has come to an end. To-night we are starting for Munich. It has been a wonderful experience in this country for me! Such fame as I have got I cannot take at all seriously. It is too readily given, and too immediately. It has not had the perspective of time. And this is why I feel frightened and tired at it—and even sad.

I am like a house-lamp, whose place is in a corner, and whose association is that of intimacy of love. But when my life is made to take part in a firework display, I apologize to the stars and feel humble.

I saw *Post Office* acted in a Berlin theatre. The girl who took the part of Amal was delightful in her acting, and altogether the whole thing was a success. But it was a different interpretation from that of ours in our own acting in Vichitra. I had been trying to define the difference in my mind, when Dr Otto of Marburg University, who was among the audience, hit upon it. He said that the German interpretation was suggestive of a fairy-story, full of elusive beauty, whereas the inner significance of this play is spiritual.

I remember, at the time when I wrote it, my own feeling which inspired me to write it. Amal represents the man whose soul has received the call of the open road—he seeks freedom from the comfortable enclosure of habits sanctioned by the prudent and from walls of rigid opinion built for him by the respectable. But Madhab, the worldly-wise, considers his restlessness to be the sign of a fatal malady; and his adviser, the physician, the custodian of conventional platitudes—with his quotations from prescribed textbooks full of maxims— gravely nods his head and says that freedom is unsafe and every care should be taken to keep the sick man within walls. And so the precaution is taken.

But there is the post office in front of his window, and Amal waits for the king's letter to come to him direct from the king, bringing to him the message of emancipation. At last the closed gate is opened by the king's own physician, and that which is "death" to the world of hoarded wealth and certified creeds brings him awakening in the world of spiritual freedom.

The only thing that accompanies him in his awakenment is the flower of love given to him by Sudha.

I know the value of this love, and therefore my petition to the Queen was:

"Let me be the gardener of thy flower garden"—the gardener, whose only reward is daily to offer his garlands to the Queen.

Do you think that *Post Office* has some meaning at this time for my country in this respect, that her freedom must come direct from the King's Messenger, and not from the British Parliament; and that when her soul awakes nothing will be able to keep her within walls? Has she received her letter yet from the King?

Ask Dinu what is the original of the following translation:

My *Vina* breaks out in strange disquiet measure,
My heart to-day is tremulous with the heart-throbs of the world.
Who is the restless youth that comes, his mantle fluttering in the breeze?
The woodland resounds with the murmur of joy at the dance lyric of the light,
The anklet-bells of the dancer quiver in the sky with an unheard tinkle,
To whose cadence the forest leaves clap their hands.
The hope for the touch of a nearing footstep spreads a whisper in the grass.
And the wind breaks its fetters, distraught with the perfume of the Unknown.

To-day is the 5th of June. Our steamer sails on the 3rd of July.

Darmstadt, *June 10th, 1921*

In Darmstadt they have a gathering of people from all parts of Germany to meet me. We have our meeting in the Grand Duke of Hesse's garden, where my audience will bring before me their questions. I give them monologues in answer, and Count Keyserling translates them into German for those who cannot follow my English.

Yesterday I reached this place, and in the afternoon we had our first meeting.

The first question put to me by a Canadian German was: "What is the future of this scientific civilization?"

After I had answered him, he again asked me: "How is the problem of over-population to be solved?"

After my answer, I was asked to give them some idea about the true character of Buddhism.

These three subjects took up fully three hours. It is delightful to feel the earnestness of these people. They have the habit of mind to think out the deeper problems of life; they deal seriously with ideas. In India, in our modern schools, we merely receive our ideas from textbooks, for the purpose of passing examinations. Besides that, our modern schoolmasters are Englishmen; and they, of all the Western nations, are the least susceptible to ideas. They are good, honest and reliable, but they have a vigorous excess of animal spirits which seek for exercise in racing, fox-hunting, boxing-matches, etc., and they offer stubborn resistance to all contagion of ideas.

Therefore our English educationalists do not inspire our minds. We do not realize that ideas are necessary in order to enable us to live a true life. We do not possess a genuine enthusiasm, which is the gift of the soul. Our principal object and occupation are going to be the dissipations of politics, whose goal is success, whose path is the zigzag of compromise— that politics which in every country has lowered the standard of morality, has given rise to a perpetual contest of lies and deception, cruelties and hypocrisies, and has increased inordinately national habits of vulgar vainglory.

S.S. "Morea," *July 5ᵗʰ, 1921*

Land has its claims upon one, in return for its hospitality, but sea has none; it repudiates humanity with a magnificent indifference; its water is solely occupied in an eternal dialogue with the sky—the two inseparable companions who retain their irresponsible infancy as on the first day of their creation.

Land imposes on us our mission of usefulness, and we have to be occupied with lectures and textbooks; and our guardians have the right to rebuke us when we waste good paper in making literary paper-boats. But the sea has no inspiration of moral obligation for us; it offers no foundation for a settled life; its waves raise their signals and have only one word of command: "Pass on."

I have observed, on board a steamer, how men and women easily give way to their instinct of flirtation, because water has the power of washing away our sense of responsibility, and those who on land resemble the oak in their firmness behave like floating seaweed when on the sea. The sea makes us forget that men are creatures who have their innumerable roots and are answerable to their soil.

For the same reason, when I used to have my dwelling on the bosom of the great river Padma, I was nothing more than a lyrical poet. But since I have taken my shelter at Santiniketan I have developed all the symptoms of growing into a schoolmaster, and there is grave danger of my ending my career as a veritable prophet! Already everybody has begun asking me for "Messages"; and the day may come when I shall be afraid to disappoint them. For when prophets do appear unexpectedly to fulfil their mission, they are stoned to death; and when those whom men warmly expect to be prophets fail to act their part to the end, they are laughed to extinction. The former have their compensation; for they fulfil their purpose, even through their martyrdom. But for the latter, their tragic end is utter wastefulness; it satisfies neither man nor Gods.

Who is there to save a poet from disaster? Can anybody give me back my good-for-nothingness? Can anyone restore to me the provision with which I began life's journey to the realm of inutility? One day I shall have to fight my way out of my own reputation; for the call of my Padma river still comes to me through this huge and growing barrier. It says to me: "Poet, where are you?" And all my heart and soul try to seek out that poet. It has become difficult to find him. For the great multitude of men have heaped honours on him, and he cannot be extricated from under them. I must stop here— for the ship's engine is throbbing in a measure which is not that of my pen.

S.S. "Morea," *July 6th, 1921*

I suppose you have read in the newspapers that in Europe I met with an enthusiastic welcome. No doubt I was thankful to the people for their kind feelings towards me; but somehow, deep in my heart I was bewildered and almost pained.

Any expression of feeling by a great multitude of men must have in it a large measure of unreality. It cannot help exaggerating itself simply because of the cumulative effect of emotion upon the crowd-mind. It is like a sound in a hall, which is echoed back from innumerable corners. An immense amount of it is only contagion—it is irrational, and every member of the crowd has the freedom to draw upon his own imagination for building up his opinion. Their idea of me cannot be the real me. I am sorry for it and for myself. It makes me feel a longing to take shelter in my former obscurity. It is hateful to have to live in a world made up of other people's illusions. I have seen people press round me to touch the hem of my robe, to kiss it in reverence—it saddens my heart. How am I to convince these people that I am of them and not above them, and that there are many among them who are worthy of reverence from me?

And yet I know for certain that there is not a single individual in their midst who is a poet as I am. But reverence of this kind is not for a poet. The poet is for conducting ceremonial in the festival of life; and for his reward he is to have his open invitation to all feasts wherever he is appreciated.

If he is successful, he is appointed to the perpetual comradeship of Man—not as a guide, but as a companion. But if, by some mad freak of fate, I am set upon an altar, I shall be deprived of my own true seat—which by right is mine and not another's. It is far better for a poet to miss his reward in this life rather than to have a false reward, or to have his reward in an excessive measure. The man who constantly receives honour from admiring crowds has the grave danger of developing a habit of mental parasitism upon such honour. He consciously, or unconsciously, grows to have a kind of craving for it, and feels injured when his allowance is curtailed or withdrawn.

I become frightened of such a possibility in me, for it is vulgar. Unfortunately, when a person has some mission of doing some kind of public good, his popularity becomes the best asset for him. His own people most readily follow him, when other people have the same readiness—and this makes it a matter of temptation for such an individual. A large number of his followers will consider themselves as deceived by him when the fickle flow of popularity changes its course.

S.S. "Morea," *July 7th, 1921*

In this modern age of the philosophy of relativity I suppose I cannot claim for myself the quality of absolute poetdom. It is evident that the poet in me changes its features and spontaneously assumes the character of the preacher with the change of its position. I have evolved in me a certain philosophy of life which has in it a strong emotional element, and therefore it can sing as well as speak. It is like a cloud that can break out in a shower of rain, or merely tinge itself in colours and offer decorations to the festival of the sky. For this reason I give rise to expectations which are almost of a contrary character—I am asked to give gladness, and I am asked to give help.

To give gladness requires inspiration; to give help requires organization—the one depends principally upon myself, and the other upon means and materials that are outside me. Here come in difficulties which make me pause. Poesy creates its own solitude for the poet. The consequent detachment of mind which is necessary for creative life is lost or broken when the poet has to choose a constructive programme. The work of construction requires continuous employment of attention and energy—it cannot afford to grant leave to the poet to retire and come to himself.

This creates conflict within my nature and very often, makes me think that the guidance of the Good is not always for the Best. And yet, its call being natural to me, I cannot ignore it altogether. But what constantly hurts me is the fact that, in a work of organization, I have to deal with and make use of men who have more faith in the material part than in the creative ideal.

My work is not for the success of the work itself, but for the realization of the ideal. But those in whose minds the reality of the ideal is not clear, and love for the ideal is not strong, try to find their compensation in the success of the work; and they are therefore ready for all kinds of compromise.

I know that the idea which I have in mind requires the elimination of all passions that have their place in the narrow range of life; but most people believe that these passions are the steam-power which gives velocity to our motives. They quote precedents; they say that pure idea has never achieved any result. But when you say that the result is not greater than the idea itself, then they laugh at you!

During the last fourteen months of my campaign for an International University, I have said to myself over and over again: "Never let your pride be hurt at any prospect of failure; for failure can never affect truth." My weakness creeps in where I love. When those whom I love feel exultant at the expectation of success, it urges me to procure this toy for them.

S.S. "Morea," *July 8th, 1921*

I must not exaggerate. Let me admit that the realization of ideals has its external part, which depends for its development upon materials. And materials—both human and non-human—offer resistance to success, and therefore must not be lightly spoken of.

But what I had in my mind was this, that the mastery of grammar and the creation of literature may not coincide. Emphasis upon grammar may hinder perfectness of expression. Success in materials may go contrary to the fulfilment of ideals. For material success has its temptation. Often our idealism is exploited for the sake of obtaining success—we have seen that in the late war. In consequence, the battle has been won, but the ideal has not been reached.

Ever since the scheme of the International University has been made public, the conflict in my mind has been unceasing—the conflict between the vision of the ideal and the vision of success. The plan itself is big and has a scope for the ambition of men who love to show their power and gain it. It is not merely ambition which lures our minds; it is the wrong value which we set upon certain results. To be certain of the inner truth requires imagination and faith, and therefore it is always in danger of being missed, even when it is near at hand; whereas external success is obvious.

You remember how Chitra, in my play of that name, became jealous of the physical beauty lent to her by the Gods—because it was a mere success, not truth itself. Truth can afford to be ignored, but not to be allied to unreality for the sake of success.

Unfortunately facts are cited to show that all over the world the prudent and the wise are in the habit of making a pact with Mephistopheles to build roads to reach their God. Only they do not know that God has *not* been reached—and that success and God are not the same thing. When I think of all this, I feel a longing for the simplicity of poverty, which, like the covering of certain fruits, conceals and protects the richness and freshness of the deeper ideal. All the same, as I have said, the pursuit of success must not be abandoned for mere want of energy and spirit. Let it represent our sacrifice for the truth, and not for itself.

S.S. "Morea," July 9th, 1921

All true ideals claim our best, and it cannot be said with regard to them that we can be content with the half, when the whole is threatened. Ideals are not like money. They are a living reality. Their wholeness is indivisible. A beggar woman may be satisfied with an eight-anna bit when sixteen annas are denied her; but a half-portion of her child she will never consent to accept!

I know that there is a call for me to work towards the true union of East and West. I have unconsciously been getting ready for this mission. When I wrote my *Sadhana* lectures, I was not aware that I had been fulfilling my destiny. All through my tour I was told that my *Sadhana* had been of real help to my Western readers. The accident which made me translate *Gitanjali* and the sudden and unaccountable longing which took me over to Europe at the beginning of my fiftieth year—all combined to push me forward to a path whose destination I did not clearly know when I first took it. This, my last tour in Europe, has made it definitely known to me.

But, as I have said before, the claims of all great ideals have to be fully paid. Not merely the negative moral injunction of non-violence will suffice. It is a truism to say that the creative force needed for true union in human society is love. Justice is only an accompaniment to it, like the beating of a tom-tom to the song. We in the East have long been suffering humiliation at the hands of the West. It is enormously difficult for us either to cultivate, or express, any love for Western races—especially as it may have the appearance of snobbishness or prudence. The talk and behaviour of the Moderate Party in India fail to inspire us because of this—because their moderation springs from the colourless principle of expediency. The bond of expediency between the powerful and the weak must have some element in it which is degrading. It brings to us gifts for which we can claim no credit whatever, except, perhaps, persistency of expectation and unbaffled employment of importunity.

Self-sacrifice on the part of the gainer, and not solely on the part of the giver, imparts true value to the gift. When our claims are feeble, and our method of realizing them is altogether unheroic, then the very boons granted to us make us poorer. That is why the Moderates in India look so pitifully obscure by the side of the Extremists.

However, my point is that, as an idealist, it is immensely difficult for me to nourish any feeling of love for those people who themselves are neither eager to offer it to us nor care to claim it from us. But never let me look at that condition as an absolute one. There are screens between us which have to be removed—possibly they are due to the too great inequality of circumstances and opportunities between the two parties. Let us, by every means in our power, struggle against our antipathies—all the while taking care to keep wide open channels of communication through which individuals, from both sides, may have facilities to meet in the spirit of good-fellowship. I cannot tell you how thankful I feel to you, who have made it easier for me to love your people. For your own relationship with India has not been based upon a sense of duty, but upon genuine love. It makes me feel sad when I see this lesson of your love being lost—when it fails to inspire our people with the realization that love of humanity is with you far truer than patriotism.

I deeply regret that you could not accompany me in my last tour in Europe, though I understand the reasons that prevented you. If you had been with me, you would have been able fully to realize the great truth of the mission we have undertaken. To the majority of my countrymen the course of experience through which I passed will ever remain vague; and my appeal to them to view the history of our own country in the large background of humanity is not likely to carry any force. For my work I shall ever depend upon your comradeship, and therefore I feel sad that the reality of the ideal which has possessed me has missed its one signal chance of coming close to your heart. The perspective against which you have been recently setting up your scheme of life has been vastly different from mine. You have taken up responsibilities that may have to follow their own channels away from those that I shall have to choose; and the loneliness of my task, which has been my fatality in my past life, will follow me to the end of my days. But I must not complain. I shall follow the call of my providence, and I know that to respond to it in my own manner is fulfilment in itself, whatever may be its results.

S.S. "Morea," July 12th, 1921

For the last fourteen months my one thought was to bring India into touch with the living activities of the larger world of humanity. It was not because I thought that India would be the sole gainer by this contact, but because I was certain that when the dormant mind of India was roused from its torpor she would be able to offer something for the needs of the human race which would be valuable.

Through different modes of political co-operation and non-co-operation India has assumed up to the present an attitude of asking boons from others. I have been dreaming of some form of co-operation through which she would be in a position to offer her own gifts to the world. In the West the mind of man is in full activity. It is vigorously thinking and working towards the solution of all the problems of life. This fullness of intellectual vigour itself gives its inspiration to mental vitality. But in our Indian Universities we simply have the results of this energy, not the living velocity itself. So our mind is burdened and not quickened by our education. This has made me realize that we do not want schoolmasters from the West, but fellow-workers in the pursuit of truth.

My own aspiration for my country is that the mind of India should join its forces to the great movement of mind which is in the present-day world. Every success that we may attain in this effort will at once lead us directly to feel the unity of Man. Whether the League of Nations acknowledges this unity or not, it is the same to us. We have to realize it through our own creative mind.

The moment that we take part in the building up of civilization we are instantly released from our own self-seclusion—from our mental solitary cell. We have not yet gained full confidence that we have the power to join hands with the great builders—the great workers of the world. Either our boastfulness breaks its voice in unnatural shrieking or our self-denunciation makes an abnormal display of itself in an aggressive flutter of humility.

But I am certain that we have every claim to this confidence, and that we must do everything to realize it. We do not want bragging; we need for ourselves the dignity of the man who knows that he has some purpose to fulfil for all people and for all time. This has made me bold to invite students and scholars from different parts of the world to an Indian University to meet there our students and scholars in a spirit of collaboration. I wonder if this idea of mine will find any response in the hearts of my countrymen of the present day.

S.S. "Morea," *July 13ᵗʰ, 1921*

In our music, each *ragini*⁵ has its special scale in which some notes are absent and some are added, and the sequence of them is different in different *raginis*. The idea of India in my mind has its different *raginis*, presenting different aspects.

During my absence in the West my idea of India had its own special grouping of notes, and consequently the vision had its own special emotional value. When, in my travels, I was communicating with you, I had not the least notion that your India and mine were vastly different at that moment. I came to be aware of this fact when, at Aden, a number of Indian newspapers of different dates came into my hands, I felt, for the first time in these fourteen months, that I should have to make another attempt between my aspiration and my country.

But misgivings come to my mind as to whether any proper adjustment will be possible. I have constant conflicts and bickerings—always to be shouting at the top of my voice in order to make myself heard above the shouts of other parties.

The India about which I had been dreaming belongs to the world. The India that I shall reach shortly belongs tremendously to itself. But which of these must I serve?

Months ago, while sitting each day at my window in a New York hotel, my heart had been aching morning after morning for the time of my return—the day that should bring me back to the arms of Mother India. But to-day, my heart is sad—like this dark heaving sea, under the rainy sky. I have been wondering in my own mind, during the last few days, whether it was not my mission to remain in Europe at least another year, where I was asked to stay. But it is too late now. From this time forward I must make the effort to train my attitude of mind to a condition for which I am not ready.

---

5. Mode or tune.

S.S. "Morea," *July 14th, 1921*

There is an idealism which is a form of egotism egregiously self-assertive. The confidence which one has in one's own ideas may not arise from an unmixed love of truth. It may be a subtle form of bigotry of self. There is an idealism ready to kill freedom in others in order to find freedom for its own plan.

I feel, at times, afraid lest such a tyranny of idealism should ever take possession of my own mind. For it would mean that my faith in truth had grown weaker than my faith in myself. Pride of self insidiously creeps into our schemes for ameliorating the conditions of our fellow-human beings; and when failure occurs, we are hurt because the schemes are *our* schemes.

Egotism of this kind is blindly oblivious of other people's missions in life. It tries to impose one vast monotony of taste upon individuals who have temperament and capacities fit for other kinds of work. It is like the tyranny of conscription which compels teachers to dig and poets to kill their fellow-men. This, being against God's own purpose, is terribly wasteful. In fact, all tyrants in idealism try to usurp the rights of Providence for their own purpose.

The gloom of sadness which has been brooding over my mind for the last few days must be the shadow of my own egotism, whose flame of hope is dimmed by a fear. For some months I had been feeling sure that everybody would think my thoughts and carry on my work. But this confidence in me and in my plan has suddenly found a check and I am apprehensive.

No, this is wrong for me, and it is also a source of wrong for others. Let me be glad because a great idea, with all its beauty and truth, has alighted upon my mind. I alone am responsible for carrying out its commands. It has its own wings of freedom to bear it to its own goal; and its call is music, and not an injunction. There is no failure for truth—failure is only for me—and what does that matter?

Henceforth, I shall have the chance of talking with you face to face. Yet distance has its own significance, and letters have their power of speech which tongues do not possess. And therefore, when we meet, some part of our thoughts will remain unuttered for the want of a great space and silence between us.

S.S. "Morea," *July 15th, 1921*

Before I finish this last letter to you, my friend, let me thank you with all my heart for your unfailing generosity in sending me letters all through my absence from India. They have been to me like a constant supply of food and water to a caravan travelling through a desert. I was sorely in need of them during the dreary months I spent in the United States. I promised to myself that I should try to pay you back in kind. I think I have kept my promise, and I hope you have got my letters in a regular weekly series, unless there have been gaps owing to the suspicions of professional eavesdroppers who watch over the destinies of the British Empire.

I suppose that the first few weeks I was lazy and depended upon Pearson to supply you with news, and therefore I am busy now in making up for the deficits. But about one thing I can never hope to compete with you. As a letter-writer you are incomparable! Mine are no more letters than lobsters are fish. They are like fragments of a book; like meteors that are shot off a planet. They are shot at you, and with a flash most of them vanish into ashes; whereas yours come down like showers of rain upon the thirsty land. Yet you must consider one thing in my favour—it is that I am heavily handicapped in my race with you, because I write in a language that is not my own, and this greatly adds to the original inertia I always have to overcome in writing any letter in any language whatsoever. On the other hand, writing letters is as easy to you as it is easy for our *Sal* avenue to put forth its leaves in the beginning of the spring months. However, I wonder, if even *you* will be able to cope with my correspondence on my return! It has grown amazingly exuberant. Good-bye.

Appendix I

[*The following letter was sent to the Editor of the* Manchester Guardian, *Mr C.P. Scott, by Rabindranath Tagore, with reference to his friend W.W. Pearson and was published on November 27, 1923.*]

The news has reached us of W.W. Pearson's death through an accident which happened while he was travelling in Italy on the eve of his departure for India. He is not known to the wide public, but we feel sure that his loss is not merely a loss to the individuals who came into intimate touch with him. We seldom met with anyone whose love of humanity was so concretely real, whose ideal of service so assimilated to his personality, as it had been with him. The gift of friendliness, which he was ever ready to bestow upon the obscure, upon those who had nothing to attract the attention of their neighbours, was spontaneous in its generosity, completely free from all tinge of conscious or unconscious egotism, enjoying the luxury of the satisfied pride of goodness. The constant help which he rendered to those who were in need of it could have no reward in public recognition; it was as simple and silent as the daily fulfilling of his own personal requirements. His patriotism was for the world of man; he intimately suffered for all injustice or cruelty inflicted upon any people in any part of the earth, and in his chivalrous attempt to befriend them he bravely courted punishment from his own countrymen. He had accepted Santiniketan Asram for his home, where he felt he could realize his desire to serve the cause of humanity and express his love for India, which was deeply genuine in his nature, all his aspirations of life centring in her.

I know he has numerous friends in this country and outside India who admire the noble unselfishness of hearts which he possessed, and who mourn his loss. I feel sure, they will appreciate our idea of setting up some permanent memorial in his name in our Asram, which was so dear to him. He had a great desire to see the hospital in connection with our institution rebuilt and equipped in an adequate manner, for which he was working and contributing money whenever possible. I believe if we can carry out this wish of his and construct a hospital building, and a special ward for children attached to it, this will be the best form of perpetuating his memory, reminding us of his sympathy for those who suffer.

Appendix II

[*The following is a letter from the Poet to his friend W.W. Pearson*]

Santiniketan, *July 4ᵗʰ*, 1923

I have just got your letter in which you ask me to give you my opinion concerning the importance of Institutional Religion. As an abstract idea, I have nothing to say against it; for it is like the Caste System, perfect when ideally represented. Men can be classified according to their inherent differences in temperament. If all the natural Brahmins came together in order to carry on the special work which was only for them to perform, then through their mutual encouragement and co-operation an immensely potent force could be generated for the good of mankind. But directly a group is formed, its own group-personality almost invariably gives rise to an egoism which judges its own value by its external success and its physical duration. The Sect struggles for bigness and self-preservation even at the cost of truth. The growing consciousness of its own distinction and importance develops into a pride which—like the pride of wealth and office—becomes a temptation.

It is extremely difficult to become truly a Christian in conduct and life; but by following the easy path of belonging to a Christian Sect one seems to acquire the merit of being a Christian and also to have the right to despise even one's betters who by chance or by choice do not profess Christianity. This has proved to be true of all religions which crystallize themselves into sectarianism. Religious communities are more often formed and established upon custom and the herd instinct than upon Truth. The children born to a Christian family are included in the religious community, not because they have shown in any way their fitness to belong to it, but because of the accident of birth. They do not have the time or the opportunity to discover their own individual inclination towards the religion they profess. They are persistently hypnotized into the belief that they are "Christians." For this reason, we often witness the scene of men preaching Christianity as missionaries—or even as bishops—to their un-Christian fellow-beings, whom they might have killed as soldiers, or held down for ever under their heels as diplomats, had they followed their own true vocations.

An Institution which brings together individuals who are profoundly true and sincere in their common aspirations is a great help to all its members. But if, by its very constitution, it offers accommodation to those who merely have uniformity of habits and not unity of true faith, it necessarily becomes a breeding-place of hypocrisy and untruth. And because all organizations, by the very virtue of their power of combination, mechanically acquire a certain amount of force, such untruths and hypocrisies find ready opportunity to create widespread mischief.

Christ, like all other spiritual personalities, was solitary in moral greatness. He had a pure relationship of love and truth with all humanity. His Spirit works in solitude in the depth of men's souls. Therefore we find great-hearted individuals on the side of those people who are oppressed and insulted. On the other hand, we often find the Christian

Church on the side of those vested interests which are engaged in exploiting the weak. This happens because the Church, as an organization, is a power which has its own natural alliance with other powers that are not only non-religious but very often irreligious. In fact, it is ready to make its bargain with those very powers that crucified Christ.

It is a truism to say that the character of the majority of the members constituting a religious community determines the level of its ideals. For this cause an Institution which is indiscriminate in the choice of its materials, and possesses an inordinate greed for the augmentation of its own numbers, very often becomes merely the most efficient organ for expressing the collective passion of its members. Have you not noticed this in the time of the late European War? And does not the profession of a sectarian Christianity fashion in the time of peace a cloak of respectability which covers a multitude of sins?

I know that a community of God-seekers is a great shelter for man. But directly this grows into an Institution it is apt to give ready access to the Devil by its back-door.

THE PARROT'S TRAINING AND
OTHER STORIES

The Parrot's Training

Once upon a time there was a bird. It was ignorant. It sang all right, but never recited scriptures. It hopped pretty frequently, but lacked manners.

Said the Raja to himself: "Ignorance is costly in the long run. For fools consume as much food as their betters, and yet give nothing in return."

He called his nephews to his presence and told them that the bird must have a sound schooling.

The pundits were summoned, and at once went to the root of the matter. They decided that the ignorance of birds was due to their natural habit of living in poor nests. Therefore, according to the pundits, the first thing necessary for this bird's education was a suitable cage.

The pundits had their rewards and went home happy.

A golden cage was built with gorgeous decorations. Crowds came to see it from all parts of the world.

"Culture, captured and caged!" exclaimed some, in a rapture of ecstasy, and burst into tears.

Others remarked: "Even if culture be missed, the cage will remain, to the end, a substantial fact. How fortunate for the bird!"

The goldsmith filled his bag with money and lost no time in sailing homewards.

The pundit sat down to educate the bird. With proper deliberation he took his pinch of snuff, as he said: "Textbooks can never be too many for our purpose!"

The nephews brought together an enormous crowd of scribes. They copied from books, and copied from copies, till the manuscripts were piled up to an unreachable height.

Men murmured in amazement: "Oh, the tower of culture, egregiously high! The end of it lost in the clouds!"

The scribes, with light hearts, hurried home, their pockets heavily laden.

The nephews were furiously busy keeping the cage in proper trim.

As their constant scrubbing and polishing went on, the people said with satisfaction: "This is progress indeed!"

Men were employed in large numbers, and supervisors were still more numerous. These, with their cousins of all different degrees of distance, built a palace for themselves and lived there happily ever after.

Whatever may be its other deficiencies, the world is never in want of fault-finders; and they went about saying that every creature remotely connected with the cage flourished beyond words, excepting only the bird.

When this remark reached the Raja's ears, he summoned his nephews before him and said: "My dear nephews, what is this that we hear?"

The nephews said in answer: "Sire, let the testimony of the goldsmiths and the pundits, the scribes and the supervisors, be taken, if the truth is to be known. Food is scarce with the fault-finders, and that is why their tongues have gained in sharpness."

The explanation was so luminously satisfactory that the Raja decorated each one of his nephews with his own rare jewels.

The Raja at length, being desirous of seeing with his own eyes how his Education Department busied itself with the little bird, made his appearance one day at the great Hall of Learning.

From the gate rose the sounds of conch-shells and gongs, horns, bugles and trumpets, cymbals, drums and kettledrums, tomtoms, tambourines, flutes, fifes, barrel-organs and bagpipes. The pundits began chanting *mantras* with their topmost voices, while the goldsmiths, scribes, supervisors, and their numberless cousins of all different degrees of distance, loudly raised a round of cheers.

The nephews smiled and said: "Sire, what do you think of it all?"

The Raja said : "It does seem so fearfully like a sound principle of Education!"

Mightily pleased, the Raja was about to remount his elephant, when the fault-finder, from behind some bush, cried out: "Maharaja, have you seen the bird?"

"Indeed, I have not!" exclaimed the Raja, "I completely forgot about the bird."

Turning back, he asked the pundits about the method they followed in instructing the bird.

It was shown to him. He was immensely impressed. The method was so stupendous that the bird looked ridiculously unimportant in comparison. The Raja was satisfied that there was no flaw in the arrangements. As for any complaint from the bird itself, that simply could not be expected. Its throat was so completely choked with the leaves from the books that it could neither whistle nor whisper. It sent a thrill through one's body to watch the process.

This time, while remounting his elephant, the Raja ordered his State Ear-puller to give a thorough good pull at both the ears of the fault-finder.

The bird thus crawled on, duly and properly, to the safest verge of inanity. In fact, its progress was satisfactory in the extreme. Nevertheless, nature occasionally triumphed over training, and when the morning light peeped into the bird's cage it sometimes fluttered its wings in a reprehensible manner. And, though it is hard to believe, it pitifully pecked at its bars with its feeble beak.

"What impertinence!" growled the kotwal.

The blacksmith, with his forge and hammer took his place in the Raja's Department of Education. Oh, what resounding blows! The iron chain was soon completed, and the bird's wings were clipped.

The Raja's brothers-in-law looked black, and shook their heads, saying: "These birds not only lack good sense, but also gratitude!"

With text-book in one hand and baton in the other, the pundits gave the poor bird what may fitly be called lessons!

The kotwal was honoured with a title for his watchfulness, and the blacksmith for his skill in forging chains.

The bird died.

Nobody had the least notion how long ago this had happened. The fault-finder was the first man to spread the rumour.

The Raja called his nephews and asked them: "My dear nephews, what is this that we hear?"

The nephews said: "Sire, the bird's education has been completed."

"Does it hop?" the Raja enquired.

"Never!" said the nephews.

"Does it fly?"

"No."

"Bring me the bird," said the Raja.

The bird was brought to him, guarded by the kotwal and the sepoys and the sowars. The Raja poked its body with his finger. Only its inner stuffing of book-leaves rustled.

Outside the window, the murmur of the spring breeze amongst the newly budded *asoka* leaves made the April morning wistful.

The Trial of the Horse

Brahma, the creator, was very near the end of his task of creation when a new idea struck him.

He sent for the Storekeeper and said: "O keeper of the stores, bring to my factory a quantity of each of the five elements. For I am ready to create another creature."

"Lord of the universe," the Storekeeper replied, "when in the first flush of creative extravagance you began to turn out such exaggerations as elephants and whales and pythons and tigers, you took no count of the stock. Now, all the elements that have density and force are nearly used up. The supply of earth and water and fire has become inconveniently scanty, while of air and ether there is as much as is good for us and a good deal more."

The four-headed deity looked perplexed and pulled at his four pairs of moustaches. At last he said: "The limitedness of material gives all the more scope to originality. Send me whatever you have left."

This time Brahma was excessively sparing with the earth, water and fire. The new creature was not given either horns or claws, and his teeth were only meant for chewing, not for biting. The prudent care with which fire was used in his formation made him necessary in war without making him warlike.

This animal was the Horse.

The reckless expenditure of air and ether, which went into his composition, was amazing. And, in consequence, he perpetually struggled to outreach the wind, to outrun space itself. The other animals run only when they have a reason, but the horse would run for nothing whatever, as if to run out of his own skin. He had no desire to chase, or to kill, but only to fly on and on till he dwindled into a dot, melted into a swoon, blurred into a shadow, and vanished into vacancy.

The creator was glad. He had given for his other creatures habitations,—to some the forests, to others the caves. But in his enjoyment of the disinterested spirit of speed in the Horse, he gave him an open meadow under the very eye of heaven.

By the side of this meadow lived Man.

Man has his delight in pillaging and piling things up. And he is never happy till these grow into a burden. So, when he saw this new creature pursuing the wind and kicking at the sky, he said to himself: "If only I can bind and secure this Horse, I can use his broad back for carrying my loads."

So one day he caught the Horse.

Then man put a saddle on the Horse's back and a spiky bit in his mouth. He regularly had hard rubbing and scrubbing to keep him fit, and there were the whip and spurs to remind him that it was wrong to have his own will.

Man also put high walls round the Horse, lest if left at large in the open the creature might escape him.

So it came to pass, that while the Tiger who had his forest remained in the forest, the Lion who had his cave remained in the cave, the Horse who once had his open meadow came to spend his days in a stable. Air and ether had roused in the horse longings for deliverance, but they swiftly delivered him into bondage.

When he felt that bondage did not suit him, the Horse kicked at the stable walls.

But this hurt his hoofs much more than it hurt the wall. Still some of the plaster came off and the wall lost its beauty.

Man felt aggrieved.

"What ingratitude!" he cried. "Do I not give him food and drink? Do I not keep highly-paid men-servants to watch over him day and night? Indeed he is hard to please."

In their desperate attempts to please the Horse, the men-servants fell upon him and so vigorously applied all their winning methods that he lost his power to kick and a great deal more besides.

Then Man called his friends and neighbours together, and said to them exultingly: "Friends, did you ever see so devoted a steed as mine?"

"Never!" they replied. "He seems as still as ditch water and as mild as the religion you profess."

The Horse, as is well known, had no horns, no claws, nor adequate teeth, at his birth. And, when on the top of this, all kicking at the walls and even into emptiness had been stopped, the only way to give vent to his feelings was to neigh.

But that disturbed Man's sleep.

Moreover, this neighing was not likely to impress the neighbours as a paean of devotion and thankfulness. So Man invented devices to shut the Horse's mouth.

But the voice cannot be altogether suppressed so long as the mistake is made of leaving any breath in the body. Therefore a spasmodic sound of moaning came from his throat now and then.

One day this noise reached Brahma's ears.

The Creator woke up from his meditation. It gave him a start when he glanced at the meadow and saw no sign of the Horse.

"This is all your doing," cried Brahma, in anger to Yama, the god of death. "You have taken away the Horse!"

"Lord of all creatures!" Death replied, "All your worst suspicions you keep only for me. But most of the calamities in your beautiful world will be explained if you turn your eyes in the direction of Man."

Brahma looked below. He saw a small enclosure, walled in, from which the dolorous moaning of his Horse came fitfully.

Brahma frowned in anger.

"Unless you set free my Horse," said he, "I shall take care that he grows teeth and claws like the Tiger."

"That would be ungodly," cried Man, "to encourage ferocity. All the same, if I may speak plain truth about a creature of your own make, this Horse is not fit to be set free. It was for his eternal good that I built him this stable—this marvel of architecture."

Brahma remained obdurate.

"I bow to your wisdom," said Man, "but if, after seven days, you still think that your meadow is better for him than my stable, I will humbly own defeat."

After this Man set to work.

He made the Horse go free, but hobbled his front legs. The result was so vastly diverting that it was enough to make even a frog burst his sides with laughter.

Brahma, from the height of his heaven, could see the comic gait of his Horse, but not the tragic rope which hobbled him. He was mortified to find his own creature openly exposing its divine maker to ridicule.

"It was an absurd blunder of mine", he cried, "closely touching the sublime."

"Grandsire," said Man with a pathetic show of sympathy, "what can I do for this unfortunate creature? If there is a meadow in your heaven, I am willing to take trouble to transport him thither."

"Take him back to your stable!" cried Brahma in dismay.

"Merciful God!" cried Man, "what a great burden it will be for mankind!"

"It is the burden of humanity," muttered Brahma.

Old Man's Ghost

At the time of the Old Man Leader's death, the entire population wailed, "What will be our lot when you go?"

Hearing this, the Old Man himself felt sad. "Who indeed," thought he, "will keep these people quiescent when I have gone?"

Death cannot be evaded, however. Yet the gods took pity and said: "Why worry? Let this fellow go on sitting on their shoulders even as a ghost. Man dies but a ghost does not."

The people of the country were greatly relieved.

For, worries come if only you believe in a future. Believing in ghosts you are freed from burden, all the worries enter the ghost's head. Yet the ghost has no head, so it does not suffer from headaches either, not for anybody's sake.

Those, who out of sheer wrong habit still attempt to think for themselves, get their ears boxed by the ghost. From this ghostly boxing you can neither free yourself nor can you escape it; against it is neither appeal nor any judgment at all.

The entire population, ghost-ridden, now walks with eyes shut. "The most ancient form of movement this, with eyes shut," the philosophers assure them, "moving like blind fate, we call it. Thus moved the first eyeless amoeba. In the grass, in the trees, this habit of movement is still customary."

Hearing which, the ghost-ridden land feels its own primitive aristocracy. And it is greatly delighted.

The Ghost's *nayeb* is the inspector of the prison. The walls of the prison-house are not visible to the eye. And so it is impossible to imagine how to pierce those walls and get free.

In the prison-house one has to slave at turning the oil-press night and day but not even an ounce of oil is produced which is marketable; only the energy of men goes out in extracting the oil. When their energy goes out, men become exceedingly peaceful. And thus in that ghost's realm whatever else there might not be—food, or clothing or health—tranquillity remains.

How great is the tranquillity is proved by one example: in other lands excessive ghostly tyranny makes men restless and seek for a medicine-man. Here such a thought cannot arise. For the medicine-man himself has already been possessed by the ghost.

Thus the days would have passed; nobody would have questioned the ghostly administration. Forever they could have taken pride that their future, like a pet lamb, was tied to the ghost's peg. Such a creature neither bleated nor baad, it sprawled dumb on the dust, useless as dust.

Only, for a slight reason, some little trouble arose. It was that the other countries of the world were not ghost-ridden. Their oil-presses turned so that the extracted oil might be used for keeping the wheels of men's chariots moving forward, not for crushing the heart and pouring heart's blood into the paws of the ghost. So, men there have not yet been completely pacified. They were terribly wakeful.

All over the ghostly empire: *the baby sleeps; quiet is the neighbourhood.*

That is comforting for the baby, and for the baby's guardian too; as to the neighbourhood, we have already seen how it is.

But there is the other line, *"the invaders enter the land."*

Thus the rhythm is completed—otherwise for lack of one foot, this history would have been crippled.

The pedants and pundits are asked: "Why is it thus?"

They toss their heads together and say: "Not the ghost's fault this, nor of the ghost-ridden land: the fault lies with the invader. Why does the invader come?"

"How right!" they all admit. And everyone feels exceedingly comforted.

Whoever the fault might be, near the back-door of the house loiter the ghost's emissaries, and in the open street outside everywhere roam the non-ghost's emissaries; the householder can hardly stay in his house, to stir out of doors is also impossible. From one side they shout "pay the taxes!" and from the other also they shout "pay the taxes!"

Now the problem is, *"how to pay the taxes?"*

Up to now, from north, south, east and west, bulbulis of all species have come in large flocks, and gorged themselves with the corn, nobody was mindful. With all those who are mindful, these people avoid contact, lest they have to do *prayashchitta* for contamination. But those other folk who are mindful have a way of coming suddenly very near to them indeed and they do not observe any penance either.

The pedants and pundits open the text and say: "Pure are the unmindful, and impure the mindful ones; so be indifferent to these latter. Remember the sacred words, 'awake are those who sleepeth.'"

And hearing this the people are hugely delighted.

But, in spite of this, the query cannot be stopped, *"how to pay the taxes?"*

From the burning-ground, from the burial-ground the wild winds bring the loud answer: "Pay the taxes with the price of your modesty, with your honour, with your conscience, with your heart's blood."

The trouble with questions is: when they come they do not come singly. So, another question has arisen : "Will the ghostly reign itself remain for ever?"

Hearing this, all the lullaby-singing aunts and uncles put their hands on their ears in horror and exclaim: "Perdition! Never in our fathers' life have we heard of such a thing! What will then have happened to our sleep, the most ancient sleep, the sleep which is earlier than all awakening?"

"That I see," the questioner persists: "but these most modern flocks of bulbulis and these very much present invaders—what about *them*?"

"To the bulbulis we shall repeat the name of Krishna," assert the aunts and uncles, "and so shall we do to the invaders."

The ignorant youths get impertinent and bluster out: "Drive the ghost out we shall—whatever the means."

The ghost's *nayeb* rolls his eyes in anger and shouts, "Shut up! The oil-press hasn't stopped grinding. No, not yet."

Hearing which the baby of the land falls silent, and then turns to sleep.

The great fact is, the Old Man is neither alive nor dead, but is a ghost. He neither stirs the country up nor ever relaxes his grip.

Inside the country, one or two men—those who never utter a word in daytime for fear of the *nayeb*—join their palms together and implore: "Old Man Leader, is it not yet time for you to leave us?"

"You fool," answers the Old Man, "I neither hold, nor let go; if you leave, then I have also left."

"But we are afraid, Old Man Leader!"

"That is where the ghost enters."—comes the answer.

Great News

Said Kusmi: "You would give me all the big news—so you promised, didn't you, Dadamashay? How else could I get educated?"

Answered Dadamashay: "But such a sack of big news there would be to carry—with so much of rubbish in it."

"Why not leave those out."

"Little else would remain, then. And that remainder you will think as small news. But that would be the real news."

"Give it to me—the real news."

"So I will."

"Well, Dadamashay, let me see what skill you have. Tell me the great news of these days, making it ever so small."

"Listen."

Work was proceeding in peace.

In a mahajani boat there started a row between the sail and the oars.

The oars came clattering to the court of the Boatman, and said: "This cannot be endured any longer. That braggart sail of yours, swelling himself, calls us *chhoto lok*. Because we, tied night and day to the lower planks, must toil, pushing the waters as we proceed, while he moves by whim, not caring for the push of any one's hand. And so he is a *bara lok*. You must decide who is more worthy. If we are *chhoto lok*, the inferior ones, we shall resign in a body. Let us see how you make your boat move."

The Boatman, seeing danger ahead, called the oars aside and whispered secretly: "Do not give ear to his words, brothers. He speaks an empty language, that sail. If you strong fellows did not work away, staking life and death, the boat would lie inert altogether. And that sail—he sits there in hallow luxury, perched on the top. At the slightest touch of stormy wind he flops, folds himself up, and lies low on the boat's thatch. Then all his vain flutterings are silenced, not a word from him at all. But in weal and woe, in danger and in crisis, on the way to the market and the ghat, you are my constant support. It is a pity that you have to carry that useless burden of luxury, to and fro. Who says you are *chhoto lok.*"

But the Boatman was afraid, lest these words be overheard by the sail. So he came to him and whispered into his ear: "Mr. Sail, none ever can be compared with you. Who says that you drive the boat, that is the work of labourers. You move at your own pleasure, and your pals and comrades follow you at your slightest gesture and bidding. And whenever you feel out of breath, you would flop down easefully, and rest. Do not lend your ear, friend, to the parleying of those low-bred oars; so firmly have I tied them up, that splutter as they might, they cannot but work as slaves."

Hearing this, the sail stretched himself, and yawned mightily.

But the signs were not good. Those oars are hard-boned fellows, now they lie aslant but who knows when they will stand up straight, slap at the sail and shatter his pride into shreds. Then the world would know that it is the oars who make the boat move, come storm come tornado, whether it be upstream or at ebb-tide.

Queried Kusmi: "Your big news, is it so small as this? You are joking."

Said Dadamashay: "Joking it seems to be. Very soon this news will become big indeed."

"And then?"

"Then your Dadamashay will practise keeping time with the strokes of those oars."

"And I?"

"Where the oars creak too much, you will pour a drop of oil."

Dadamashay continued: "True news appears small, like the seeds. And then comes the tree with its branches and foliage. Do you understand now?"

"So I do," said Kusmi. Her face showed that she had not understood. But Kusmi had one virtue, she would not easily admit it to her Dadamashay that she would not understand. That she is less clever than *Iru Mashi* is better kept concealed.

Glossary

Bulbuli—A species of Indian nightingale; these birds often do
    great harm to the crops.
    The social significance of this folksong is brought out in
a popular Bengali nursery rhyme:

"The baby sleeps, the neighbourhood is quiet;
The invaders enter the land;
The *bulbulis* have eaten the corn,
How to pay the taxes?"

Chhotolok—Literally iterally, small people; a common term
    used abusingly with regard to the working classes by
    the so-called "big people", or *"bara-lok"*.
Dadamashay—Grandfather.
Iru Mashi—Aunt Iru (Mashi—mother's sister).
Kotwal—Chief of the Police.
Mahajani boat—Boat for carrying merchandise.
Mantras—sacred texts from ancient Hindu scriptures, which
    are often to be found in abbreviated verse-form.
Nayeb—Manager.
Prayashchitta—Penance and purification.
Pundit—Pedant.

THE KING OF THE DARK CHAMBER

I

A street. CITY GUARD *on duty*
[*A band of wandering mendicants enter and pass out
singing*]

My beloved is ever in my heart
  That is why I see him everywhere,
He is in the pupils of my eyes
  That is why I see him everywhere.

*I thought I heard his voice come from beyond the
sky*
  I tried to retrace it in vain
When I came back to the quiet of my heart
  I heard it in my own songs.

Who are you who seek him like a
  beggar from door to door!
Come to my heart and see his face in the
  tears of my eyes!

[*Enter* WAYFARERS]

1ST MAN: Ho, sir!
C.-G: What do you want?

2ND MAN: We are from a foreign land—Would you kindly tell us the way?

C.-G: Where do you want to go?

3RD MAN: To the place where those great festivities are to be held, you know.

C.-G: Any street will lead you there. Go straight ahead, and you can't possibly miss it.

[CITY GUARD *goes out*]

1ST MAN: Did you hear what the fool said? "Any street will lead you there"! Where then is the sense of having so many streets?

2ND MAN: My dear friend, you need not make so much of a small point like that! A country is free to order its own affairs in its own way. As for roads in our country—well, they might as well not have been there at all: narrow and crooked lanes, a maze of ruts and tracks. Our King does not believe in open thoroughfares, not he!—he thinks that streets are just so many openings for his subjects to fly away from his kingdom.

1ST MAN: My dear Janardan, I have long noticed that this is a great defect in your character.

2ND MAN: What is?

1ST MAN: That you are always having a fling at your own country. Look here, Kaundilya, here's a man who actually believes that open highways are the salvation of a country!

3RD MAN: I know, Bhavadatta, Janardan is blessed with an intelligence which is sure to get him into trouble some day or other. If the King comes to hear of our worthy friend, he will make it pretty hard for him to find anyone to perform his funeral rites after he is dead.

1ST MAN: I somehow feel that life would grow quite burdensome in this country—one misses the joys of privacy in these streets—this jostling and brushing of shoulders with strange people day and night makes one long for a bath. And you never can tell exactly *what* class of people you may be meeting in these public roads—ugh!

3RD MAN: Why it was Janardan himself who persuaded us to come to this precious country. We never had anyone like him in our family. You knew my father, of course: he was a great man, a pious man if ever there was one. He spent his whole life within a circle of a radius of 49 cubits drawn with a rigid adherence to the injunctions of the scriptures, and never for a single day did he cross this circle. After his death a serious difficulty arose—how to cremate him within the limits of the 49 cubits and yet outside the house? At length the priests decided that though we could not go beyond the scriptural number, the only way out of the difficulty was to reverse the figure and make it 94 cubits; only thus could we cremate him outside the house without violating the sacred books. *That* was indeed strict observance! Ours is no common country!

1ST MAN: And yet, though Janardan comes from the very same soil, he actually thinks it wise to declare that open highways are best.

[*Enter* THĀKURDĀDĀ, *with the Boys of the Hermitage*]

DĀDĀ: Boys, we shall have to vie with the wild breeze of the south today—and we are not going to be beaten. We will sing till we have flooded all the streets with our mirth and song.

[*Song*]

The southern gate is unbarred. Come, my spring,
come!
Swing on the swing of my heart, come, my spring,
come!
Come in the lisping leaves, in the youthful
surrender of flowers,
Come in the flute songs of shepherds and wistful
sighs of the woodlands!
Let your ungirded robe toss in the drunken wind!
Come, my spring, come!

[*Enter a band of* CITIZENS]

1ST CIT: After all, we can't help wishing that the king had allowed himself to be seen at least on this one day. What bad luck is ours to live in his kingdom and yet not to have seen him even once!

2ND CIT: Dādā, this year every country has sent its people to our festival, but everyone asks, "Where is your King"? And we do not know what to answer. That is the one great lack which cannot help making itself felt in our rejoicings.

DĀDĀ: Lack! What a word to use! The whole country is filled and crammed with the King: and you call him a "lack"! Why, he has made everyone of us a crowned King!

[*Sings*]

We are all Kings in the kingdom of our King,
Were it not so, how could we hope to meet him
in our hearts?
We do our own will, yet we do his will,

We are not bound with the chain of fear at the
feet of a slave-owning King.
Were it not so, how could we hope in our heart
to meet him!

Our King honours each one of us, and thus
honours his own very self.
Our littleness cannot immure us for ever in the
deceitful walls.
Were it not so, how could we hope to meet him
in our hearts?
We struggle and dig our own path, and thus reach
his path in the end.
We can never be utterly lost in the dark night.
Were it not so, how could we hope to meet him
in our hearts?

[GRANDFATHER *and* BOYS *go out*]
[*Enter* HERALDS *and* ADVANCE GUARD *of the Pretender*]

1ST HER: Stand on one side! Get out of the way, all of you!

1ST CIT: Hullo, what a lot you think of yourself? Who are you, you're nobody! Don't give yourself airs; my good Sir! Leave us alone. Why should we stand aside, we're not street dogs.

2ND HER: Our King is coming this way.

2ND CIT: King? Which King!

1ST HER: Our King, the King of this country.

1ST CIT: What, is the fellow mad! Whoever heard of our King coming out heralded by these rowdies?

2ND HER: The King will no longer deny himself to his subjects. He is coming to attend the festivities in person.

2ND CIT: What! Is that so?

2ND HER: Look, his banner is flying over there.

2ND CIT: Hullo! Yes! You're right. There is a flag.

2ND HER: Do you see the sign of the red *Kimshuk* flower on it?

3RD CIT: Yes, yes, it is indeed the *Kimshuk!*—what a bright scarlet flower it has.

1ST HER: Well! Won't you believe us now?

3RD CIT: I never said I didn't. It was that fellow Kumbha who started all this disturbance. I never said a word.

2ND HER: Who's Kumbha? Is he any kinsman of yours?

2ND CIT: Oh, dear no! He is just a cousin of our village chief's father-in-law, and he does not even live in the same part of our village.

2ND HER: That's exactly what I thought. He quite looks the seventh cousin of somebody's father-in-law and his understanding appears also to bear the stamp of uncle-in-law-hood.

4TH CIT: Alas, my friends blow upon blow of bitter sorrow has given my poor mind a twist. Only the other day that a King came and paraded the streets, with as many titles in front of him as the drums that made the town hideous by their din ... I rained down offerings upon him, I hung about him like a beggar—But how did it all end? When people sought grants and presents from him, somehow he was not able to discover an auspicious day in the Calendar: yet everyday was a red-letter day when it came to our paying him our dues.

2ND HER: Do you mean to say that our King's a false King, like the one you speak of?

1ST HER: Mr. Uncle-in-Law, I believe the time has come for you to say good-bye to Aunty-in-Law.

4TH CIT: My good Sirs, forgive me! I apologize with all my heart. I am willing to move away as far as you like.

2ND HER: All right, come here and form up in line. The King will soon come now—We're on our way to prepare the way for him.

[*They go out*]

2ND CIT: My dear good Kumbha, your tongue will really be the death of you one of these days.

4TH CIT: Oh, my dear Madhav, it's not my tongue! It's not my tongue! It's fate! When the false King appeared I never said a word. And now, when perhaps the real King has come, I must blurt out treason! It's fate, Madhav, it's fate!

2ND CIT: I believe in absolute obedience—it does not matter whether the King is a real one or a false one. What do we know of Kings? We're no judges of Kings. You can only be sure of hitting your aim in the dark if you throw a lot of stones. I go on obeying; if it is a real King, well and good: if not, what harm is done?

3RD CIT: Oh, look! There comes the King! Ah, a King indeed! What a splendid figure, what a glorious face! Whoever saw such beauty—lily white, creamy-soft! What now, Kumbha? What do you think now?

2ND CIT: He looks all right enough—yes, he may be the real King for all I know.

3RD CIT: He looks as though he were designed and moulded for kingship, a figure too exquisite for the common light of day.

[*Enter* SUVARNA, *the Pretender*]

Prosperity and victory attend you, O King! We have been standing here to see your royal highness since the early morning. Forget us not, your Majesty, in your favours.

[*Enter another* BAND OF MEN]

1ST MAN: The King, the King! Come quickly, the King is passing this way.

2ND MAN: Do not forget me, your royal highness! I am Viraj, the grandson of Udaya of Kushalivastu. I hurried here at the first report of your coming—I did not stop to hear what people were saying: and the loyalty in me went out towards you, and brought me here.

3RD MAN: What stuff and nonsense! I came here much earlier than you did—before cock-crow. I am Bhadrasena, your Majesty of Vikramasthali. Deign to remember your humble servant!

KING: I am much pleased with your loyalty and devotion.

1ST MAN: Your Majesty, there are many grievances which we have to lay before you; to whom could we turn our prayers all this while, when we could not see you?

KING: Your grievances will all be redressed.

[Exit]

1ST MAN: It won't do to lag behind, lads—The King will lose sight of us if we get mixed up with the mob.

2ND MAN: Look there—just look what that fool Narottam is doing! He has actually elbowed his way through the lot of us and is now busy fanning the King with a palm leaf!

3RD CIT: Good heavens! Well, I declare, the sheer audacity of the man is enough to take one's breath away.

2ND MAN: We shall have to pitch the fellow out of that place—He's not fit to stand beside the King.

2ND CIT: Do you imagine his Majesty won't see through him? His loyalty is obviously too showy and profuse.

1ST MAN: Nonsense! That won't make any difference! Kings can't scent out hypocrites as we can! I should not be surprised if the King were to be taken in by that fool's strenuous fanning.

II

The dark chamber. Queen SUDARSHANA *and* SURANGAMA

SUDARSHANA: Light, light! Where is the light? Will the lamp never be lighted in this chamber?

SURANGAMA: My Queen, you can meet others in the lighted rooms; but only in this dark room can you meet your lord.

SUDARSHANA: It is so still here! still and dark as the depth of the dark sea.

SURANGAMA: It is waiting to be filled with the music of love.

SUDARSHANA: Living in this dark room you have grown to speak darkly and strangely Surangama, I cannot understand you. No, no—I cannot live without light—I am restless in this stifling darkness. Surangama, if only you can bring a light into this room, will this necklace of mine be yours.

SURANGAMA: It is not in my power, O Queen. How can I bring light to a place which he wishes kept dark!

SUDARSHANA: Strange devotion! And yet, is it not true that the King punished your father?

SURANGAMA: Yes, that is true. My father used to gamble. All the young men of the country used to gather at my father's house—and they used to drink and gamble.

SUDARSHANA: And when the King sent away your father in exile, did it not make you feel bitterly oppressed?

SURANGAMA: O, it made me feel mad with rage. For I was on the road to ruin—and when that path was closed for me I seemed left without any support.

SUDARSHANA: How then did you get this devotion towards the King who treated you thus?

SURANGAMA: How can I explain? Perhaps I could rely on him just because he was so inflexible.

SUDARSHANA: When did this change of feeling take place?

SURANGAMA: I cannot tell you—I do know not myself. A day came when all the rebel in me knew itself beaten, and then I saw that he was as matchless in sweetness as in terror. Ah, I was saved!

SUDARSHANA: Surangama, I implore you, won't you tell me what is the King like? I have not seen him yet for a single day. He comes to me in darkness, and leaves me in this dark room again. How many people have I not asked— but they all give me vague answers—it seems to me that they all keep something back.

SURANGAMA: To tell you the truth, Queen, I hardly know what he is like. No—he is not what men call handsome.

SUDARSHANA: You say that he is not handsome?

SURANGAMA: No, my Queen, to call him beautiful would be to say far too little about him.

SUDARSHANA: All you say is like that—dark and strange. I cannot understand what you mean.

SURANGAMA: And it is because he is not beautiful that he is so wonderful.

SUDARSHANA: I do not understand you Surangama and yet I like to hear you talk thus about him. But I must see him at any cost.

SURANGAMA: Do you feel a faint breeze blowing?

SUDARSHANA: A breeze? Where?

SURANGAMA: Is there not a soft fragrance in the air?

SUDARSHANA: No.

SURANGAMA: The outer door has opened ... he is coming, he is coming, my king is coming in.

SUDARSHANA: How can you perceive when he comes?

SURANGAMA: I cannot say: I seem to hear his footsteps in my heart. Serving him in this dark chamber, I have gained this new sense—I know and feel without seeing.

SUDARSHANA: Would that I had such sense too Surangama!

SURANGAMA: You will have it, O Queen ... this sense will waken in you one day. Your longing to have a sight of him has affected your mind. When this state of restlessness is past everything will seem quite easy.

SUDARSHANA: How is it that it is easy to you, who are a servant, and so difficult to me, who am a Queen?

SURANGAMA: It is because I am a mere servant that no difficulty baulks me. ...O here he comes! ... he is standing outside, before the door. Lord! O King!

[*Song outside*].

Open your door. I am waiting.
The ferry that bears light from the dawn to the
dark has crossed this day.
The evening star is up.
Have you gathered your flowers, braided your hair,
And donned your white robe for the night?
The cattle are back in their folds and birds in their
nests.
The cross paths that run to all quarters have
merged into one in the dark.
Open your door. I am waiting.

SURANGAMA: O King, who can keep your own doors shut against you? They are not locked or bolted—they will swing wide at the touch of your finger. Will you not even touch them? Will you not enter unless we open the doors? (*Turning to the queen*) Then do you go, O Queen, and open the door for him: he will not enter otherwise.

SUDARSHANA: I do not see things distinctly in the dark—I do not know where the door is. You know everything here— go and open the door for me.

[SURANGAMA *opens the door, bows to the* KING, *and goes out*]

Why do you not allow me to see you in the light?

KING: Do you wish to see me one among a thousand things? Why should I not be the only thing you can feel in this darkness?

SUDARSHANA: But I *must,* I must see you—I am longing for a *sight* of you.

KING: You will not be able to bear the sight of me—it will only give you pain, poignant and over-powering.

SUDARSHANA: Oh, how can you say so? I feel even in this dark how lovely and wonderful you are—why should I be afraid of you in the light? But tell me, can you see me in this darkness?

KING: Yes, I can.

SUDARSHANA: What is it that you see?

KING: I see the darkness of the infinite heavens whirled into life and being in the form of a perfect body. And in that form, what aeons of thought and striving, what yearnings of limitless skies, what countless gifts of unnumbered seasons!

SUDARSHANA: Am I so wonderful? When I hear you speak so, my heart swells with gladness and pride. But how can I believe the things you tell of me? I cannot find all these in myself!

KING: *Your* mirror cannot reflect them—it dwindles you, limits you. But could you see yourself in *my* heart, how perfect would you appear!

SUDARSHANA: O show me for one instant how to see with your eyes! Is nothing dark to you? I am afraid when I think of this darkness which is to me real and strong as death—is it nothing to you? Then how can there be any union between us in a place like this? No, no—it is

impossible here, where there is this barrier betwixt us—
I want to find you and see you where I see trees and
animals, birds and stones and the Earth—

KING: You may try to find me—but none must point me out to
you. You will have to recognize me, if you can, yourself,
And, even if any one professes to show me to you how
can you be sure he is right?

SUDARSHANA: I should pick you out among a million men. I
could never be mistaken.

KING: So be it. To-night, during the festival of the full moon
of the spring, try to find me out from the high turret of
my palace—seek me with your own eyes amongst the
crowd.

SUDARSHANA: Will you be there among them?

KING: I shall show myself again and again, from every side of
the crowd. Surangama!

[*Enter* SURANGAMA]

SURANGAMA: What is your pleasure, lord?

KING: To-night is the full moon festival of the spring.

SURANGAMA: What have I to do to-night?

KING: The pleasure gardens are in full bloom—you will join
in my festivities there.

SURANGAMA: I shall do as you wish, lord.

KING: The Queen desires to see me to-night with her own
eyes.

SURANGAMA: Where can you be seen O King?

KING: She would see me there in the pleasure garden.

SURANGAMA: But my lord, what can be seen in that hide-and-
seek of darkness and light? There the wind is wild and
restless, everything is dance and swift movement—will it
not puzzle the eyes?

KING: The Queen is curious to search me out.

SURANGAMA: Her curiosity must come home baffled and in tears!

III

Before the pleasure-garden
[*Enter the princes of* KANCHI, AVANTI, KOSHALA, VIDARBHA *and* KALINGA]

AVANTI: Will not the King of this place receive us?

KANCHI: What manner of governing a country is this? The King holds his festival in a forest, where even the meanest people have easy access!

KOSHALA: We, sovereign rulers of this earth, should have found a place set apart and ready for our reception.

KANCHI: If he has set apart no such place as yet, we should compel him to have one prepared for us.

KOSHALA: Such things make one doubt whether these people really have any King at all—it looks as if an unfounded rumour has led us astray.

AVANTI: It may be so with regard to the King; but the existence of the Queen of this place Sudarshana is by no means an unfounded rumour!

KOSHALA: It is only for her sake that I cared to come at all. I do not mind failing to see one who takes such a great care to hide himself.

KANCHI: Let us make some definite plan, then.

AVANTI: A plan is an excellent thing, so long as you do not get yourself entangled in it.

KANCHI: Who are these vermin swarming this way? Here! who are you!

[Enter DĀDĀ *and the* BOYS]

DĀDĀ: We are the Jolly Band of Have-Nothings.
AVANTI: That is perfectly evident. But you will please take yourself a little further away and leave us in peace.
DĀDĀ: We never suffer from want of space: we can afford to give you as wide a berth as you please. What little suffices for us is not enough to quarrel about. Is not that so, my little friends!

[They sing]

[Song]

We have nothing, indeed we have nothing at all!
    We sing merrily fol de rol de rol!
Some build high walls to their houses
    On the bog of the sands of gold.
We stand before them and sing
    fol de rol de rol.
Pickpockets hover about us
    And honour us with covetous glances.
We shake out our empty pockets and sing
    Fol de rol de rol.
When death, the old hag, steals to our doors
    We snap our fingers in her face,
And we sing in a chorus with gay flourishes
    Fol de rol de rol.

[They go out]

KANCHI: Look over there, Koshala, who are these others coming this way? A pantomime? Somebody is out masquerading as a King.

KOSHALA: The King of this place may tolerate all this tomfoolery, but we will not.

AVANTI: It may be some rural chief.

[*Enter* FOOTGUARDS]

KANCHI: What country does your King come from?

1ST SOLDIER. He is the King of this country. He is going to preside over the festivities.

[*They go out*]

KOSHALA: What! The King of this country come out for the festivities!

AVANTI: Indeed! Then we shall be obliged to return having only seen him and leave the delectable Queen unseen.

KANCHI: Do you really think that fellow spoke the truth? Anybody can pass himself off as the King of this kingless country. Can you not see that the man looks like a dressed up King—much too overdressed?

AVANTI: Oh, but he looks handsome—his appearance is not without a certain attractiveness.

KANCHI: He may be pleasing to your eye, but if you look at him closely enough there can be no mistaking him. You will see how I shall expose him before you.

[*Enter* SUVARNA *the Pretender*]

PRETENDER: Welcome, princes, to our kingdom! I trust that your reception has been all that you desired?

KING: [*with feigned courtesy*] Yes, indeed: nothing was lacking in the reception.

KANCHI: If there were any shortcoming, it is atoned for by the honour of seeing your Majesty, in person.

PRETENDER: We do not show ourselves to the general public, but your great devotion of loyalty to us has made it our pleasure not to deny ourselves to you.

KANCHI: It is truly hard for us, your Majesty, to bear the weight of your gracious favours.

PRETENDER: We fear we shall not be able to stop here long. In the meantime, if you have any favour to ask of us—

KANCHI: We have; but we would speak in private.

PRETENDER: [to his attendants] Retire a little from our presence.

[They retire]

Now you can express without reserve.

KANCHI: There will be no reserve on our part—our only fear is that you might think reserve necessary for yourself.

PRETENDER: Oh no, you need have no scruples on that score.

KANCHI: Come then, do us homage by placing your head on the ground.

PRETENDER: It seems my servants have been distributing the Varuni spirits too liberally.

KANCHI: False pretender, it is you who are suffering from an excess of arrogant spirits. Your head will soon roll on the dust.

PRETENDER: Princes, such jokes are not worthy of kings.

KANCHI: Those who will jest with you indeed are near at hand. Soldiers!

PRETENDER: No more, I beg you. It is plain that I owe you homage. [Bows to the ground] Only allow me to escape, and I shall trouble you no more with my presence.

KANCHI: Why should you escape? We will make you King of this place—let us carry our joke to its finish. Have you got any following?

PRETENDER: I have. Everyone who sees me in the streets flocks after me. At first when I had a meagre retinue everyone regarded me with suspicion, but now with the increasing crowd their doubts are dissolving. The crowd is being hypnotized by its own magnitude.

KANCHI: Excellent! From this moment we all promise to help and stand by you. But you will have to do us a service in return.

PRETENDER: Your commands and the crown you are placing on my head will be equally binding and sacred.

KANCHI: At present we want nothing more than a sight of the Queen Sudarshana. You will have to see to this.

PRETENDER: I shall spare no pains.

KANCHI: We cannot put much faith in your pains—you will be solely directed by our instructions. But now you can go and join the festivities in the royal arbour with all possible splendour and magnificence.

[*They go out*]

IV

Turret of the royal palace.
[*Queen* SUDARSHANA *and* ROHINI]

SUDARSHANA: You may make mistakes, Rohini, but I cannot be mistaken: Am I not the Queen? [*Pointing to a figure in the distance*] That, of course, *must* be my King.

ROHINI: He who has conferred such high honour upon you cannot be long in showing himself to you.

SUDARSHANA: His very form makes me restless like a caged bird. Did you try well to ascertain who he is?

ROHINI: Yes, I did. Everyone I asked said he was the King—he whose flag has the *Kimshuk* flower on it.

SUDARSHANA: I recognized him at once of course, but I do wish that Surangama were here. There would remain no room for doubt then.

ROHINI: Do you think her cleverer than all of us?

SUDARSHANA: Oh no, but she would recognize him instantly.

ROHINI: I cannot believe that! She merely pretends to know him, for there are none to test her knowledge. If we were as shameless as she is it would not have been difficult for us to boast about our acquaintance with the King.

SUDARSHANA: But no, she never boasts.

ROHINI: It is sheer affectation, which often goes a longer way than open boasting. She is up to all manner of tricks: that is why we could never get to like her.

SUDARSHANA: Whatever you may say, I should have liked to ask her.

ROHINI: But is not everyone saying it? Listen! The acclamations of the people mount even to this height!

SUDARSHANA: Then do this for me: put these flowers on a lotus leaf, and take them to him.

ROHINI: And what am I to say if he asks me who sends them?

SUDARSHANA: You will not have to say anything—he will know. He thought that I would not be able to recognize him. I cannot spare him the knowledge that I have found him out.

[ROHINI *goes out with the flowers*]

My heart is all a-quiver tonight: I have never felt like this before: The light of the full moon is flooding the heavens and brimming over like the bubbling foam of wine ... It rushes to my blood. It intoxicates me.—Here, who is there?

[*Enter a* SERVANT]

SERVANT: What is your Majesty's pleasure?

SUDARSHANA: Do you see those boys singing and moving through the avenues of the mango trees? Call them hither, bring them to me. I want to hear them sing.

[SERVANT *goes out and enters with the* BOYS]

Come, living emblems of youthful spring, begin your festive song! All my mind and body is music to- night—but its ineffable melody eludes my voice. Do you then sing for me.

[*Song*]

My sorrow is sweet to me in this spring night.
My pain smites at the chords of my love and
softly sings.
Visions take birth from my yearning eyes and flit
in the moonlit sky.
The scents from the deep of the woodlands have
lost their way in my dreams.
Words come to my ears in whispers I know not
whence,
And bells in my anklets tremble and tinkle in time
with my throbbing heart.

SUDARSHANA: Enough, enough—I cannot bear it any more! Your song has filled my eyes with tears ... a fancy comes to me that desire can never attain its object—it need never attain it. Dear boys of the hermitage! How shall I reward you? This necklace is but made of jewels, hard stones—its hardness will give you pain—I have got nothing like the garlands of flowers which you wear.

[*The* BOYS *bow and go out*]
[*Enter* ROHINI]

I have done ill Rohini—I have done ill. I feel ashamed to ask what happened. I have just realized that no hand can really give the greatest of gifts. Still, let me hear all.

ROHINI: When I gave the King those flowers he did not appear to understand.

SUDARSHANA: What! He did not understand?

ROHINI: No, he sat there silent like an idol. I think he did not wish to show that he understood not, so he kept silence.

SUDARSHANA: Ah my shame! My forwardness has been justly punished. Why did you not bring back my flowers?

ROHINI: How could I? The Prince of Kanchi, a very clever man, who was sitting by him, took in everything at a glance. He smiled and said, "King, Queen Sudarshana sends your Majesty her greetings with blossoms that belong to the God of Love." The King seemed to awake with a start and said, "Ah! This indeed the crown of all my regal glory to-night".

I was coming back, all out of countenance, when the Prince of Kanchi took off this necklace of jewels from the King's person, and said to me, "Friend, the King's garland is bestowed upon you, in return for the happy greetings you have brought".

SUDARSHANA: What, Kanchi had to make the King understand all this? What else could I expect? Leave me, Rohini, I would be alone for a time.

[ROHINI *goes out*]

A great blow has shattered my pride today, and yet ... I cannot efface from my mind that fascinating form! I am vanquished, utterly helpless ... I cannot even turn away from him. O how the wish comes back to me again and again to beg that garland of Rohini! ... But what would she think of me! ... Rohini!

[*Enter* ROHINI]

ROHINI: What is your wish?

SUDARSHANA: What reward do you deserve for your services today?

ROHINI: Nothing from you—but I had my reward from the King, as it should be.

SUDARSHANA: That was no free gift, but an extortion. I do not like to see you wear what was given with such want of grace. Take it off—I give you my bracelets, take them and go now.

[ROHINI *goes out*]

Another defeat! I should have thrown this necklace away— but I could not! It is pricking me as if it were a garland of thorns—but I cannot throw it away. This is what the good of the festival has awarded me to-night—this necklace of shame!

V

[*The Pretender and the Prince of* KANCHI]

KANCHI: You must do exactly as I have said. Let there be no mistake.

PRETENDER: There shall be none.

KANCHI: The Queen Sudarshana's chambers are in the...

PRETENDER: Yes, Prince, I have marked the place well.

KANCHI: What you have got to do is to set fire to the garden, and then you will take advantage of the confusion to accomplish your object.

PRETENDER: I shall remember.

KANCHI: Look here, Sir Pretender, I cannot help thinking that a needless fear is troubling you—there is really no King in this country.

PRETENDER: My sole aim shall be to rid the country of this anarchy. Your common man cannot live without a King, whether a real one or a fraud! Anarchy is always a source of danger.

KANCHI: Pious benefactor of the people! Your wonderful self-sacrifice should really be an example to all of us. I am almost persuaded to do this extra-ordinary service to the people myself.

[They go out]

VI

The inner garden
[GARDENERS *preparing to leave. Enter* ROHINI]

ROHINI: What is the matter? I cannot understand what is happening.

[*To the* GARDENERS] Where are you all going in such haste?

1ST GARDENER: We are going away out of the garden.

ROHINI: Where to?

2ND GARDENER: We do not know whither—the King has called us.

ROHINI: Why, the King is in the garden. Which King has called you?

1ST GARDENER: Which King we cannot say.

2ND GARDENER: The King we have been serving all our life, of course.

ROHINI: Are you all going?

1ST GARDENER: Yes, all—we must be gone instantly, or we might get into trouble.

[*They go out*]

ROHINI: I cannot understand their words ... I am afraid. They are scampering off like wild animals flying from the bank of a river before it is washed away by the torrent.

[*Enter Prince of* KOSHALA]

KOSHALA: Rohini, do you know where your King and Kanchi have gone?

ROHINI: They are somewhere in the garden, but I could not tell you where.

KOSHALA: I really cannot understand their intentions:
I have not done well to put my trust in Kanchi.

[*Exit*]

ROHINI: What is this dark affair going on amongst these kings? Something dreadful is going to happen soon.

[*Enter Prince of* AVANTI]

AVANTI: Rohini, do you know where the other princes are?

ROHINI: It is difficult to say which of them is where. The Prince of Koshala just passed by in this direction.

AVANTI: I am not thinking of Koshala. Where are your King and Kanchi?

ROHINI: I have not seen them for some time.

AVANTI: Kanchi seems to be avoiding us. He is certainly planning some deception. I have not done well to get into his hands. Friend, could you tell me any way out of this garden?

ROHINI: I know of none.

AVANTI: Is there no man here who can show me the way out?

ROHINI: The servants have all left the garden.

AVANTI: Why?

ROHINI: I could not exactly understand. They said the King had commanded them to leave the garden at once.

AVANTI: The King? Which King?

ROHINI: That they could not exactly say.

AVANTI: This does not sound well, I must find my way out at all costs. I must not stay here another instant.

[Goes out hurriedly]

ROHINI: Where shall I find the King? He did not seem much interested in me when I gave him the flowers the Queen had sent—but ever since he has been showering gifts on me. This causeless generosity makes me much afraid ... Whither are the birds flying at such an hour of the night? What has frightened them all of a sudden? Why is the Queen's pet deer running that way? Chapalā! Chapalā! She does not even hear my call. Never have I seen a night like this! All the horizon has suddenly become red, like a madman's eye! The sun seems to be setting at this untimely hour in every direction all at once! What madness of the Almighty is this! O, I am frightened! ... Where am I to find the King?

VII

At the door of the Queen's palace
[*The* PRETENDER *and the Prince of* KANCHI]

PRETENDER: What is this you have done, Lord Kanchi?

KANCHI: I wanted to set fire to only this part of the garden near the palace—I had no idea that it would spread so quickly on all sides. Tell me, quick, the way out of this garden.

PRETENDER: I know nothing at all about it. Those who brought us here have all fled.

KANCHI: You are a native of this country—you must know the way.

PRETENDER: I have never entered these inner gardens before.

KANCHI: I will have no excuses—you must show me the way, or I shall split you in two.

PRETENDER: But that would not help you out of the garden.

KANCHI: How is it then that you went about claiming that you were the King of this country?

PRETENDER: I am not the King—I am not the King. [*Throwing himself on the ground with folded hands*] Where art thou, my King? Save me, oh save me! I am a rebel— punish me, but spare my life!

KANCHI: What is the use of shouting and cringing to the empty air?

PRETENDER: I shall lie down here—I shall not move a step. I give myself up to the King's mercy.

KANCHI: I will not endure this folly. If I must be burnt to death, you shall bear me company to the very end.

[*From the outside—"Oh, save us, our King!*
The Fire is closing in on us."]

KANCHI: Fool, get up, lose no more time.

[*Enter Queen* SUDARSHANA]

SUDARSHANA: King, O my King! Save me. Save me from this death! I am surrounded by fire.
PRETENDER: Where is the King? I am no King!
SUDARSHANA: You not the King?
PRETENDER: No, I am a hypocrite, a scoundrel.

[*Flings his crown on the ground and goes out with the Prince of* KANCHI]

SUDARSHANA: No King! He is not the King? Then, O thou God of fire, burn me to ashes! I throw myself into thy hands, O thou great purifier; burn to ashes my shame, my desire.

[*Enter* ROHINI]

ROHINI: Queen, where are you going? Your inner chambers are shrouded in raging fire—enter not there.
SUDARSHANA: Yes! Yes! I will enter those burning chambers! To the fire of my death!

[*Exit into the palace*]

VIII

The dark chamber
[*The* KING, *and Queen* SUDARSHANA]

KING: Do not be afraid—you have no cause for fear. The fire cannot reach this room.
SUDARSHANA: I need no longer fear—but oh my shame has accompanied me like a raging fire.

KING: It will be long before this burning ceases.

SUDARSHANA: This fire will never cease—will never cease!

KING: Despair not, Queen!

SUDARSHANA: O King, I would hide nothing from you ... I have another's garland round my neck.

KING: That garland too is mine—how else could he have got it?

SUDARSHANA: But it is *his* gift to me: yet I could not fling it away! When the fire came raging round me, I thought of throwing this garland into it. But no, I could not. My heart whispered. "Let that garland be on you in your death" ... What fire is this, O King, into which I, who had come out to see you, leaped like a moth that could not resist the flame?

KING: But you have seen me at last—has not your desire been fulfilled?

SUDARSHANA: But did I seek to see you in the midst of this dreadful doom? I know not what I saw, but my heart is still beating fast with fear.

KING: What did you see?

SUDARSHANA: Terrible, oh, it was terrible! I am afraid even to think of it again.—Oh you are dark and terrible as the everlasting night! I only looked on you for one dreadful instant. The blaze of the fire fell on your features—they were like the awful night when a comet swings fearfully into our ken—oh then I closed my eyes—I could not look on you any more. Dread, as the threatening storm-cloud, dark as the shoreless sea with the spectral tint of twilight on its tumultuous waves!

KING: Did I not warn you that you could not bear the sight of me unless really prepared? This is why I wished to reveal myself to you slowly, not with too great a suddenness.

SUDARSHANA: But my sin came and destroyed all your hopes— the very possibility of a union with you has now become unthinkable to me.

KING: It will be possible in time, my Queen. The utter darkness that has to-day shaken you to your soul will one day be your solace and salvation. What else can my love exist for?

SUDARSHANA: It cannot be, it is impossible. What can your love alone do? *My* love has now turned away from you. Beauty has cast its spell on me. I have told you all: now punish me as you will.

KING: Your punishment has already begun.

SUDARSHANA: But if you do not cast me off. I will leave you—

KING: You are free; do as you choose.

SUDARSHANA: I cannot bear your presence! You fill my heart with anger. Why did they tell me you were fair? You are dark, dark as night—I shall never, I can never, desire you. I have seen what I love—it is soft as cream, delicate as the *Shirisha* flower, beautiful as a butterfly.

KING: It is false as a mirage, empty as a bubble.

SUDARSHANA: Let it be so—still I cannot stand near you. I cannot! Union with you! It is not possible. It cannot be anything but a false union—my heart turns from you in spite of itself.

KING: Will you not even try a little?

SUDARSHANA: I have been trying since yesterday—but the more I try, the more rebellious does my heart become. If I stay with you I shall constantly be pursued by the thought that I am impure, that I am false.

KING: Well, then, you can go as far from me as you like.

SUDARSHANA: I cannot fly from you—just because you do not prevent my going. Why do you not hold me back, hold me by the hair, saying, "You shall not go"? Why do you not strike me? O punish me, strike me, beat me with violent hands! But your unresisting silence exasperates me—I cannot bear it!

KING: Why do you think that I am really silent? How do you know that I am not trying to keep you back?

SUDARSHANA: Oh, no, no—I cannot bear this—tell me aloud, command me with the voice of thunder, compel me with words that will drown everything else in my ears.

KING: I leave you free, but why should I help you to break away from me?

SUDARSHANA: You will not? Well then, I must go!

KING: Go then!

SUDARSHANA: If I go thus, am I to blame? You could have held me back by force, but you did not! You have not hindered me—and now I shall go away. Command your sentinels to prevent my going.

KING: No one will stand in your way. You can go as free as the broken storm-cloud driven by the tempest.

SUDARSHANA: I can resist no more—something in me is impelling me forward—I am breaking away from my anchor! Perhaps I shall sink, but I shall return no more.

[*She rushes out and comes back with* SURANGAMA]

SUDARSHANA [*re-entering*] King, O King!

SURANGAMA: He has gone.

SUDARSHANA: Gone? Has he gone? Has he left me? Well then … then he has cast me off for good! I came back; but he could not wait for me, even for an instant! Since that is so, now I am utterly free. Surangama, did he ask you to keep me back?

SURANGAMA: No, he said nothing.

SUDARSHANA: Why should he say anything? Why should he care for me? … I am then free, perfectly free. But, Surangama, I wanted to ask one thing of the King, but could not utter it in his presence. Tell me if he has punished the prisoners with death.

SURANGAMA: Death? My King never punishes with death.

SUDARSHANA: What has he done to them, then?

SURANGAMA: He has set them at liberty. The Prince of Kanchi has acknowledged his defeat and gone back to his kingdom.

SUDARSHANA: Ah, what a relief! What a joy that I am free!

SURANGAMA: But are you not afraid of your freedom?

SUDARSHANA: No, why should I be afraid?

SURANGAMA: Do you not fear to meet the monstrous Many?

SUDARSHANA: O, do not talk like that.

SURANGAMA: The monster Many with its hundred licking tongues!

SUDARSHANA: O stop!

SURANGAMA: I already feel its hissing breath all around us. Ah, you have left the refuge of the one!

SUDARSHANA: Refuge! Why, I am fleeing from it. The multitude is my salvation. I will lose and forget myself in its arms.

SURANGAMA: Never more shall you forget yourself. Every moment will hit you, every step will lead you to doubt and uncertainty.

SUDARSHANA: Ah, the mad delight of uncertainty! I am in love with it.

SURANGAMA: My Queen, I have one prayer to make to you.

SUDARSHANA: You need not utter your prayer in words, Surangama. Whatever jewels the King gave me, I leave to you—I am not worthy to wear them now.

SURANGAMA: No, I do not want them, my Queen. My unadorned plainness is good enough for me. My master has not given me anything of which I can boast before people.

SUDARSHANA: What do you want of me then?

SURANGAMA: I too shall go with you, my Queen.

SUDARSHANA: Consider what you are saying; You want to leave your master. What a prayer for you to make!

SURANGAMA: I shall not go far from him—when you go out unguarded he will be with you, close by your side.

SUDARSHANA: You are talking nonsense, my child. I wanted to take Rohini with me, but she would not come. What gives you courage enough to wish to come with me?

SURANGAMA: I have got neither courage nor strength. But I shall go—courage will come of itself, and strength too will come.

SUDARSHANA: No, how can I take you with me; your presence will constantly remind me of my shame. I shall never endure that.

SURANGAMA: O, my Queen, I have made all your good and all your evil my own, will you treat me as a stranger still? I must go with you.

IX

A room in the palace of KANYAKUVJA
[*The King of* KANYAKUVJA *and his* MINISTER]

MINISTER: Sire, do not be angry with her. Princess Sudarshana has come to you as your daughter.

KANYAKUVJA: Do not plead for her. She has left her husband, she has lost her place in the world.

MINISTER: But still she is a princess.

KANYAKUVJ: No, she has burst through her bonds, she has no more claims upon her past.

MINISTER: What arrangements shall I make for her residence in the palace?

KANYAKUVJA: Do not trouble yourself about that. I have already sent her word that she will have to live here as a maidservant if she must stay in my house.

MINISTER: It will be hard and bitter for her.

KANYAKUVJA: You do not know with what deadly fear this daughter of mine has inspired me. She is coming to my home laden with peril.

MINISTER: What do you fear, Sire?

KANYAKUVJA: I feel that she has entered this house by breaking its wall, and the security and peace of my home is endangered. She has dug a hole in the dyke and the flood will follow; already I seem to hear its roar.

[*Enter* ATTENDANT]

ATTENDANT: Victory be to you. Sire, a messenger from a foreign land is waiting to have an audience.

KANYAKUVJA: God grant that it be not a messenger of evil.

[*They go out and enter* SUDARSHANA *dressed as a maidservant, and* SURANGAMA]

SUDARSHANA: Go from me, Surangama! It drives me to fury to see you so patient and so submissive.

SURANGAMA: With whom are you angry?

SUDARSHANA: I do not know, but I long to see everything involved in destruction! I felt my place on the throne as the queen in a moment's time—did I lose my all to sweep the dust, to sweat and slave in this dismal hole? Alone, I am all alone. O, I am terribly alone!

SURANGAMA: I wish you were alone, my Queen! You are surrounded on all sides—the whole world is pressing upon you—it is suffocating you.

SUDARSHANA: Surangama, I shall not keep anything from you. When he set the palace on fire, I could not be angry with him. A great inward joy set my heart a-flutter all the while. What a stupendous crime! How glorious! It was this terrible joy that enabled me to leave everything behind me in a moment's time. But is all this nothing but my own imagining? Why is there so sign of his coming anywhere?

SURANGAMA: He of whom you are thinking did not set fire to
the palace—it was the Prince of Kanchi who did it.

SUDARSHANA: Ah! Coward! But is it possible? Have I deceived
myself? But Surangama, don't you think your King should
yet have come to take me back?

[SURANGAMA *remains silent*]

You think I am anxious to go back? Never! Even if the
King really came I should not return. Not even once did he
forbid me to depart and I found all the doors wide open to
let me out! And the stony and dusty road over which I
walked—it cared not at all that a Queen was treading on it.
It is hard—like your King—it is unfeeling! The meanest who
walks upon it is the same as the highest. You are silent, silent?
Well, I tell you, your King's behaviour is—mean, brutal,
shameful!

SURANGAMA: Everyone knows that my King is hard and
pitiless—no one has ever been able to move him.

SUDARSHANA: Surangama, look a cloud of dust seems to rise
over the Eastern horizon across the fields.

SURANGAMA: Yes, I see it.

SUDARSHANA: Is that not like the banner of a chariot?

SURANGAMA: Yes, indeed, a banner it is.

SUDARSHANA: Then he is coming. He has come at last!

SURANGAMA: Who is coming?

SUDARSHANA: Our King, who else? How could he live without
me?

SURANGAMA: No, no, this cannot be the King. I see it plain,
Sudarshana, it is that Monster.

SUDARSHANA: Monster!

SURANGAMA: Yes, it has smelt your flesh, it has come out of its
hole with its greedy glaring eyes. It is the Many.

SUDARSHANA: You always talk in riddles.

SURANGAMA: It is no riddle of mine, my Queen. *You* yourself have made your life a riddle, its meaning is all upset.

SUDARSHANA: Ah! How you frighten me, Surangama. I feel I am pursued, but I do not clearly see by whom. Go out, Surangama, and see what is happening and come back and tell me everything.

[SURANGAMA *goes out and enters the* DOORKEEPER]

DOORKEEPER: You must be her maid.

SUDARSHANA: Whose maid?

DOORKEEPER: Of Princess Sudarshana.

SUDARSHANA: That is possible.

DOORKEEPER: Do not evade my question. It is no longer a secret that the Princess has left her husband and is living in this palace.

SUDARSHANA: If it were true I should not talk about it.

DOORKEEPER: Yes, it is a shame that should be hidden—but it glows like a blush and spreads all over the country—this country of her father.

SUDARSHANA: I know, it is her curse, she cannot remain concealed, even her hiding place betrays her.

DOORKEEPER: Has she no love for her father, and her father's people?

SUDARSHANA: What makes you doubt that?

DOORKEEPER: Does she not see that she has come here as an evil fate?

SUDARSHANA: The wretched creature has no power to do harm to anybody but herself. She is too destitute. Why are you afraid of her?

DOORKEEPER: We are afraid of her as we are afraid of the dead who have no business to come back to the land of the living. Tell her she must leave this country without delay. Since she has been here there seems to be an unrest in the air—ugly rumours are flying all about. Men from watch towers say that dust is seen in the horizon, in the east and in the west. Some danger is marching upon us from all sides.

[*Sound of a horn outside*]

Ah! do you hear the war horn? It has come already.

[*Rushes out*]

SUDARSHANA: It must be my King. His anger has been aroused at last. He is coming to punish me. It is a terror and a delight. He must bring his whole army to get this weak woman back. But I will not be defeated.

[*Enters* SURANGAMA]

SURANGAMA: It is not the King, my Queen.
SUDARSHANA: Not the King? What, has he not come yet! Are you quite sure?
SURANGAMA: No, my King never raises these clouds of dust by his advent. None knows when he comes.
SUDARSHANA: Then this is—
SURANGAMA: The same: he is coming with the Prince of Kanchi.
SUDARSHANA: Do you know his name?
SURANGAMA: His name is Suvarna.
SUDARSHANA: It is he then. My hero is coming now, to release me. Did you know Suvarna?
SURANGAMA: When I was at my father's home, in the gambling den—

SUDARSHANA: No, no, I won't hear anything of him from you. He is my own hero, my only salvation. I shall know him without your telling stories about him. But see, what manner of man your King is! You cannot condemn me now. How could I have waited for him here all my life, toiling like a bondslave. I shall never have *your* meek and weak submissiveness.

[*Enter King of* KANYAKUVJA]

[*Bowing to him*] Father!

KANYAKUVJA: Yes, I am that unfortunate being, your father. I have come to tell you that the Prince Kanchi is at my door claiming you as his by right.

SUDARSHANA: I know not what right he has.

KANYAKUVJA: The right of having set you free from the bond that held you fast and true.

SUDARSHANA: If that be so then I am mine own.

KANYAKUVJA: No, you are like a lotus cut from its stem, at the mercy of every clamorous wave.

SUDARSHANA: Then give me up, father.

KANYAKUVJA: You are but one, one, and your claimants many. I have letters from the Princes of Avanti, Koshala, Vidarbha and Kalinga as well—and they are following with their armies. I wish I could cut you into five pieces to meet their claims.

SUDARSHANA: Father, send no army to fight them; let me go alone to meet these Princes.

MINISTER: Victory be to you. The Princes of Kanchi, Koshala, Avanti, Vidarbha and Kalinga have met in the mango grove across the river. They have agreed among themselves that he whom the Princess accepts as her husband will have her. And they have sent a message saying that they are holding an assembly for the occasion, and the Princess Sudarshana is to be sent there without delay.

KANYAKUVJA: Call up the army, we must get ready to fight.

MINISTER: It is hopeless, sire; we are one against so many, and we are unprepared.

KANYAKUVJA: But it takes no time to prepare to die. Come, we have no time for hesitation.

[KANYAKUVJA *and his* MINISTER *go out*]

SUDARSHANA: Surangama, I must go to this assembly.

SURANGAMA: And bravely meet your fate and defy it, my Queen.

SUDARSHANA: You take my message to the Princes—salute them for me and tell them that I accept their invitation.

SURANGAMA: I am ready.

[SURANGAMA *goes out*]

SUDARSHANA: O King, my only King! [*Taking out a dagger from within her bosom*] This body of mine has received a stain—I shall make a sacrifice of it to-day in the dust before all these princes! But shall I never be able to tell you that I know of no stain of faithlessness within the innermost chamber of my heart? That dark chamber where you used to come to meet me lies cold and empty within my bosom to-day—but O my Lord! none has opened its doors, none has entered it but you, O King! Will you never come again to open those doors? Then, let death come, for death is dark like yourself.—You are death—O King!

X

A grove of trees
[*All the princes, and* SUVARNA, *the Pretender, as the Prince of* KANCHI'S *umbrella-bearer*]

VIDARBHA: Kanchi, how is it that you have got no single ornament on your person?

KANCHI: Because I entertain no hopes at all, my friend. Ornaments would but double the shame of my defeat.

KALINGA: But your umbrella-bearer seems to have made up for that—his is loaded with gold and jewellery.

VIRAT: The vanity of the Prince of Kanchi has made him discard all outer embellishments.

PANCHALA: I cannot command his wisdom. Everyone knows that a woman's eyes are like a moth, they fling themselves headlong upon the glare and glitter or jewel and gold.

KALINGA: How much longer shall we have to wait?

KANCHI: Do not grow impatient, Kalinga—sweet are the fruits of delay.

KOSHALA: Kanchi, did you feel as if something shook your seat just now? Is it an earthquake?

KANCHI: Earthquake? I do not know.

VIDARBHA: I cannot regard this as a very auspicious omen.

KANCHI: Everything looks inauspicious to the eye of fear.

VIDARBHA: I fear none except Fate, before which courage is as futile as it is absurd.

PANCHALA: Vidarbha, do not darken today's happy proceedings with your unwelcome auguries.

KANCHI: I never take the unseen into account till it has become "seen".

VIDARBHA: But then it might be too late to do anything.

KALINGA: Isn't that music somewhere outside?

PANCHALA: Yes, it certainly sounds like music.

KANCHI: Then at last it must be Queen Sudarshana approaching near. [*Aside to* Suvarna] Suvarna, you must not hide and cower behind me like that. Mind, the umbrella in your hand is shaking!

[*Enters* DĀDĀ *dressed as a warrior*]
[*Exits* SUVARNA *unperceived*]

KALINGA: Who is that?—Who are you?

PANCHALA: Who is this that dares to enter this hall unbidden?

VIRAT: Amazing impudence! Kalinga, prevent that fellow from advancing further.

KALINGA: That duty I resign to you, my elders all.

VIDARBHA: Let us rather hear what he has to say.

DĀDĀ: The King has come.

VIDARBHA: [*starting*] The King?

PANCHALA: Which King?

KALINGA: Where does he come from?

DĀDĀ: My King!

VIRAT: Your King?

KALINGA: Who is he?

KOSHALA: What do you mean?

DĀDĀ: Who all know whom I mean. He has come.

VIDARBHA: He has come?

KOSHALA: With what intention?

DĀDĀ: He has summoned you all to come to him.

KANCHI: Summoned us, indeed? In what terms has he been pleased to summon us, pray?

DĀDĀ: You can take his call in any way you like—he is prepared to give all kinds of welcome to suit your various tastes.

VIRAT: But who are you?

DĀDĀ: I am one of his generals.

KANCHI: General indeed! Do you think you can frighten us?

Do you imagine that I cannot see through your disguise?
You dare to pose as a "general" before us who know you
so well!

DĀDĀ: You have recognized me to perfection. Who is so
unworthy as I to bear my King's commands? And yet it
is he who has invested me with these robes of a
general and sent me here choosing me before mightier
warriors.

KANCHI: It is well. We shall observe the proprieties on a more
fitting occasion—but at present we are in the midst of a
pressing engagement. The King must wait until our
business is at an end.

DĀDĀ: When he sends out his call he does not wait.

KOSHALA: We had better obey his call, I am going at once.

VIDARBHA: Kanchi, I cannot agree with your proposal to wait
till this function is over. I am going too.

KALINGA: You are older than I am—I shall follow you.

PANCHALA: Look behind you, Kanchi, your regal umbrella is
lying in the dust: you have not noticed when your
umbrella-holder has stolen away.

KANCHI: All right, general. I too am going—but not to do him
homage. I go to fight him on the field of battle.

DĀDĀ: My King will meet you then in the field of battle; that
is no mean place for your reception.

VIRAT: Look here, friends, perhaps we are all flying before an
imaginary terror—it looks as if Kanchi will have the best
of it.

PANCHALA: Possibly. When the fruit is so near the hand, it is
cowardly and foolish to go away without plucking it.

KALINGA: No, no, it is better to join Kanchi. He cannot be
without a definite plan when he is so daring.

XI

[*The palace of* KANYAKUVJA]
[Queen SUDARSHANA *and* SURANGAMA]

SUDARSHANA: The fight is over. When will the King come?

SURANGAMA: I also look for his coming.

SUDARSHANA: I feel such a throb of joy, Surangama, that my very heart is aching. Yet I am dying with shame too; how shall I show my face to him?

SURANGAMA: Go to him in utmost humility and all shame will vanish in a moment.

SUDARSHANA: I confess to you, Surangama, that I have met with a defeat which must endure for the rest of my life. Pride made me claim the largest share in his love so long. Everyone used to say I had wonderful grace and charm; everyone used to say that the King showed me unlimited kindness—this makes it difficult for me to bend my heart in humility before him.

SURANGAMA: This difficulty, My Queen, will pass away.

SUDARSHANA: Oh, yes, it will pass—the day has arrived for me to humble myself before the whole world. But why does not the King come to take me back? For what is he still waiting for yet?

SURANGAMA: Have I not told you, my King is cruel?

[*Enters* DĀDĀ]

SUDARSHANA: I have heard that you are my King's friend. Give me good news. Tell me when the King will come to take me back.

DĀDĀ: You ask me a hard question, indeed! I hardly understand my friend yet. His fight was fought, but how, I do not know. The battle is over, but no one can tell where he was or where he is.

SUDARSHANA: Is he then gone away?

DĀDĀ: I find no trace of him here.

SUDARSHANA: Has he gone? And you call such a person your friend?

DĀDĀ: That is why he gets abuse as well as suspicion. But my King is regardless of both.

SUDARSHANA: Has he gone away? Ah! how hard, how cruel, how cruel! He is made of stone! I tried to move him with my own bosom—my breast is torn and bleeding—but I could not move him at all. Dādā, tell me, how can you endure such a friend?

DĀDĀ: I know him now—I have known him through my griefs and joys—he can make me weep no more.

SUDARSHANA: Will he not let me know him also?

DĀDĀ: Of course he will. Nothing less will satisfy him.

SUDARSHANA: Very well, I shall see how hard he can be! I shall stay here near the window. I shall not say a word; I shall not move a step; let me see if he will not come to me!

DĀDĀ: You are young still—you can afford to wait for him; but to me, an old man, a moment's loss is an age. I must set out to seek him, whether I succeed or fail.

[*Exits* DĀDĀ]

SUDARSHANA: I do not want him—I will not seek him! Surangama, I have no need of your King! Why did he fight with the Princes? Was it for me at all? Did he want to show off his prowess and strength?

SURANGAMA: Show off! Why he was nowhere even seen! And imagine, it was Dādā, the playmate of all the village boys who acted as his general.

SUDARSHANA: Go from me—I cannot bear the sight of you. He has humbled me to the dust and still he is not content.

XII

A street
[A band of CITIZENS]

1ST CIT: When so many Princes met together, we thought some great matter was afoot, but somehow everything took such a turn that nobody knows what happened!

2ND CIT: Did you not see, they could not come to an agreement among themselves—everyone distrusted everyone else.

3RD CIT: None kept to their original plan, one wanted to advance, another thought it better policy to recede, some went to the right, others made a rush to the left; and they did not know with whom they were fighting, nor do we know even now. How can you call that a fight?

1ST CIT: They had no eye to real fighting—each had his eyes on the others.

2ND CIT: Each was thinking, "Why should I die to enable others to reap the harvest?"

3RD CIT: But you must all admit that the Prince of Kanchi fought like a real hero.

1ST CIT: Yes! For a long time after his defeat he seemed loth to acknowledge himself beaten.

2ND CIT: He was at last pierced to the heart by a deadly missile.

3RD CIT: But before that he did not seem to realize that he had been losing ground at every step.

1ST CIT: As for the other Princes—well, nobody knows where they fled, leaving poor Kanchi alone in the field.

2ND CIT: But I have heard that he did not die.

3RD CIT: No, the physicians saved him—but he will carry the mark of his defeat on his breast till his dying day.

1ST CIT: None of the other Princes who fled escaped, they have all been taken prisoners. But what sort of justice is this that was meted out to them?

2ND CIT: I heard that everyone was punished except Kanchi, whom the judge placed on his right on the throne of justice, putting a crown on his head.

3RD CIT: This beats all mystery hollow.

1ST CIT: Just so. The greatest offender was certainly the Prince of Kanchi; as for the others, greed of gain now pressed them to advance, then again they drew back in fear.

2ND CIT: What kind of justice is this, I ask? It is as the tiger came off scot-free, while his tail was punished.

3RD CIT: They are great, high justices, my friends; their brains are of a different stamp from ours.

1ST CIT: Have they got any brains at all I wonder? They simply indulge their whims as there is no one above them.

2ND CIT: Whatever you may say, had the power been in our hands we should certainly have governed much better than this.

3RD CIT: There can be no doubt at all about that! It goes without saying.

XIII

A road
[Queen SUDARSHANA and SURANGAMA]

SUDARSHANA: What a relief, Surangama! It is my defeat that has brought me freedom. O what an iron pride was mine! All through yesternight I lay alone on the dusty

floor before that window—lay there through the desolate
hours and wept!

SURANGAMA: Last night's heavy and melancholy air seemed as
though it would last for an eternity—oh, what a dismal
night!

SUDARSHANA: But would you believe it—I seemed to hear the
soft strains of the *vina* floating through the dark. Could
he play such tender tunes, he who is so dark and terrible?
The world knows only my indignity—but none but my
own heart could hear those strains that called me through
the lone and wailing night. Did you too, Surangama,
hear that *vina*? Or was that but a dream of mine?

SURANGAMA: It is for this call of music that I have all along
been listening with an eager ear.

SUDARSHANA: He did at last send me on to the open road—I
could not withstand his will. When I shall find him, the
first words that I shall tell him will be, "I have come of
my own will—I have not awaited your coming". I shall
say, "For your sake have I trodden the hard and weary
road, and bitter and ceaseless has been my weeping all
the way". I shall at least have this pride in me when I
meet him.

SURANGAMA: But even that pride will not last. He came before
you did—who else could have sent you on the road?

SUDARSHANA: Perhaps he did. As long as a sense of offended
pride remained with me, I could not help thinking that
he had left me for good—but when I flung my dignity to
the winds and came out on the common streets, then it
seemed to me that he too had come out: I have been
finding him since the moment I was on the road. Ah, yes,
he has come—he has held me by the hand, just as he used
to do in that chamber of darkness, when, at his touch, all
my body would start with a sudden thrill: it is the same,
the same touch again! Who says that he is not here?—

Surangama, can you not see that he has come, in silence
and secret? ... Who is that there? Look, Surangama,
there is a third traveller on this dark road at this hour of
night.

SURANGAMA: I see, it is the Prince of Kanchi, my Queen.

SUDARSHANA: Kanchi?

SURANGAMA: Do not be afraid, my Queen!

SUDARSHANA: Afraid! Why should I be afraid? The days of
fear are gone for ever from me.

KANCHI: [entering] Queen-mother, I see you too on this road!
I travel the same way as yourself. Have no fear of me, O
Queen!

SUDARSHANA: It is well, Prince of Kanchi, that we should be
going together, side by side—this is but right. I crossed
your path when first I left my home, and now I meet you
again on my way back. Who could have dreamed that
first meeting of ours would augur so well?

KANCHI: But, Queen-mother, it is not meet that you should
walk this road on foot. Will you permit me to get a
chariot for you?

SUDARSHANA: Oh, do not say so: I shall never be happy if I
cannot on my way back home tread every particle of the
dust of the road that led me away from my King.

SURANGAMA: But, Prince, you too are walking in the dust
today: This road has never known anybody driving a
chariot over it. Look, my Queen, there on the Eastern
horizon comes the dawn. We have not long to walk: I see
the spires of the golden turrets of the King's palace.

[Enter DĀDĀ]

DĀDĀ: My child, it is dawn—at last!

SUDARSHANA: Your benedictions have given me god speed,
Dādā, and here I am, at last.

DĀDĀ: But see how discourteous our King is! He has sent no chariot, no band of music, no royal pomp to meet you.

SUDARSHANA: How can you say that? The sky is crimson from end to end, the air is full of the welcoming fragrance of flowers.

DĀDĀ: Yes. But however cruel our King may be, we cannot but feel pain at seeing you thus, my child. How can we bear to see you going to the King's palace in this poor attire? Wait a little—I am running to fetch you your Queenly garments.

SUDARSHANA: Oh, no, no, no! He has taken away those regal robes from me for ever—he has attired me in a servant's dress before the eyes of the whole world: what a relief this has been to me! I am his servant now, no longer his Queen. Today I stand at the feet of all those who can claim any relationship with him.

DĀDĀ: But your enemies will laugh at you now.

SUDARSHANA: May their laughter be immortal—let them throw dust at me in the streets: this dust will today be the powder with which I shall deck myself to meet my lord.

DĀDĀ: Well then, let us play the last game of our spring festival—instead of the pollen of flowers let the south breeze blow and scatter the lowly dust in its every direction! We shall go to the lord clad in common grey. And we shall find him too covered all over with dust.

KANCHI: Dādā, do not forget me in this game of yours! I also will have to get this royal garment of mine soiled beyond recognition.

DĀDĀ: That will not take long, my brother. Now that you have come down so far—you will quickly change your colour. Look at our Queen—she was displeased with herself and thought that she could spoil her matchless beauty by flinging away her ornaments: but this insult has made it shine forth in tenfold radiance, and now it is in its unadorned perfection.

SURANGAMA: Lo, there rises the sun!

XIV

The dark chamber
[*The* KING *and Queen* SUDARSHANA]

SUDARSHANA: Lord, do not give me back the honour which you once turned away from me! I am the servant of your feet—I only seek the privilege of serving you.

KING: Will you be able to bear me now?

SUDARSHANA: Oh, yes, yes, I can. I was repelled from you because I had sought to find you in the pleasure garden, in my Queen's chamber; there even your meanest servant looks fairer than you. That fever of longing has left my eyes for ever. You are not beautiful, my lord—you are beyond compare.

KING: That which can be matched with me lies within yourself.

SUDARSHANA: If this be so, then that too is beyond compare. Your love lives in me—you are mirrored in that love, and you see your face reflected in me; nothing of this is mine, it is all yours, O Lord!

KING: I open the doors of this dark room today—the game is finished here! Come, come with me now, come outside—*into the light!*

SUDARSHANA: Before I go, let me bow at the feet of my lord of darkness, my cruel, my terrible, my peerless one!

POEMS OF KABIR

Introduction

The poet Kabīr, a selection from whose songs is here for the first time offered to English readers, is one of the most interesting personalities in the history of Indian mysticism. Born in or near Benares, of Mohammedan parents, and probably about the year 1440, he became in early life a disciple of the celebrated Hindu ascetic Rāmānanda. Rāmānanda had brought to northern India the religious revival which Rāmānuja, the great twelfth-century reformer of Brāhmanism, had initiated in the south. This revival was in part a reaction against the increasing formalism of the orthodox cult, in part an assertion of the demands of the heart as against the intense intellectualism of the Vedānta philosophy, the exaggerated monism which that philosophy proclaimed. It took in Rāmānuja's preaching the form of an ardent personal devotion to the God Vishnu, as representing the personal aspect of the Divine Nature: that mystical "religion of love" which everywhere makes its appearance at a certain level of spiritual culture, and which creeds and philosophies are powerless to kill.

Though such a devotion is indigenous in Hinduism, and finds expression in many passages of the Bhagavad Gītā, there was in its mediaeval revival a large element of syncretism. Rāmānanda, through whom its spirit is said to have reached Kabīr, appears to have been a man of wide religious culture, and full of missionary enthusiasm. Living at the moment in which the impassioned poetry and deep philosophy of the great Persian mystics, Attār, Sādi, Jalālu'ddīn Rūmī, and Hāfiz, were exercising a powerful influence on the religious thought of India, he dreamed of reconciling this intense and personal Mohammedan mysticism with the traditional theology of Brāhmanism. Some have regarded both these great religious leaders as influenced also by Christian thought and life: but as this is a point upon which competent authorities hold widely divergent views, its discussion is not attempted here. We may safely assert, however, that in their teachings, two—perhaps three—apparently antagonistic streams of intense spiritual culture met, as Jewish and Hellenistic thought met in the early Christian Church: and it is one of the outstanding characteristics of Kabīr's genius that he was able in his poems to fuse them into one.

A great religious reformer, the founder of a sect to which nearly a million northern Hindus still belong, it is yet supremely as a mystical poet that Kabīr lives for us. His fate has been that of many revealers of Reality. A hater of religious exclusivism, and seeking above all things to initiate men into the liberty of the children of God, his followers have honoured his memory by re-erecting in a new place the barriers which he laboured to cast down. But his wonderful songs survive, the spontaneous expressions of his vision and his love; and it is by these, not by the didactic teachings associated with his name, that he makes his immortal appeal to the heart. In these poems a wide range of mystical emotion is brought into play: from the loftiest abstractions, the most other-worldly passion for the Infinite, to the most intimate and personal realisation of God, expressed in homely metaphors and religious symbols drawn indifferently from Hindu and Mohammedan belief. It is impossible to say of their author that he was Brāhman or Sūfi, Vedāntist or Vaishnavite. He is, as he says himself, "at once the child of Allah and of Rām." That Supreme Spirit Whom he knew and adored, and to Whose joyous friendship he sought to induct the souls of other men, transcended whilst He included all metaphysical categories, all credal definitions; yet each contributed something to the description of that Infinite and Simple Totality Who revealed Himself, according to their measure, to the faithful lovers of all creeds.

Kabīr's story is surrounded by contradictory legends, on none of which reliance can be placed. Some of these emanate from a Hindu, some from a Mohammedan source, and claim him by turns as a Sūfi and a Brahman saint. His name, however, is practically a conclusive proof of Moslem ancestry: and the most probable tale is that which represents him as the actual or adopted child of a Mohammedan weaver of Benares, the city in which the chief events of his life took place.

In fifteenth-century Benares the syncretistic tendencies of Bhakti religion had reached full development. Sūfīs and Brāhmans appear to have met in disputation: the most spiritual members of both creeds frequenting the teachings of Rāmānanda, whose reputation was then at its height. The boy Kabīr, in whom the religious passion was innate, saw in Rāmānanda his destined teacher; but knew how slight were the chances that a Hindu guru would accept a Mohammedan as disciple. He therefore hid upon the steps of the river Ganges, where Rāmānanda was accustomed to bathe; with the result that the master, coming down to the water, trod upon his body unexpectedly, and exclaimed in his astonishment, 'Rām! Rām!'—the name of the incarnation under which he worshipped God. Kabīr then declared that he had received the mantra of initiation from Rāmānanda's lips, and was by it admitted to discipleship. In spite of the protests of orthodox Brāhmans and Mohammedans, both equally annoyed by this contempt of theological landmarks, he persisted in his claim; thus exhibiting in action that very principle of religious synthesis which Rāmānanda had sought to establish in thought. Rāmānanda appears to have accepted him, and though Mohammedan legends speak of the famous Sūfi Pīr, Takkī of Jhansī, as Kabīr's master in later life, the Hindu saint is the only human teacher to whom in his songs he acknowledges indebtedness.

The little that we know of Kabīr's life contradicts many current ideas concerning the Oriental mystic. Of the stages of discipline through which he passed, the manner in which his spiritual genius developed, we are completely ignorant. He seems to have remained for years the disciple of Rāmānanda, joining in the theological and philosophical arguments which his master held with all the great Mullahs and Brāhmans of his day; and to this source we may perhaps trace his acquaintance with the terms of Hindu and Sūfi philosophy. He may or may not have submitted to the traditional education of the Hindu or the Sūfi contemplative: it is clear, at any rate, that he never adopted the life of the professional ascetic, or retired from the world in order to devote himself to bodily modifications and the exclusive pursuit of the contemplative life. Side by side with his interior life of adoration, its artistic expression in music and words— for he was a skilled musician as well as a poet—he lived the sane and diligent life of the Oriental craftsman. All the legends agree on this point: that Kabīr was a weaver, a simple and unlettered man, who earned his living at the loom. Like Paul the tentmaker, Boehme the cobbler, Bunyan the tinker, Tersteegen the ribbon-maker, he knew how to combine vision and industry; the work of his hands helped rather than hindered the impassioned meditation of his heart. Hating mere bodily austerities, he was no ascetic, but a married man, the father of a family—a circumstance which Hindu legends of the monastic type vainly attempt to conceal or explain—and it was from out of the heart of the common life that he sang his rapturous lyrics of divine love. Here his works corroborate the traditional story of his life. Again and again he extols the life of home, the value and reality of diurnal existence, with its opportunities for love and renunciation; pouring contempt upon the professional sanctity of the Yogi, who "has a great beard and matted locks, and looks like a goat," and on all who think it necessary to flee a world pervaded by love, joy, and beauty—the proper theatre of man's quest—in order to find that One Reality Who has "spread His form of love throughout *all* the world."[1]

It does not need much experience of ascetic literature to recognise the boldness and originality of this attitude in such a time and place. From the point of view of orthodox sanctity, whether Hindu or Mohammedan, Kabīr was plainly a heretic; and his frank dislike of all institutional religion, all external observance—which was as thorough and as intense as that of the Quakers themselves—completed, so far as ecclesiastical opinion was concerned, his reputation as a dangerous man. The "simple union" with Divine reality which he perpetually extolled, as alike the duty and the joy of every soul, was independent both of ritual and of bodily austerities; the God whom he proclaimed was "neither in Kaaba nor in Kailāsh." Those who sought Him needed not to go far; for He awaited discovery everywhere, more accessible to "the washerwoman and the carpenter" than to the self-righteous holy man.[2] Therefore the whole apparatus of piety, Hindu and Moslem alike—the temple and mosque, idol and holy water, scriptures and priests—were denounced by this inconveniently clear-

---

1. Cf. Poems 21, 40, 43, 66, 76.
2. Poems 1, 2, 41.

sighted poet as mere substitutes for reality; dead things
intervening between the soul and its love—

> The images are all lifeless, they cannot speak: I know,
> for I have cried aloud to them.
> The Purana and the Koran are mere words: lifting up
> the curtain, I have seen.[3]

This sort of thing cannot be tolerated by any organised
church; and it is not surprising that Kabīr, having his head-
quarters in Benares, the very centre of priestly influence, was
subjected to considerable persecution. The well-known legend
of the beautiful courteasan sent by the Brāhmans to tempt his
virtue, and converted, like the Magdalen, by her sudden
encounter with the initiate of a higher love, preserves the
memory of the fear and dislike with which he was regarded
by the ecclesiastical powers. Once at least, after the performance
of a supposed miracle of healing, he was brought before the
emperor Sikandar Lodī, and charged with claiming the possession
of divine powers. But Sikandar Lodī, a ruler of considerable
culture, was tolerant of the eccentricities of saintly persons
belonging to his own faith. Kabīr, being of Mohammedan birth,
was outside the authority of the Brāhmans, and technically
classed with the Sūfis, to whom great theological latitude was
allowed. Therefore, though he was banished in the interests
of peace from Benares, his life was spared. This seems to have
happened in 1495, when he was nearly sixty years of age;
it is the last event in his career of which we have definite
knowledge. Thenceforth he appears to have moved about
amongst various cities of northern India, the centre of a group
of disciples; continuing in exile that life of apostle and poet
of love to which, as he declares in one of his songs, he was

---

3. Poems 42, 65, 67.

destined "from the beginning of time." In 1518, an old man, broken in health, and with hands so feeble that he could no longer make the music which he loved, he died at Maghar near Gorakhpur.

A beautiful legend tells us that after his death his Mohammedan and Hindu disciples disputed the possession of his body; which the Mohammedans wished to bury, the Hindus to burn. As they argued together, Kabīr appeared before them, and told them to lift the shroud and look at that which lay beneath. They did so, and found in the place of the corpse a heap of flowers; half of which were buried by the Mohammedans at Maghar, and half carried by the Hindus to the holy city of Benares to be burned—fitting conclusion to a life which had made fragrant the most beautiful doctrines of two great creeds.

II

The poetry of mysticism might be defined on the one hand as a temperamental reaction to the vision of Reality: on the other, as a form of prophecy. As it is the special vocation of the mystical consciousness to mediate between two orders, going out in loving adoration towards god and coming home to tell the secrets of Eternity to other men; so the artistic self-expression of this consciousness has also a double character. It is love-poetry, but love-poetry which is often written with a missionary intention.

Kabīr's songs are of this kind: outbirths at once of rapture and of charity. Written in the popular Hindi, not in the literary tongue, they were deliberately addressed—like the vernacular poetry of Jacopone da Todi and Richard Rolle—to the people rather than to the professionally religious class; and all must be struck by the constant employment in them of imagery drawn from the common life, the universal experience. It is by the simplest metaphors, by constant appeals to needs, passions, relations which all men understand—the bridegroom and bride, the guru and disciple, the pilgrim, the farmer, the migrant bird—that he drives home his intense conviction of the reality of the soul's intercourse with the Transcendent. There are in his universe no fences between the 'natural' and 'supernatural' worlds; everything is a part of the creative Play of God, and therefore—even in its humblest details—capable of revealing the Player's mind.

This willing acceptance of the here-and-now as a means of representing supernal realities is a trait common to the greatest mystics. For them, when they have achieved at last the true theopathetic state, all aspects of the universe possess equal authority as sacramental declarations of the Presence of God; and their fearless employment of homely and physical symbols—often startling and even revolting to the unaccustomed taste—is in direct proportion to the exaltation of their spiritual life. The works of the great Sūfis, and amongst the Christians of Jacopone da Todi, Ruysbroeck, Boehme, abound in illustrations of this law. Therefore we must not be surprised to find in Kabīr's songs—his desperate attempts to communicate his ecstasy and persuade other men to share it—a constant juxtaposition of concrete and metaphysical language; swift alternations between the most intensely anthropomorphic, the most subtly philosophical, ways of apprehending man's communion with the Divine. The need for this alternation; and its entire naturalness for the mind which employs it, is rooted in his concept, or vision, of the Nature of God; and unless we make some attempt to grasp this, we shall not go far in our understanding of his poems.

Kabīr belongs to that group of supreme mystics—amongst whom St. Augustine, Ruysbroeck, and the Sūfi poet Jalālu'ddīn Rūmī are perhaps the chief—who have achieved that which we might call the synthetic vision of God. These have resolved the perpetual opposition between the personal and impersonal, the transcendent and immanent, static and dynamic aspects of the Divine Nature; between the Absolute of philosophy and the "sure true Friend" of devotional religion. They have done this, not by taking these apparently incompatible concepts one after the other; but by ascending to a height of spiritual intuition at which they are, as Ruysbroeck said, "melted and merged in the Unity," and perceived as the completing opposites of a perfect Whole. This proceeding entails for them—and both Kabīr and Ruysbroeck expressly acknowledge it—a universe of three orders: Becoming, Being, and that which is "More than Being," i.e, God.[4] God is here felt to be not the final abstraction, but the one actuality. He inspires, supports, indeed inhabits, both the durational, conditioned, finite world of Becoming and the unconditioned, non-successional, infinite world of Being; yet utterly transcends them both. He is the omnipresent reality, the "All-pervading" within Whom "the worlds are being told like beads." In His personal aspect He is the "beloved Fakīr," teaching and companioning each soul. Considered as Immanent Spirit, He is "the Mind within the mind." But all these are at best partial aspects of His nature, mutually corrective: as the Persons in the Christian doctrine of the Trinity—to which this theological diagram bears a striking resemblance—represent different and compensating experiences of the Divine Unity within which they are resumed. As Rusybroeck discerned a plane of reality upon which "we can speak no more of Father, Son, and Holy Spirit, but only of One being, the very substance of the Divine Persons"; so Kabīr says that "beyond both the limited *and* the limitless is He, the Pure Being."[5]

---

4. Nos. 7 and 49.
5. No. 7.

Brahma, then, is the Ineffable Fact compared with which "the distinction of the conditioned from the Unconditioned is but a word": at once the utterly transcendent one of Absolutist philosophy, and the personal Lover of the individual soul—"common to all and special to each," as one Christian mystic has it. The need felt by Kabīr for both these ways of describing reality is a proof of the richness and balance of his spiritual experience; which neither cosmic nor anthropomorphic symbols, taken alone, could express. More absolute than the Absolute, more personal than the human mind, Brahma therefore exceeds whilst He includes all the concepts of philosophy, all the passionate intuitions of the heart. He is the great Affirmation, the fount of energy, the source of life and love, the unique satisfaction of desire. His creative word is the *Om* or "Everlasting Yea." The negative philosophy, which strips from the Divine Nature all Its attributes and—defining Him only by that which He is not—reduces Him to an "Emptiness," is abhorrent to this most vital of poets. Brahma, he says, "may never be found in abstractions." He is the One Love who pervades the world, discerned in His fullness only by the eyes of love; and those who know Him thus share, though they may never tell, the joyous and ineffable secret of the universe.[6]

Now Kabīr, achieving this synthesis between the personal and cosmic aspects of the Divine Nature, eludes the three great dangers which threaten mystical religion.

First, he escapes the excessive emotionalism, the tendency to an exclusively anthropomorphic devotion, which results from an unrestricted cult of Divine Personality, especially under an incarnational form; seen in India in the exaggerations of Krishna worship, in Europe in the sentimental extravagances of certain Christian saints. Next, he is protected from the

---

6. Nos. 7, 26, 76, 90.

soul-destroying conclusions of pure monism, inevitable if its logical implications are pressed home: that is, the total absorption of that soul in the Being of God as the goal of the spiritual life. For the thorough-going monist the soul, in so far as it is real, is substantially identical with God; and the true object of existence is the making patent of this latent identity, the realisation which finds expression in the Vedantist formula "That art thou." But Kabīr says that Brahma and the creature are "ever distinct, yet ever united"; that the wise man knows the spiritual as well as the material world to "be no more than his footstool."[7] The soul's union with Him is a love union, a mutual inhabitation; that essentially dualistic relation which all mystical religion expresses, not a self-mergence which leaves no place for personality. This eternal distinction, the mysterious union-in-separateness of God and the soul, is a necessary doctrine of all sane mysticism; for no scheme which fails to find a place for it can represent more than a fragment of that soul's intercourse with the spiritual world. Its affirmation was one of the distinguishing features of the Vaishnavite reformation preached by Rāmānuja; the principle of which had descended through Rāmānanda to Kabīr.

Last, the warmly human and direct apprehension of God as the supreme Object of love, the soul's comrade, teacher, and bridegroom, which is so passionately and frequently expressed in Kabīr's poems, balances and controls those abstract tendencies which are inherent in the metaphysical side of his vision of Reality: and prevents it from degenerating into that sterile worship of intellectual formulae which became the curse of the Vedantist school. For the mere intellectualist, as for the mere pietist, he has little approbation.[8] Love is throughout his "absolute sole Lord": the unique source of the

---

7. Nos. 7 and 9.
8. Cf. especially Nos. 59, 69, 75, 90, 91.

more abundant life which he enjoys, and the common factor which unites the finite and infinite worlds. All is soaked in love: that love which he described in almost Johannine language as the "Form of God." The whole of creation is the Play of the Eternal Lover; the living, changing, growing expression of Brahma's love and joy. As these twin passions preside over the generation of human life, so "beyond the mists of pleasure and pain" Kabīr finds them governing the creative acts of God. His manifestation is love; His activity is joy. Creation springs from one glad act of affirmation: the Everlasting Yea, perpetually uttered within the depths of the Divine Nature.[9] In accordance with this concept of the universe as a Love-Game which eternally goes forward, a progressive manifestation of Brahma—one of the many notions which he adopted from the common stock of Hindu religious ideas, and illuminated by his poetic genius—movement, rhythm, perpetual change, forms an integral part of Kabīr's vision of Reality. Though the Eternal and Absolute is ever present to his consciousness, yet his concept of the Divine nature is essentially dynamic. It is by the symbols of motion that he most often tries to convey it to us: as in his constant reference to dancing, or the strangely modern picture of that Eternal Swing of the Universe which is "held by the cords of love."[10]

It is a marked characteristic of mystical literature that the great contemplatives, in their effort to convey to us the nature of their communion with the supersensuous, are inevitably driven to employ some form of sensuous imagery: coarse and inaccurate as they know such imagery to be, even at the best. Our normal human consciousness is so completely committed to dependence on the senses, that the fruits of intuition itself are instinctively referred to them. In that intuition it seems

---

9. Nos. 17, 26, 76, 82.
10. No. 16.

to the mystics that all the dim cravings and partial apprehensions of sense find perfect fulfilment. Hence their constant declaration that they *see* the uncreated light, they *hear* the celestial melody, they *taste* the sweetness of the Lord, they know an ineffable fragrance, they feel the very contact of love. "Him verily seeing and fully feeling, Him spiritually hearing and Him delectably smelling and sweetly swallowing," as Julian of Norwich has it. In those amongst them who develop psycho-sensorial automatisms these parallels between sense and spirit may present themselves to consciousness in the form of hallucinations: as the light seen by Suso, the music heard by Rolle, the celestial perfumes which filled St. Teresa. These are excessive dramatisations of the symbolism under which the mystic tends instinctively to represent his spiritual intuition to the surface consciousness. Here, in the special sense-perception which he feels to be most expressive of Reality, his peculiar idiosyncrasies come out.

Now Kabīr, as we might expect in one whose reactions to the spiritual order were so wide and various, uses by turn all the symbols of sense. He tells us that he has "seen without sight" the effulgence of Brahma, tasted the divine nectar, felt the ecstatic contact of Reality, smelt the fragrance of the heavenly flowers. But he was essentially a poet and musician: rhythm and harmony were to him the garments of beauty and truth. Hence in his lyrics he shows himself to be, like Richard Rolle, above all things a musical mystic. Creation, he says again and again, is full of music: it *is* music. At the heart of the Universe "white music is blossoming": love weaves the melody, whilst renunciation beats the time. it can be heard in the home as well as in the heavens; discerned by the ears of common men as well as by the trained senses of the ascetic. Moreover, the body of every man is a lyre on which Brahma, "the source of all music," plays. Everywhere Kabīr discerns the "Unstruck Music of the Infinite"—that celestial melody which the angel played to St. Francis, that ghostly symphony which filled the soul of Rolle with ecstatic joy.[11] The one figure which he adopts from the Hindu Pantheon and constantly uses, is that of Krishna the Divine Flute Player.[12] He sees the supernal music, too, in its visual embodiment, as rhythmical movement: that mysterious dance of the universe before the face of Brahma, which is at once an act of worship and an expression of the infinite rapture of the Immanent God.[13]

Yet in this wide and rapturous vision of the universe Kabīr never loses touch with diurnal existence, never forgets the common life. His feet are firmly planted upon earth; his lofty and passionate apprehensions are perpetually controlled by the activity of a sane and vigorous intellect, by the alert commonsense so often found in persons of real mystical genius. The constant insistence on simplicity and directness, the hatred of all abstractions and philosophisings,[14] the ruthless criticism of external religion: these are amongst his most marked characteristics. God is the Root whence all manifestations, "material" and "spiritual," alike proceed; and God is the only need of man—"happiness shall be yours when you come to the Root."[15] Hence to those who keep their eye on the "one thing needful," denominations, creeds, ceremonies, the conclusions of philosophy, the disciplines of asceticism, are matters of comparative indifference. They represent merely the different angles from which the soul may approach that simple union with Brahma which is its goal; and are useful only in so far as they contribute to this consummation. So thorough-going is Kabīr's eclecticism, that he seems by turns

11. Nos. 17, 18, 39, 41, 54, 76, 83, 89, 97.
12. Nos. 50, 53, 68.
13. Nos. 26, 32, 76.
14. Nos. 75, 78, 80, 90.
15. No. 80.

Vedāntist and Vaishnavite, Pantheist and Transcendentalist,
Brāhman and Sūfi. In the effort to tell the truth about that
ineffable apprehension, so vast and yet so near, which controls
his life, he seizes and twines together—as he might have
woven together contrasting threads upon his loom—symbols
and ideas drawn from the most violent and conflicting
philosophies and faiths. All are needed, if he is ever to suggest
the character of that One whom the Upanishad called "the
Sun-coloured Being who is beyond this Darkness": as all the
colours of the spectrum are needed if we would demonstrate
the simple richness of white light. In thus adapting traditional
materials to his own use he follows a method common amongst
the mystics; who seldom exhibit any special love for originality
of form. They will pour their wine into almost any vessel that
comes to hand: generally using by preference—and lifting to
new levels of beauty and significance—the religious or
philosophic formulae current in their own day. Thus we find
that some of Kabīr's finest poems have as their subjects the
commonplaces of Hindu philosophy and religion: the Līlā,
or Sport, of God, the Ocean of Bliss, the Bird of the Soul,
Māyā, the Hundred-petalled Lotus, and the "Formless Form."
Many, again, are soaked in Sūfi imagery and feeling. Others
use as their material the ordinary surroundings and feeling.
Others use as their material the ordinary surroundings and
incidents of Indian life: the temple bells, the ceremony of the
lamps, marriage, suttee, pilgrimage, the characters of the
seasons; all felt by him in their mystical aspect, as sacraments
of the soul's relation with Brahma. In many of these a
particularly beautiful and intimate feeling for Nature is shown.[16]

In the collection of songs here translated there will be
found examples which illustrate nearly every aspect of Kabīr's
thought, and all the fluctuations of the mystic's emotion: the

---

16. Nos. 15, 23, 67, 87, 98.

ecstasy, the despair, the still beatitude, the eager self-devotion, the flashes of wide illumination, the moments of intimate love. His wide and deep vision of the universe, the "Eternal Sport" of creation (82), the worlds being "told like beads" within the Being of God (14, 16, 17, 76), is here seen balanced by his lovely and delicate sense of intimate communion with the Divine Friend, Lover, teacher of the soul (10, 11, 23, 35, 51, 85, 86, 88, 92, 93; above all, the beautiful poem 34). As these apparently paradoxical views of Reality are resolved in Brahma, so all other opposites are reconciled in Him: bondage and liberty, love and renunciation, pleasure and pain (17, 25, 40, 89). Union with Him is the one thing that matters to the soul, its destiny and its need (51, 52, 54, 70, 74, 93, 96); and this union, this discovery of God, is the simplest and most natural of all things, if we would but grasp it (41, 46, 56, 72, 76, 78, 97). The union, however, is brought about by love, not by knowledge or ceremonial observances (38, 54, 55, 59, 91); and the apprehension which that union confers is ineffable—"neither This nor That," as Ruysbroeck has it (9, 46, 76). Real worship and communion is in Spirit and in Truth (40, 41, 56, 63, 65, 70), therefore idolatry is an insult to the Divine Lover (42, 69) and the devices of professional sanctity are useless apart from charity and purity of soul (54, 65, 66). Since all things, and especially the heart of man, are God-inhabited, God-possessed (26, 56, 76, 89, 97), He may best be found in the here-and-now: in the normal, human bodily existence, the "mud" of material life (3, 4, 6, 21, 39, 40, 43, 48, 67). "We can reach the goal without crossing the road" (76)—not the cloister but the home is the proper theatre of man's efforts: and if he cannot find God there, he need not hope for success by going farther afield. "In the home is reality." There love and detachment, bondage and freedom, joy and pain play by turns upon the soul; and it is from their conflict that the

Unstruck Music of the Infinite proceeds. "Kabīr says: None but Brahma can evoke its melodies."

III

This version of Kabīr's songs is chiefly the work of Mr. Rabīndranāth Tagore, the trend of whose mystical genius makes him—as all who read these poems will see—a peculiarly sympathetic interpreter of Kabīr's vision and thought. It has been based upon the printed Hindi text with Bengali translation of Mr. Kshiti Mohan Sen; who has gathered from many sources—sometimes from books and manuscripts, sometimes from the lips of wandering ascetics and minstrels—a large collection of poems and hymns to which Kabīr's name is attached, and carefully sifted the authentic songs from the many spurious works now attiributed to him. These painstaking labours alone have made the present undertaking possible.

We have also had before us a manuscript of English translation of 116 songs made by Mr. Ajit Kumār Chakravarty from Mr. Kshiti Mohan Sen's text, and a prose essay upon Kabīr from the same hand. From these we have derived great assistance. A considerable number of readings from the translation have been adopted by us; whilst several of the facts mentioned in the essay have been adopted by us; whilst several of the facts mentioned in the essay have been incorporated into this introduction. Our most grateful thanks are due to Mr. Ajit Kumār Chakravarty for the extremely generous and unselfish manner in which he has placed his work at our disposal.

Evelyn Underhill

1

I. 13. *mo ko kahāṉ ḍhuṉro bande*

O SERVANT, where dost thou seek Me?
Lo! I am beside thee.
I am neither in temple nor in mosque: I am neither in
Kaaba nor in Kailash:
Neither am I in rites and ceremonies, nor in Yoga and
renunciation.
If thou art a true seeker, thou shalt at once see Me: thou
shalt meet Me in a moment of time.
Kabir says, "O Sadhu! God is the breath of all breath."

2

I .16. *santan jāt na pūcho nirguṉiyāṉ*

IT IS NEEDLESS to ask of a saint the caste to which he belongs;
For the priest, the warrior, the tradesman, and all the
thirty-six castes, alike are seeking for God.
It is but folly to ask what the caste of a saint may be;
The barber has sought God, the washer-woman, and the
carpenter—
Even Raidas was a seeker after God.
The Rishi Swapacha was a tanner by caste.
Hindus and Moslems alike have achieved that End, where
remains no mark of distinction.

3

I.57. *sādho bhāī, jīvat hī karo āśā*

O FRIEND! Hope for Him whilst you live, know whilst you
live, understand whilst you live: for in life deliverance
abides.

If your bonds be not broken whilst living, what hope of deliverance in death?

It is but an empty dream, that the soul shall have union with Him because it has passed from the body:

If He is found now, He is found then,
If not, we do but go to dwell in the City of Death.

If you have union now, you shall have it hereafter.

Bathe in the truth, know the true Guru, have faith in the true Name!

Kabir says: "It is the Spirit of the quest which helps; I am the slave of this Spirit of the quest."

4

I. 58. bāgo nā ja re nā jā

DO NOT GO to the garden of flowers!
O Friend! Go not there;
In your body is the garden of flowers.

Take your seat on the thousand petals of the lotus, and there gaze on the Infinite Beauty.

5

I. 63. avadhū, māyā tajī na jāy

TELL ME, Brother, how can I renounce Maya?

When I gave up the tying of ribbons, still I tied my garment about me:

When I gave up tying my garment, still I covered my body in its folds.

So, when I give up passion, I see that anger remains;

And when I renounce anger, greed is with me still;

And when greed is vanquished, pride and vain-glory remain;

When the mind is detached and casts Maya away, still it clings to the letter.
Kabir says, "Listen to me, dear Sadhu! The true path is rarely found."

6

I. 83. *candā jhalkai yahi ghaṭ māhiṉ*

THE MOON shines in my body, but my blind eyes cannot see it:
The moon is within me, and so is the sun.
The unstruck drum of Eternity is sounded within me; but my deaf ears cannot hear it.
So long as man clamours for the *I* and the *Mine*, his works are as naught:
When all love of the *I* and the *Mine* is dead, then the work of the Lord is done.
For work has no other aim than the getting of knowledge:
When that comes, then work is put away.

The flower blooms for the fruit: when the fruit comes, the flower withers.
The musk is in the deer, but it seeks it not within itself: it wanders in quest of grass.

7

I. 85. *sādho, Brahm alakh lakhāyā*

WHEN HE HIMSELF reveals, Himself, Brahma brings into manifestation That which can never be seen.
As the seed is in the plant, as the shade is in the tree, as the void is in the sky, as infinite forms are in the void—
So from beyond the Infinite, the Infinite comes; and from the Infinite the finite extends.

The creature is in Brahma, and Brahma is in the creature:
they are ever distinct, yet ever united.
He Himself is the tree, the seed, and the germ.
He Himself is the flower, the fruit, and the shade.
He Himself is the sun, the light, and the lighted.
He Himself is Brahma, creature, and Maya.
He Himself is the manifold form, the infinite space;
He is the breath, the word, and the meaning.
He Himself is the limit and the limitless: and beyond both
the limited and the limitless is He, the Pure Being.
He is the Immanent Mind in Brahma and in the creature.
The Supreme Soul is seen within the soul,
The Point is seen within the Supreme Soul,
And within the Point, the reflection is seen again.
Kabir is blest because he has this supreme vision!

8

I. 101. *is ghaṭ antar bāg bagīce*

WITHIN THIS earthen vessel are bowers and groves, and within
it is the Creator:
Within this vessel are the seven oceans and the
unnumbered stars.
The touchstone and the jewel-appraiser are within;
And within this vessel the eternal soundeth, and the
spring wells up.
Kabir says: "Listen to me, my friend! My beloved
Lord is within."

9

I. 104. *aisā lo nahīn taisā lo*

O HOW MAY I ever express that secret word?
O how can I say He is not like this, and He is like that?

If I say that He is within me, the universe is ashamed:
If I say that He is without me, it is falsehood.
He makes the inner and the outer worlds to be indivisible
one;
The conscious and the unconscious, both are His footstools.
He is neither manifest nor hidden, He is neither revealed
nor unrevealed:
There are no words to tell that which He is.

10

I. 121. *tohi mori lagan lagāye re phakīr wā*

TO THEE Thou hast drawn my love, O Fakir!
I was sleeping in my own chamber, and Thou didst awaken
me; striking me with Thy voice, O Fakir!
I was drowning in the deeps of the ocean of this world,
and thou didst save me: upholding me with Thine arm,
O Fakir!
Only one word and no second—and thou hast made me
tear off all my bonds, O Fakir!
Kabir says, "Thou hast united Thy heart to my heart,
O Fakir!"

11

I. 131. *niś din khelat rahī sakhiyān sang*

I PLAYED day and night with my comrades, and now I am
greatly afraid.
So high is my Lord's palace, my heart trembles to mount
its stairs:
Yet I must not be shy, if I would enjoy His love.
My heart must cleave to my Lover; I must withdraw my
veil, and meet Him with all my body:

Mine eyes must perform the ceremony of the lamps of love.

Kabir says: "Listen to me, friend: he understands who loves. If you feel not love's longing for your Beloved One, it is vain to adorn your body, vain to put unguent on your eyelids."

12

II. 24. *hamsā, kaho puratan bāt*

TELL ME, O Swan, your ancient tale.

From what land do you come, O Swan? To what shore will you fly?

Where would you take your rest, O Swan, and what do you seek?

Even this morning, O Swan, awake, arise, follow me!

There is a land where no doubt nor sorrow have rule: where the terror of Death is no more.

There the woods of spring are a-bloom, and the fragrant scent "He is I" is borne on the wind:

There the bee of the heart is deeply immersed, and desires no other joy.

13

II. 37. *angaḍhiyā devā*

O LORD Increate, who will serve Thee?

Every votary offers his worship to the God of his own creation: each day he receives service—

None seek Him, the Perfect: Brahma, the Indivisible Lord.

They believe in ten Avatars; but no Avatar can be the Infinite Spirit, for he suffers the results of his deeds:

The Supreme One must be other than this.

The Yogi, the Sanyasi, the Ascetics, are disputing one with another:
Kabir says, "O brother! He who has seen that radiance of love, he is saved."

14

II. 56. *dariyā kī lahar dariyāo hai jī*

THE RIVER and its waves are one surf: where is the difference between the river and its waves?

When the waves rise, it is the water; and when it falls, it is the same water again. Tell me, Sir, where is the distinction?

Because it has been named as wave, shall it no longer be considered as water?

Within the Supreme Brahma, the worlds are being told like beads:
Look upon that rosary with the eyes of wisdom.

15

II. 57. *jaṇh khelat vasant ṛiturāj*

WHERE SPRING, the lord of the seasons, reigneth, there the Unstruck Music sounds of itself,
There the streams of light flow in all directions;
Few are the men who can cross to that shore!
There, where millions of Krishnas stand with hands folded,
Where millions of Vishnus bow their heads,
Where millions of Brahmas are reading the Vedas,
Where millions of Shivas are lost in contemplation,
Where millions of Indras dwell in the sky,
Where the demi-gods and the munis are unnumbered,
Where millions of Saraswatis, Goddess of Music, play on the vina—

There is my Lord self-revealed: and the scent of sandal and flowers dwells in those deeps.

16

II. 59. *jaṉh cet acet khambh dōū*

BETWEEN THE poles of the conscious and the unconscious, there has the mind made a swing:

Thereon hang all beings and all worlds and that swing never ceases its sway.

Millions of beings are there: the sun and the moon in their courses are there:

Millions of ages pass, and the swing goes on.

All swing! The sky and the earth and the air and the water; and the Lord Himself taking form:

And the sight of this has made Kabir a servant.

17

II. 61. *grah candra tapan jot barat hai*

THE LIGHT of the sun, the moon, and the stars shines bright:

The melody of love swells forth, and the rhythm of love's detachment beats the time.

Day and night, the chorus of music fills the heavens; and Kabir says, "My Beloved One gleams like the lightning flash in the sky."

Do you know how the moments perform their adoration?

Waving its row of lamps, the universe sings in worship day and night,

There are the hidden banner and the secret canopy:

There the sound of the unseen bells is heard.

Kabir says: "There adoration never ceases; there the Lord of the Universe sitteth on His throne."

The whole world does its works and commits its errors: but few are the lovers who know the Beloved.

The devout seeker is he who mingles in his heart the double currents of love and detachment, like the mingling of the streams of Ganges and Jumna;

In his heart the sacred water flows day and night; and thus the round of births and deaths is brought to an end. Behold what wonderful rest is in the Supreme Spirit! And he enjoys it, who makes himself meet for it.

Held by the cords of love, the swing of the Ocean of Joy sways to and fro; and a mighty sound breaks forth in song.

See what a lotus blooms there without water! and Kabīr says "My heart's bee drinks its nectar."

What a wonderful lotus it is, that blooms at the heart of the spinning wheel of the universe! Only a few pure souls know of its true delight.

Music is all around it, and there the heart partakes of the joy of the Infinite Sea.

Kabir says: "Dive thou into that Ocean of sweetness: thus let all errors of life and of death flee away."

Behold how the thirst of the five senses is quenched there! And the three forms of misery are no more!

Kabir says: "It is the sport of the Unattainable One: look within, and behold how the moon-beams of that Hidden One shine in you."

There falls the rhythmic beat of life and death:

Rapture wells forth, and all space is radiant with light.

There the Unstruck Music is sounded; it is the music of the love of the three worlds.

There millions of lamps of sun and of moon are burning;

There the drum beats, and the lover swings in play.

There love-songs resound, and light rains in showers; and the worshipper is entranced in the taste of the heavenly nectar.

Look upon life and death; there is no separation between them,

The right hand and the left hand are one and the same.

Kabir says: "There the wise man is speechless; for this truth may never be found in Vedas or in books."

I have had my Seat on the Self-poised One,

I have drunk of the Cup of the Ineffable,

I have found the Key of the Mystery,

I have reached the Root of Union.

Travelling by no track, I have come to the Sorrowless Land: very easily has the mercy of the great Lord come upon me.

They have sung of Him as infinite and unattainable: but I in my meditations have seen Him without sight.

That is indeed the sorrowless land, and none know the path that leads there:

Only he who is on that has surely transcended all sorrow.

Wonderful is that land of rest, to which no merit can win;

It is the wise who has seen it, it is the wise who has sung of it.

This is the Ultimate Word: but can any express its marvellous savour?

He who has savoured it once, he knows what joy it can give.

Kabir says: "Knowing it, the ignorant man becomes wise, and the wise man becomes speechless and silent,

The worshipper is utterly inebriated,

His wisdom and his detachment are made perfect;

He drinks from the cup of the inbreathings and the outbreathings of love."

There the whole sky is filled with sound, and there that music is made without fingers and without strings;

There the game of pleasure and pain does not cease.

Kabir says: "If you merge your life in the ocean of Life, you will find your life in the Supreme Land of Bliss."

What a frenzy of ecstacy there is in every hour! And the worshipper is pressing out and drinking the essence of the hours: he lives in the life of Brahma.

I speak truth, for I have accepted truth in life; I am now attached to truth, I have swept all tinsel away.

Kabir says: "Thus is the worshipper set free from fear; thus have all errors of life and of death left him."
There the sky is filled with music:

There it rains nectar:

There the harp-strings jingle, and there the drums beat.

What a secret splendour is there, in the mansion of the sky!

There no mention is made of the rising and the setting of the sun;

In the ocean of manifestation, which is the light of love, day and night are felt to be one.

Joy for ever, no sorrow, no struggle!

There have I seen joy filled to the brim, perfection of joy;

No place for error is there.

Kabir says: "There have I witnessed the sport of One Bliss!"

I have known in my body the sport of the universe: I have escaped from the error of this world.

The inward and the outward are become as one sky, the Infinite and the finite are united: I am drunken with the sight of this All!

This Light of Thine fulfils the universe: the lamp of love that burns on the salver of knowledge.

Kabir says: "There error cannot enter, and the conflict of life and death is felt no more."

18

II. 77. *maddh ākāś ap jahān baithe*

THE MIDDLE region of the sky, wherein the spirit dwelleth, is radiant with the music of light;

There, where the pure and white music blossoms, my Lord takes His delight.

In the wondrous effulgence of each hair of His body, the brightness of millions of suns and of moons is lost.

On that shore there is a city, where the rain of nectar pours and pours, and never ceases.

Kabir says: "Come, O Dharmadas! And see my great Lord's Durbar."

19

III. 20. *paramātama guru nikat virājain*

O MY HEARt! The Supreme Spirit, the great Master, is near you: wake, oh wake!

Run to the feet of your Beloved: for your Lord stands near to your head.

You have slept for unnumbered ages; this morning will you not wake?

20

II. 22. *man tu pār utar kānh jaiho*

TO WHAT shore would you cross, O my heart? There is no traveller before you, there is no road:

Where is the movement, where is the rest, on that shore?

There is no water; no boat, no boatman, is there;

There is not so much as a rope to tow the boat, nor a man to draw it.

No earth, no sky, no time, no thing, is there: no shore,
no ford!

There, there is neither body nor mind: and where is the
place that shall still the thirst of the soul? You shall find naught
in that emptiness.

Be strong, and enter into your own body: for there your
foothold is firm. Consider it well, O my heart! go not elsewhere.

Kabir says: "Put all imaginations away, and stand fast in
that which you are."

21

II. 33. *ghar ghar dīpak barai*

LAMPS BURN in every house, O blind one! And you cannot
see them.

One day your eyes shall suddenly be opened, and you
shall see: and the fetters of death will fall from you.

There is nothing to say or to hear, there is nothing to
do: it is he who is living, yet dead, who shall never die
again.

Because he lives in solitude, therefore the Yogi says that his
home is far away.

Your Lord is near: yet you are climbing the palm-tree to
seek Him.

The Brahman priest goes from house to house and initiates
people into faith:

Alas! The true fountain of life is beside you, and you have
set up a stone to worship.

Kabir says: "I may never express how sweet my Lord is.
Yoga and the telling of beads, virtue and vice—these are
naught to Him."

22

II. 38. *sādho, so satgur mohi bhāwai*

O BROTHER, my heart yearns for that true Guru, who fills the
cup of true love, and drinks of it himself, and offers it then
to me.

He removes the veil from the eyes, and gives the true
Vision of Brahma:

He reveals the worlds in Him, and makes me hear the
Unstruck Music:

He shows joy and sorrow to be one:

He fills all utterance with love.

Kabir says: "Verily he has no fear, who has such a Guru
to lead him to the shelter of safety!"

23

II. 40. *tinwir sānjh kā ghirā āwai*

THE SHADOWS of evening fall thick and deep, and the darkness
of love envelops the body and the mind.

Open the window to the west, and be lost in the sky of love;

Drink the sweet honey that steeps the petals of the lotus
of the heart.

Receive the waves in your body: what splendour is in the
region of the sea!

Hark! the sounds of conches and bells are rising.

Kabir says: "O brother, behold! the Lord is in this vessel
of my body."

24

II. 48. *jis se rahani apār jagat men*

MORE THAN all else do I cherish at heart that love which
makes me to live a limitless life in this world.

It is like the lotus, which lives in the water and blooms
in the water:

Yet the water cannot touch its petals, they open beyond its reach.

It is like a wife, who enters the fire at the bidding of love. She burns and lets others grieve, yet never dishonours love.

This ocean of the world is hard to cross: its waters are very deep. Kabir says: "Listen to me, O Sadhu! Few there are who have reached its end."

25

II. 45. *Hari ne apnā āp chipāyā*

MY LORD hides Himself, and my Lord wonderfully reveals Himself:

My Lord has encompassed me with hardness, and my Lord has cast down my limitations.

My Lord brings to me words of sorrow and words of joy, and He Himself heals strife.

I will offer my body and mind to my Lord: I will give up my life, but never can I forget my Lord!

26

II. 75. *ōṅkār siwāe kōī sirjai*

ALL THINGS are created by the Om;
The love-form is His body.
He is without form, without quality, without decay:
Seek thou union with Him!

But that formless God takes a thousand forms in the eyes of His creatures:
He is pure and indestructible,
His form is infinite and fathomless,
He dances in rapture, and waves of form arise from His dance:

The body and the mind cannot contain themselves, when they are touched by His great joy.

He is immersed in all consciousness, all joys, and all sorrows;

He has no beginning and no end;

He holds all within His bliss.

27

II. 81. *satgur sōī daya kar dīnhā*

IT IS THE MERCY of my true Guru that has made me to know the unknown;

I have learned from Him how to walk without feet, to see without eyes,

to hear without ears, to drink without mouth, to fly without wings;

I have brought my love and my meditation into the land where there

Is no sun and moon, nor day and night.

Without eating, I have tasted of the sweetness of nectar; and without water, I have quenched my thirst.

Where there is the response of delight, there is the fullness of joy.

Before whom can that joy be uttered?

Kabir says: "The guru is great beyond words, and great is the good fortune of the disciple."

28

II. 85. *nirgun āge sargun nācai*

BEFORE THE Unconditioned, the Conditioned dances:

"Thou and I are one!" this trumpet proclaims.

The Guru comes, and bows down before the disciple:

This is the greatest of wonders.

29

II. 87. *Kabīr kab se bhaye vairāgī*

GORAKHNATH ASKS Kabir:

"Tell me, O Kabir, when did your vocation begin? Where did your love have its rise?"

Kabir answers:

"When He whose forms are manifold had not begun His play: when there was no Guru, and no disciple: when the world was not spread out: when the Supreme One was alone—

Then I became an ascetic; then O Gorakh, my love was drawn to Brahma.

Brahma did not hold the crown on his head; the god Vishnu was not anointed as king; the power of Shiva was still unborn; when I was instructed in Yoga.

"I became suddenly revealed in Benares, and Ramananda illumined me;

I brought with me the thirst for the Infinite, and I have come for the meeting with Him.

In simplicity will I unite with the Simple One; my love will surge up.

O Gorakh, march thou with His music!"

30

II. 95. *yā tarvar men ek pakherū*

ON THIS TREE is a bird: it dances in the joy of life.

None knows where it is: and who knows what the burden of its music may be?

Where the branches throw a deep shape, there does it have its nest: and it comes in the evening and flies away in the morning, and says not a word of that which it means.

None tell me of this bird that sings within me.

It is neither coloured nor colourless: it has neither form nor outline:

It sits in the shadow of love.

It dwells within the Unattainable, the Infinite, and the Eternal; and no one marks when it comes and goes.

Kabir says: "O brother Sadhu! deep is the mystery. Let wise men seek to know where rests that bird."

31

II. 100. *niś din sālai ghāw*

A SORE PAIN troubles me day and night, and I cannot sleep;

I long for the meeting with my Beloved, and my father's house gives pleasure no more.

The gates of the sky are opened, the temple is revealed:

I meet my husband, and leave at His feet the offering of my body and my mind.

32

II. 103. *nāco re mero man, matta hoy*

DANCE, MY heart! dance to-day with joy.

The strains of love fill the days and the nights with music, and the world is listening to its melodies:

Mad with joy, life and death dance to the rhythm of this music. The hills and the sea and the earth dance. The world of man dances in laughter and tears.

Why put on the robe of the monk, and live aloof from the world in lonely pride?

Behold! my heart dances in the delight of a hundred arts; and the Creator is well pleased.

33

II. 105. *man mast huā tab kyon bole*

WHERE IS the need of words, when love has made drunken the heart?

I have wrapped the diamond in my cloak; why open it again and again?

When its load was light, the pan of the balance went up: now it is full, where is the need for weighing?

The swan has taken its flight to the lake beyond the mountains; why should it search for the pools and ditches any more?

Your Lord dwells within you: why need your outward eyes be opened?

Kabir says: "Listen, my brother! my Lord, who ravishes my eyes, has united Himself with me."

34

II. 110. *mohi tohi lāgī kaise chuṭe*

HOW COULD the love between Thee and me sever?

As the leaf of the lotus abides on the water: so thou art my Lord, and I am Thy servant.

As the night-bird Chakor gazes all night at the moon: so Thou art my Lord and I am Thy servant.

From the beginning until the ending of times, there is love between

Thee and me; and how shall such love be extinguished?

Kabir says: "As the river enters into the ocean, so my heart touches Thee."

35

II. 113. vālam, āwo hamāre geh re

MY BODY AND my mind are grieved for the want of Thee;
    O my Beloved! come to my house.
When people say I am Thy bride, I am ashamed; for I
have not touched
    Thy heart with my heart.
    Then what is this love of mine? I have no taste for food,
I have no sleep; my heart is ever restless within doors and
without.
    As water is to the thirsty, so is the lover to the bride. Who
is there that will carry my news to my Beloved?
    Kabir is restless: he is dying for sight of Him.

36

II. 126. jāg piyārī, ab kān sowai

O FRIEND, awake, and sleep no more!
    The night is over and gone, would you lose your day also?
    Others, who have wakened, have received jewels;
    O foolish woman! You have lost all whilst you slept.
    Your lover is wise, and you are foolish, O woman!
    You never prepared the bed of your husband:
    O mad one! you passed your time in silly play.
    Your youth was passed in vain, for you did not know your
Lord;
    Wake, wake! See! your bed is empty: He left you in the
night.
    Kabir says: "Only she wakes, whose heart is pierced with
the arrow of His music."

37

I. 36. *sūr parkās, tānh rain kahān pāïya*

WHERE IS THE night, when the sun is shining? If it is night, then the sun withdraws its light.

Where knowledge is, can ignorance endure? If there be ignorance, then knowledge must die.

If there be lust, how can love be there? Where there is love, there is no lust.

Lay hold on your sword, and join in the fight. Fight, O my brother, as long as life lasts.

Strike off your enemy's head, and there make an end of him quickly: then come, and bow your head at your King's Durbar.

He who is brave, never forsakes the battle: he who flies from it is no true fighter.

In the field of this body a great war goes forward, against passion, anger, pride, and greed:

It is in the kingdom of truth, contentment and purity, that this battle is raging; and the sword that rings forth most loudly is the sword of His Name.

Kabir says: "When a brave knight takes the field, a host of cowards is put to flight.

It is a hard fight and a weary one, this fight of the truth-seeker: for the vow of the truth-seeker is more hard than that of the warrior, or of the widowed wife who would follow her husband.

For the warrior fights for a few hours, and the widow's struggle with death is soon ended:

But the truth-seeker's battle goes on day and night, as long as life lasts it never ceases."

38

I. 50. *bhram kā tālā lagā mahal re*

THE LOCK of error shuts the gate, open it with the key of love:
  Thus, by opening the door, thou shalt wake the Beloved.
  Kabir says: "O brother! do not pass by such good fortune as this."

39

I. 59. *sādho, yah tan thāṭh tanvure ka*

O FRIEND THIS body is His lyre;
  He tightens its strings, and draws from it the melody of Brahma.
  If the strings snap and the keys slacken, then to dust must this instrument of dust return:
  Kabir says: "None but Brahma can evoke its melodies."

40

I. 65. *avadhū bhūle ko ghar lāwe*

HE IS DEAR TO me indeed who can call back the wanderer to his home. In the home is the true union, in the home is enjoyment of life: why should I forsake my home and wander in the forest? If Brahma helps me to realise truth, verily I will find both bondage and deliverance in home.
  He is dear to me indeed who has power to dive deep into Brahma; whose mind loses itself with ease in His contemplation.
  He is dear to me who knows Brahma, and can dwell on His supreme truth in meditation; and who can play the melody of the Infinite by uniting love and renunciation in life.

Kabir says: "The home is the abiding place; in the home is reality; the home helps to attain Him Who is real. So stay where you are, and all things shall come to you in time."

41

I. 76. santo, sahaj samādh bhalī

O SADHU! THE simple union is the best.

Since the day when I met with my Lord, there has been no end to the sport of our love.

I shut not my eyes, I close not my ears, I do not mortify my body;

I see with eyes open and smile, and behold His beauty everywhere:

I utter His Name, and whatever I see, it reminds me of Him; whatever I do, it becomes His worship.

The rising and the setting are one to me; all contradictions are solved.

Wherever I go, I move round Him,

All I achieve is His service:

When I lie down, I lie prostrate at His feet.

He is the only adorable one to me: I have none other.

My tongue has left off impure words, it sings His glory day and night:

Whether I rise or sit down, I can never forget Him; for the rhythm of His music beats in my ears.

Kabir says: "My heart is frenzied, and I disclose in my soul what is hidden. I am immersed in that one great bliss which transcends all pleasure and pain."

42

I. 79. *tīrath men to sab pānī hai*

THERE IS nothing but water at the holy bathing places; and I know that they are useless, for I have bathed in them.

The images are all lifeless, they cannot speak; I know, for I have cried aloud to them.

The Purana and the Koran are mere words; lifting up the curtain, I have seen.

Kabir gives utterance to the words of experience; and he knows very well that all other things are untrue.

43

I. 82. *panī vic mīn piyāsī*

I LAUGH WHEN I hear that the fish in the water is thirsty:

You do not see that the Real is in you home, and you wander from forest to forest listlessly!

Here is the truth! Go where you will, to Benares or to Mathura; if you do not find your soul, the world is unreal to you.

44

I. 93. *gagan math gaib nisān gade*

THE HIDDEN Banner is planted in the temple of the sky; there the blue canopy decked with the moon and set with bright jewels is spread.

There the light of the sun and the moon is shining: still your mind to silence before that splendour.

Kabir says: "He who has drunk of this nectar, wanders like one who is mad."

45

I. 97. *sādho, ko hai kānh se āyo*

WHO ARE YOU, and whence do you come?

Where dwells that Supreme Spirit, and how does He have His sport with all created things?

The fire is in the wood; but who awakens it suddenly? Then it turns to ashes, and where goes the force of the fire?

The true guru teaches that He has neither limit nor infinitude.

Kabir says: "Brahma suits His language to the understanding of His hearer."

46

I. 98. *sādho, sahajai kāyā śodho*

O SADHU! purify your body in the simple way.

As the seed is within the banyan tree, and within the seed are the flowers, the fruits, and the shade:

So the germ is within the body, and within that germ is the body again.

The fire, the air, the water, the earth, and the aether; you cannot have these outside of Him.

O Kazi, O Pundit, consider it well: what is there that is not in the soul?

The water-filled pitcher is placed upon water, it has water within and without.

It should not be given a name, lest it call forth the error of dualism.

Kabir says: "Listen to the Word, the Truth, which is your essence. He speaks the Word to Himself; and He Himself is the Creator."

47

I. 102. *tarvar ek mūl bin ṭhāḍā*

THERE IS A strange tree, which stands without roots and bears fruits without blossoming;
It has no branches and no leaves, it is lotus all over.
Two birds sing there; one is the Guru, and the other the disciple:
The disciple chooses the manifold fruits of life and tastes them, and the Guru beholds him in joy.
What Kabir says is hard to understand: "The bird is beyond seeking, yet it is most clearly visible. The Formless is in the midst of all forms. I sing the glory of forms."

48

I. 107. *calat mansā acal kīnhī*

I HAVE STILLED my restless mind, and my heart is radiant: for in That-ness I have seen beyond That-ness, in company I have seen the Comrade Himself.
Living in bondage, I have set myself free: I have broken away from the clutch of all narrowness.
Kabir says: "I have attained the unattainable, and my heart is coloured with the colour of love."

49

I. 105. *jo dīsai, so to hai nāhīṉ*

THAT WHICH you see is not: and for that which is, you have no words.
Unless you see, you believe not: what is told you you cannot accept.
He who is discerning knows by the word; and the ignorant stands gaping.

Some contemplate the Formless, and others meditate on form: but the wise man knows that Brahma is beyond both.

That beauty of His is not seen of the eye: that metre of His is not heard of the ear.

Kabir says: "He who has found both love and renunciation never descends to death."

50

I. 126. *muralī bajat akhaṇḍ sadāye*

THE FLUTE OF the Infinite is played without ceasing, and its sound is love:

When love renounces all limits, it reaches truth.

How widely the fragrance spreads! It has no end, nothing stands in its way.

The form of this melody is bright like a million suns: incomparably sounds the vina, the vina of the notes of truth.

51

I. 129. *sakhiyo, ham hūṉ bhāī vālamāsī*

DEAR FRIEND, I am eager to meet my Beloved! My youth has flowered, and the pain of separation from Him troubles my breast.

I am wandering yet in the alleys of knowledge without purpose, but

I have received His news in these alleys of knowledge.

I have a letter from my Beloved: in this letter is an unutterable message, and now my fear of death is done away.

Kabir says: "O my loving friend! I have got for my gift the Deathless One."

52

I. 130. *saīn bin dard kareje hoy*

WHEN I AM parted from my Beloved, my heart is full of misery: I have no comfort in the day, I have no sleep in the night. To whom shall I tell my sorrow?

The night is dark; the hours slip by. Because my Lord is absent, I start up and tremble with fear.

Kabir says: "Listen, my friend! there is no other satisfaction, save in the encounter with the Beloved."

53

I. 122. *kaun muralī śabd śun ānand bhayo*

WHAT IS THAT flute whose music thrills me with joy?

The flame burns without a lamp;

The lotus blossoms without a root;

Flowers bloom in clusters;

The moon-bird is devoted to the moon;

With all its heart the rain-bird longs for the shower of rain;

But upon whose love does the Lover concentrate His entire life?

54

I. 112. *śuntā nahi dhun kī khabar*

HAVE YOU NOT heard the tune which the Unstruck Music is playing? In the midst of the chamber the harp of joy is gently and sweetly played; and where is the need of going without to hear it?

If you have not drunk of the nectar of that One Love, what boots it though you should purge yourself of all stains?

The Kazi is searching the words of the Koran, and instructing other: but if his heart be not steeped in that love, what does it avail, though he be a teacher of men?

The Yogi dyes his garments with red: but if he knows naught of that colour of love, what does it avail though his garments be tinted?

Kabir says: "Whether I be in the temple or the balcony, in the camp or in the flower garden, I tell you truly that every moment my Lord is taking His delight in me."

55

I. 73. bhakti kā mārag jhīnā re

SUBTLE IS the path of love!

Therein there is no asking and no not-asking,

There one loses one's self at His feet,

There one is immersed in the joy of the seeking; plunged in the deeps of love as the fish in the water.

The lover is never slow in offering his head for his Lord's service.

Kabir declares the secret of this love.

56

I. 68. bhāī koī satguru sant kahāwai

HE IS THE real Sadhu, who can reveal the form of the Formless to the vision of these eyes:

Who teaches the simple way of attaining Him, that is other than rites or ceremonies:

Who does not make you close the doors, and hold the breath, and renounce the world:

Who makes you perceive the Supreme Spirit wherever the mind attaches itself:

Who teaches you to be still in the midst of all your activities.
Ever immersed in bliss, having no fear in his mind, he keeps the spirit of union in the midst of all enjoyments.
The infinite dwelling of the Infinite Being is everywhere: in earth, water, sky, and air:
Firm as the thunderbolt, the seat of the seeker is established above the void.
He who is within is without: I see Him and none else.

57

I. 66. sādho, śabd sādhanā kījai

RECEIVE THAT Word from which the Universe springeth!
That Word is the Guru; I have heard it, and become the disciple.
How many are there who know the meaning of that Word?
O Sadhu! practise that Word!
The Vedas and the Puranas proclaim it,
The world is established in it,
The Rishis and devotees speak of it:
But none knows the mystery of the Word.
The householder leaves his house when he hears it,
The Six Philosophies expound it,
The Spirit of Renunciation points to that Word,
From that Word the world-form has sprung,
That Word reveals all.
Kabir says: "But who knows whence the Word cometh?"

58

I. 63. pī le pyālā, ho matwālā

EMPTY THE Cup! O be drunken!
Drink the divine nectar of His Name!
Kabir says: "Listen to me, dear Sadhu!

From the sole of the foot to the crown of the head this mind is filled with poison."

59

I. 52. *khasm na cīnhai bāwarī*

O MAN, IF thou dost not know thine own Lord, whereof art thou so proud?

Put thy cleverness away: mere words shall never unite thee to Him.

Do not deceive thyself with the witness of the Scriptures:

Love is something other than this, and he who has sought it truly has found it.

60

I. 56. *sukh sindh kī sair kā*

THE SAVOUR of wandering in the ocean of deathless life has rid me of all my asking:

As the tree is in the seed, so all diseases are in this asking.

61

I. 48. *sukh sāgar men āīke*

WHEN AT last you are come to the ocean of happiness, do not go back thirsty.

Wake, foolish man! For Death stalks you. Here is pure water before you; drink it at every breath.

Do not follow the mirage on foot, but thirst for the nectar;

Dhruva, Prahlad, and Shukadeva have drunk of it, and also Raidas has tasted it:

The saints are drunk with love, their thirst is for love.

Kabir says: "Listen to me, brother! The nest of fear is broken.

Not for a moment have you come face to face with the world:

You are weaving your bondage of falsehood, your words are full of deception:

With the load of desires which you hold on your head, how can you be light?"

Kabir says: "Keep within you truth, detachment, and love."

62

I. 35. satī ko kaun śikhāwtā hai

WHO HAS EVER taught the widowed wife to burn herself on the pyre of her dead husband?

And who has ever taught love to find bliss in renunciation?

63

I. 39. are man, dhīraj kāhe na dharai

WHY SO impatient, my heart?

He who watches over birds, beasts, and insects,

He who cared for you whilst you were yet in your mother's womb,

Shall He not care for you now that you are come forth?

Oh my heart, how could you turn from the smile of your Lord and wander so far from Him?

You have left your Beloved and are thinking of others: and this is why all your work is in vain.

64

I. 117. sāīn se lagan kathin hai, bhāī

HOW HARD IT is to meet my Lord!

The rain-bird wails in thirst for the rain: almost she dies of her longing, yet she would have none other water than the rain.

Drawn by the love of music, the deer moves forward: she dies as she listens to the music, yet she shrinks not in fear.

The widowed wife sits by the body of her dead husband: she is not afraid of the fire.

Put away all fear for this poor body.

65

I. 22. *jab main bhūlā, re bhāī*

O BROTHER! when I was forgetful, my true Guru showed me the Way.

Then I left off all rites and ceremonies, I bathed no more in the holy water:

Then I learned that it was I alone who was mad, and the whole world beside me was sane; and I had disturbed these wise people.

From that time forth I knew no more how to roll in the dust in obeisance:

I do not ring the temple bell:

I do not set the idol on its throne:

I do not worship the image with flowers.

It is not the austerities that mortify the flesh which are pleasing to the Lord,

When you leave off your clothes and kill your senses, you do not please the Lord:

The man who is kind and who practises righteousness, who remains passive amidst the affairs of the world, who considers all creatures on earth as his own self,

He attains the Immortal Being, the true God is ever with him.

Kabir says: "He attains the true Name whose words are pure, and who is free from pride and conceit."

66

I. 20. *man na rangāye*

THE YOGI dyes his garments, instead of dyeing his mind in the colours of love:

He sits within the temple of the Lord, leaving Brahma to worship a stone.

He pierces holes in his ears, he has a great beard and matted locks, he looks like a goat:

He goes forth into the wilderness, killing all his desires, and turns himself into an eunuch:

He shaves his head and dyes his garments; he reads the Gita and becomes a mighty talker.

Kabir says: "You are going to the doors of death, bound hand and foot!"

67

I. 9. *nā jāne sāhab kaisā hai*

I DO NOT KNOW what manner of God is mine.

The Mullah cries aloud to Him: and why? Is your Lord deaf? The subtle anklets that ring on the feet of an insect when it moves are heard of Him.

Tell your beads, paint your forehead with the mark of your God, and wear matted locks long and showy: but a deadly weapon is in your heart, and how shall you have God?

68

III. 102. *ham se rahā na jāy*

I HEAR THE melody of His flute, and I cannot contain myself:

The flower blooms, though it is not spring; and already the bee has received its invitation.

The sky roars and the lightning flashes, the waves arise
in my heart,
The rain falls; and my heart longs for my Lord.
Where the rhythm of the world rises and falls, thither my
heart has reached:
There the hidden banners are fluttering in the air.
Kabir says: "My heart is dying, though it lives."

69

III. 2. *jo khodā masjid vasat hai*

IF GOD BE within the mosque, then to whom does this world
belong?
If Rām be within the image which you find upon your
pilgrimage,
Then who is there to know what happens without?
Hari is in the East: Allah is in the West. Look within your
heart, for there you will find
both Karim and Rām:
All the men and women of the world are His living forms.
Kabir is the child of Allah and of Rām: He is my Guru,
He is my Pir.

70

III. 9. *śil santosh sadā samadrishṭi*

HE WHO IS meek and contented, he who has an equal vision,
whose mind is filled with the fullness of acceptance and of
rest;
He who has seen Him and touched Him, he is freed from
all fear and trouble.
To him the perpetual thought of God is like sandal paste
smeared on the body, to him nothing else is delight:

His work and his rest are filled with music: he sheds abroad the radiance of love.

Kabir says: "Touch His feet, who is one and indivisible, immutable and peaceful; who fills all vessels to the brim with joy, and whose form is love."

71

III. 13. *sādh sangat pītam*

GO THOU TO the company of the good, where the Beloved One has His dwelling place:

Take all thy thoughts and love and instruction from thence.

Let that assembly be burnt to ashes where His Name is not spoken!

Tell me, how couldst thou hold a wedding-feast, if the bridegroom himself were not there?

Waver no more, think only of the Beloved;

Set not thy heart on the worship of other gods, there is no worth in the worship of other masters.

Kabir deliberates and says: "Thus thou shalt never find the Beloved!"

72

III. 26. *tor hīrā hirāilwā kīcaḍ meṉ*

THE JEWEL IS lost in the mud, and all are seeking for it;

Some look for it in the east, and some in the west; some in the water and some amongst stones.

But the servant Kabir has appraised it at its true value, and has wrapped it with care in the end of the mantle of his heart.

73

III. 26. *āyau din gaune kā ho*

THE PALANQUIN came to take me away to my husband's home, and it sent through my heart a thrill of joy;

But the bearers have brought me into the lonely forest, where I have no one of my own.

O bearers, I entreat you by your feet, wait but a moment longer: let me go back to my kinsmen and friends, and take my leave of them.

The servant Kabir sings: "O Sadhu! finish your buying and selling, have done with your good and your bad: for there are no markets and no shops in the land to which you go."

74

III. 30. *are dil, premnagar kā ant na pāyā*

O MY HEART! you have not known all the secrets of this city of love: in ignorance you came, and in ignorance you return.

O my friend, what have you done with this life? You have taken on your head the burden heavy with stones, and who is to lighten it for you?

Your Friend stands on the other shore, but you never think in your mind how you may meet with Him:

The boat is broken, and yet you sit ever upon the bank; and thus you are beaten to no purpose by the waves.

The servant Kabīr asks you to consider; who is there that shall befriend you at the last?

You are alone, you have no companion: you will suffer the consequences of your own deeds.

75

III. 55. *ved kahe sargun ke āge*

THE VEDAS say that the Unconditioned stands beyond the world of Conditions.

O woman, what does it avail thee to dispute whether He is beyond all or in all?

See thou everything as thine own dwelling place: the mist of pleasure and pain can never spread there.

There Brahma is revealed day and night: there light is His garment, light is His seat, light rests on thy head.

Kabir says: "The Master, who is true, He is all light."

76

III. 48. *tū surat nain nihār*

OPEN YOUR eyes of love, and see Him who pervades this world! Consider it well, and know that this is your own country.

When you meet the true Guru, he will awaken your heart;

He will tell you the secret of love and detachment, and then you will know indeed that He transcends this universe.

This world is the City of Truth, its maze of paths enchants the heart:

We can reach the goal without crossing the road, such is the sport unending.

Where the ring of manifold joys ever dances about Him, there is the sport of Eternal Bliss.

When we know this, then all our receiving and renouncing is over;

Thenceforth the heat of having shall never scorch us more.

He is the Ultimate Rest unbounded:

He has spread His form of love throughout all the world.

From that Ray which is Truth, streams of new forms are perpetually springing: and He pervades those forms.

All the gardens and groves and bowers are abounding with blossom; and the air breaks forth into ripples of joy.

There the swan plays a wonderful game,

There the Unstruck Music eddies around the Infinite One;

There in the midst the Throne of the Unheld is shining, whereon the great Being sits—

Millions of suns are shamed by the radiance of a single hair of His body.

On the harp of the road what true melodies are being sounded! And its notes pierce the heart:

There the Eternal Fountain is playing its endless life-streams of birth and death.

They call Him Emptiness who is the Truth of truths, in Whom all truths are stored!

There within Him creation goes forward, which is beyond all philosophy; for philosophy cannot attain to Him:

There is an endless world, O my Brother! and there is the Nameless Being, of whom nought can be said.

Only he knows it who has reached that region: it is other than all that is heard and said. No form, no body, no length, no breadth is seen there: how can I tell you that which it is?

He comes to the Path of the Infinite on whom the grace of the Lord descends: he is freed from births and deaths who attains to Him.

Kabir says: "It cannot be told by the words of the mouth, it cannot be written on paper:

It is like a dumb person who tastes a sweet thing—how shall it be explained?"

77

III. 60. *cal haṃsā wā deś jahān*

O MY HEART let us go to that country where dwells the Beloved, the ravisher of my heart!

There Love is filling her pitcher from the well, yet she has no rope wherewith to draw water;

There the clouds do not cover the sky, yet the rain falls down in gentle showers;

O bodiless one! do not sit on your doorstep; go forth and bathe yourself in that rain!

There it is ever moonlight and never dark; and who speaks of one sun only? that land is illuminate with the rays of a million suns.

78

III. 63. *kahaiṉ Kabīr, śuno ho sādho*

KABIR SAYS: "O Sadhu! hear my deathless words. If you want your own good, examine and consider them well.

You have estranged yourself from the Creator, of whom you have sprung: you have lost your reason, you have bought death.

All doctrines and all teachings are sprung from Him, from Him they grow: know this for certain, and have no fear.

Hear from me the tidings of this great truth!

Whose name do you sing, and on whom do you meditate? O, come forth from this entanglement!

He dwells at the heart of all things, so why take refuge in empty desolation?

If you place the Guru at a distance from you, then it is but the distance that you honour:

If indeed the Master be far away, then who is it else that is creating this world?

When you think that He is not here, then you wander
further and further away, and seek Him in vain with tears.
Where He is far off, there He is unattainable: where He
is near, He is very bliss."
Kabir says: "Lest His servant should suffer pain He pervades
him through and through."
Know yourself then, O Kabir; for He is in you from head
to foot.
Sing with gladness, and keep your seat unmoved within
your heart.

79

III. 66. nā maiṉ dharmī nahīṉ adharmī

I AM NEITHER pious nor ungodly,
 I live neither by law nor by sense,
 I am neither a speaker nor hearer,
 I am neither a servant nor master,
 I am neither bond nor free,
 I am neither detached nor attached.
 I am far from none: I am near to none.
 I shall go neither to hell nor to heaven.
 I do all works; yet I am apart from all works.
 Few comprehend my meaning: he who can comprehend
it, he sits unmoved.
Kabir seeks neither to establish nor to destroy.

80

III. 69. satta nām hai sab ten nyara

THE TRUE Name is like none other name!
 The distinction of the Conditioned from the Unconditioned
is but a word:
 The Unconditioned is the seed, the Conditioned is the
flower and the fruit.

Knowledge is the branch, and the Name is the root.

Look, and see where the root is: happiness shall be yours when you come to the root.

The root will lead you to the branch, the leaf, the flower, and the fruit:

It is the encounter with the Lord, it is the attainment of bliss, it is the reconciliation of the Conditioned and the Unconditioned.

81

III. 74. *pratham ek jo āpai āp*

IN THE beginning was He alone, sufficient unto Himself: the formless, colourless, and unconditioned Being.

Then was there neither beginning, middle, nor end;

Then were no eyes, no darkness, no light;

Then were no ground, air, nor sky; no fire, water, nor earth; no rivers like the Ganges and the Jumna, no seas, oceans, and waves.

Then was neither vice nor virtue; scriptures there were not, as the Vedas and Puranas, nor as the Koran.

Kabir ponders in his mind and says, "Then was there no activity: the Supreme Being remained merged in the unknown depths of His own self."

The Guru neither eats nor drinks, neither lives nor dies:

Neither has He form, line, colour, nor vesture.

He who has neither caste nor clan nor anything else— how may I describe His glory?

He has neither form nor formlessness,

He has no name,

He has neither colour nor colourlessness,

He has no dwelling-place.

82

III. 76. *kahaiṉ Kabīr vicār ke*

KABIR PONDERS and says: 'He who has neither caste nor country, who is formless and without quality, fills all space.'

The Creator brought into being the Game of Joy: and from the word Om the Creation sprang.

The earth is His joy; His joy is the sky;
His joy is the flashing of the sun and the moon;
His joy is the beginning, the middle, and the end;
His joy is eyes, darkness, and light.

Oceans and waves are His joy: His joy the Sarasvati, the Jumna, and the Ganges.

The Guru is One: and life and death, union and separation, are all His plays of joy!

His play the land and water, the whole universe!
His play the earth and the sky!

In play is the Creation spread out, in play it is established. The whole world, says Kabir, rests in His play, yet still the Player remains unknown.

83

III. 84. *jhī jhī jantar bājai*

THE HARP gives forth murmurous music; and the dance goes on without hands and feet.

It is played without fingers, it is heard without ears: for He is the ear, and He is the listener.

The gate is locked, but within there is fragrance: and there the meeting is seen of none.

The wise shall understand it.

84

III. 89. *mor phakīrwā mānigi jay*

THE BEGGAR goes a-begging, but I could not even catch sight
of Him:
And what shall I beg of the Beggar? He gives without
my asking.
Kabir says: "I am His own: now let that befall which
may befall!"

85

III. 90. *naihar se jiyarā phaṭ re*

MY HEART cries aloud for the house of my lover; the open
road and the shelter of a roof are all one to her who has lost
the city of her husband.
My heart finds no joy in anything: my mind and my body
are distraught.
His place has a million gates, but there is a vast ocean
between it and me:
How shall I cross it, O friend? for endless is the
outstretching of the path.
How wondrously this lyre is wrought! When its strings
are rightly strung, it maddens the heart: but when the keys
are broken and the strings are loosened, none regard it
more.
I tell my parents with laughter that I must go to my Lord
in the morning;
They are angry, for they do not want me to go, and they
say: "She thinks she has gained such dominion over her
husband that she can have whatsoever she wishes: and therefore
she is impatient to go to him."
Dear friend, lift my veil lightly now; for this is the night
of love.

Kabir says: "Listen to me! My heart is eager to meet my lover: I lie sleepless upon my bed. Remember me early in the morning!"

86

III. 96. *jīv mahal men Śiv pahunwā*

SERVE YOUR God, who has come into this temple of life!
Do not act the part of a madman, for the night is thickening fast.

He has awaited me for countless ages, for love of me He has lost His heart:
Yet I did not know the bliss that was so near to me, for my love was not yet awake.
But now, my Lover has made known to me the meaning of the note that struck my ear:
Now, my good fortune is come.
Kabir says: "Behold! how great is my fortune! I have received the unending caress of my beloved!"

87

I. 71. *gagan ghaṭā ghaharānī, sādho*

CLOUDS THICKEN in the sky! O, listen to the deep voice of their roaring;
The rain comes from the east with its monotonous murmur.
Take care of the fences and boundaries of your fields, lest the rains
Overflow them;
Prepare the soil of deliverance, and let the creepers of love and renunciation be soaked in this shower.
It is the prudent farmer who will bring his harvest home; he shall fill both his vessels, and feed both the wise men and the saints.

88

III. 118. *āj din ke main jāun balihārī*

THIS DAY is dear to me above all other days, for to-day the
Beloved Lord is a guest in my house;
My chamber and my courtyard are beautiful with His
presence.
My longings sing His Name, and they are become lost in
His great beauty:
I wash His feet, and I look upon His Face; and I lay
before Him as an offering my body, my mind, and all that
I have.
What a day of gladness is that day in which my Beloved,
who is my treasure, comes to my house!
All evils fly from my heart when I see my Lord.
"My love has touched Him; my heart is longing for the
name which is Truth."
Thus sings Kabir, the servant of all servants.

89

I. 100. *Kōī śuntā hai jnānī rāg gagan men*

IS THERE any wise man who will listen to that solemn music
which arises in the sky?
For He, the Source of all music, makes all vessels full
fraught, and rests in fullness Himself.
He who is in the body is ever athirst, for he pursues that
which is in part:
But ever there wells forth deeper and deeper the sound
"He is this—this is He"; fusing love and renunciation into
one.
Kabir says: "O brother! that is the Primal Word."

90

I. 108. *main̤ kā se būjhaun̤*

TO WHOM shall I go to learn about my beloved?

Kabir says: "As you never may find the forest if you ignore the tree, so He may never be found in abstraction."

91

III. 12. *saṃskirit bhāshā paḍhi līnhā*

I HAVE learned the Sanskrit language, so let all men call me wise:

But where is the use of this, when I am floating adrift, and parched with thirst, and burning with the heat of desire?

To no purpose do you bear on your head this load of pride and vanity.

Kabir says: "Lay it down in the dust, and go forth to meet the beloved.

Address Him as your Lord."

92

III. 110. *carkhā calai surat virahin kā*

THE WOMAN who is parted from her lover spins at the spinning wheel.

The city of the body arises in its beauty; and within it the palace of the mind has been built.

The wheel of love revolves in the sky, and the seat is made of the jewels of knowledge:

What subtle threads the woman weaves, and makes them fine with love and reverence!

Kabir says: "I am weaving the garland of day and night. When my Lover comes and touches me with His feet, I shall offer Him my tears."

93

III. 111. *koṭīn bhānu candra tārāgaṇ*

BENEATH THE great umbrella of my King millions of suns and
moons and stars are shining!

He is the Mind within my mind: He is the Eye within
mine eye.

Ah, could my mind and eyes be one! Could my love but
reach to my Lover! Could but the fiery heat of my heart be
cooled!

Kabir says: "When you unite love with the Lover, then
you have love's perfection."

94

I. 92. *avadhū begam deś hamārā*

O SADHU! my land is a sorrowless land.

I cry aloud to all, to the king and the beggar, the emperor
and the Fakir—

Whosoever seeks for shelter in the Highest, let all come
and settle in my land!

Let the weary come and lay his burdens here!

So live here, my brother, that you may cross with ease to that
other shore.

It is a land without earth or sky, without moon or stars;

For only the radiance of Truth shines in my Lord's Durbar.

Kabir says: "O beloved brother! naught is essential save
Truth."

95

I. 109. *sāin ke sangat sāsur āī*

I CAME with my Lord to my Lord's home: but I lived not with
Him and I tasted Him not, and my youth passed away like
a dream.

On my wedding night my women-friends sang in chorus, and I was anointed with the unguents of pleasure and pain:

But when the ceremony was over, I left my Lord and came away, and my kinsman tried to console me upon the road.

Kabir says, "I shall go to my Lord's house with my love at my side;

Then shall I sound the trumpet of triumph!"

96

I. 75. *samajh dekh man mīt piyarwā*

O FRIEND, dear heart of mine, think well! If you love indeed, then why do you sleep?

If you have found Him, then give yourself utterly, and take Him to you.

Why do you lose Him again and again?

If the deep sleep of rest has come to your eyes, why waste your time making the bed and arranging the pillows?

Kabir says: "I tell you the ways of love! Even though the head itself must be given, why should you weep over it?"

97

II. 90. *sāhab ham men, sāhab tum men*

THE LORD is in me, the Lord is in you, as life is in every seed. O servant! put false pride away, and seek for Him within you.

A million suns are ablaze with light,

The sea of blue spreads in the sky,

The fever of life is stilled, and all stains are washed away; when I sit in the midst of that world.

Hark to the unstruck bells and drums! Take your delight in love!

Rains pour down without water, and the rivers are streams of light.

One Love it is that pervades the whole world, few there are who know it fully:

They are blind who hope to see it by the light of reason, that reason which is the cause of separation—

The House of Reason is very far away!

How blessed is Kabir, that amidst this great joy he sings within his own vessel.

It is the music of the meeting of soul with soul;

It is the music of the forgetting of sorrows;

It is the music that transcends all coming in all going forth.

98

II. 98. ṛitu phāgun niyar ānī

THE MONTH of March draws near: ah, who will unite me to my Lover?

How shall I find words for the beauty of my beloved? For He is merged in all beauty.

His colour is in all the pictures of the world, and it bewitches the body and the mind.

Those who know this, know what is this unutterable play of the Spring.

Kabir says: "Listen to me, brother! there are not many who have found this out."

99

II. 111. Nārad, pyār so antar nāhī

OH NARAD! I know that my Lover cannot be far:

When my Lover wakes, I wake: when He sleeps, I sleep.

He is destroyed at the root who gives pain to my Beloved.

Where they sing His praise, there I live;
When He moves, I walk before Him: my heart yearns for
my Beloved.

The infinite pilgrimage lies at His feet, a million devotees
are seated there.

Kabir says: "The Lover Himself reveals the glory of true
love."

100

II. 122. *koī prem kī peng jhulāo re*

HANG UP the swing of love to-day!

Hang the body and the mind between the arms of the
Beloved, in the ecstasy of love's joy:

Bring the tearful streams of the rainy clouds to your eyes,
and cover your heart with the shadow of darkness:

Bring your face nearer to His ear, and speak of the deepest
longings of your heart.

Kabir says: "Listen to me, brother! bring the vision of the
Beloved in your heart."

Made in the USA
Lexington, KY
27 May 2016